CW00551845

FORSTER'S STRATA.

A Treatise

ON A

SECTION OF THE STRATA

FROM

NEWCASTLE-UPON-TYNE TO CROSS FELL,

WITH REMARKS ON MINERAL VEINS;

ALSO,

TABLES OF THE STRATA IN NORTHUMBERLAND, DURHAM, YORKSHIRE, DERBYSHIRE, WEST CUMBERLAND, AND FIFESHIRE; TO WHICH IS ADDED, A TREATISE ON THE DISCOVERY, THE OPENING, AND THE WORKING OF LEAD MINES, AND THE DRESSING AND SMELTING OF LEAD ORES.

By WESTGARTH FORSTER.

Third Edition, Revised and Corrected to the present time,

BY THE

REV. W. NALL, M.A.,

WITH A MEMOIR OF THE AUTHOR'S LIFE.

NEWCASTLE-UPON-TYNE: ANDREW REID, PRINTING COURT BUILDINGS.
LONDON: EDWARD STANFORD, 55, CHARING CROSS.
1883.

Republished 1985

DAVIS BOOKS LTD
140 Westgate Road
Newcastle upon Tyne

ISBN 0 946865 04 3

*The fact that Plates 1, 2, & 11 are missing is not an
error, these Plates did not appear in the original edition.*

*For convenience of use the illustrations have been
printed as part of the book rather than on fold out plates
as in the original.*

Printed & Bound by
SMITH SETTLE
Otley, West Yorkshire

TO THE

COMMISSIONERS AND GOVERNORS

OF

THE ROYAL HOSPITAL FOR SEAMEN,

AT GREENWICH,

IN THE COUNTY OF KENT.

———

MY LORDS AND GENTLEMEN,

I return you my most sincere thanks, for the honour and great favour you have pleased to confer upon me, in your having granted me permission to dedicate to you, a new edition of my Treatise on a Section of the Strata, from Newcastle-upon-Tyne to Cross Fell, in Cumberland. You, my Lords and Gentlemen, undoubtedly, of all others, have the best claim to a work of this nature, who are most justly looked up to as the encouragers of the industrious miner, and whose judicious system, generosity, and benevolence, have been so conspicuous in promoting the welfare and good of the mining districts under your direction.

There are many who can bear testimony to the truth of these sentiments, but no one with more unfeigned respect, than, my Lords and Gentlemen,

Your most devoted, much obliged,

And most obedient Servant,

WESTGARTH FORSTER.

EDITOR'S PREFACE.

—

Some alterations have been made in this edition of the "Strata." Parts I. and II. have been revised and rearranged; Part III. has been partially recast: some of the old sections have been extended, and other sections have been given: obsolete matter has been expunged, and new matter, in the form of notes, has been added.

In the revision of the text care has been taken to preserve the characteristics of the author's style, alterations having been made only where the meaning was obscure, or where there was a too frequent repetition of the same word or phrase.

Forster was eminently practical in his treatment of the subjects upon which he wrote. Any serious disturbance of the text would, therefore, have impaired the value of the book in the estimation of those for whom it was specially intended, namely, the practical geologist and miner. Such disturbance has been studiously avoided. The case was somewhat different with regard to some portions of the subject matter.

The controversy between the Huttonians and the Wernerians respecting the origin of the rocks composing the crust of the earth, which raged during the closing years of the

last, and the opening years of the present century, is now as
dead as the controversies of the ancients concerning the shape
of the earth. The statement of the two theories which Forster
inserted in the second edition of the "Strata," has, therefore,
been left out of the present edition.

Four short paragraphs quoted from Werner "On Mineral
Veins," and the "Tabular Representation of the Order of the
Superposition of the Strata, according to the Wernerian
Theory," have also been omitted. The Table of Highest
Mountains has shared the same fate, because more accurate
and complete Tables of the heights of mountains are contained
in the modern Atlas and Geographical Reader.

In 1821 almost every mining company had its own
smelting house for the smelting of its own ore. It was, therefore, desirable that in a book which treated of the "smelting of
ore," a list of smelting houses should be given. The smelting
is now done in a comparatively small number of large houses.
Fourteen of the twenty-one houses which Forster mentioned
have been closed. A list of the remaining seven is contained
in Hunt's "Mineral Statistics," which is issued annually.
Under these circumstances I felt justified in omitting the list
altogether.

The omission of obsolete matter left room for the admission
of new.

During the sixty years which have elapsed since the issue
of the last edition of the "Strata," the development of the
mineral resources of the British Isles has proceeded at a rapid
rate, many new mining fields having been opened out, and
many old fields extended. One of great extent has been opened
out in the North of England under the magnesian limestone.

Mr. Winch, in the paper which is quoted by Forster, stated that "no coal mine had," prior to 1821, "been won in Northumberland, or Durham, by sinking a shaft through the magnesian limestone," and that "it was a circumstance too well ascertained to admit of a doubt, though difficult to be accounted for, that the coal is deteriorated in quality when covered by the limestone."

In 1835 the late Mr. Thomas Forster (nephew of our author) sank a shaft through the limestone and discovered that the coal underneath was as good as the coal found elsewhere in the same seams.

Since 1835 many more shafts have been put down through the limestone, with similar results. The sinking of new and deeper shafts in the North of England and elsewhere, afforded opportunities for the taking of new and more complete sections of the strata—opportunities which mining engineers, following the example of our author, gladly availed themselves of in order to place their knowledge of the strata upon a broader basis than that upon which it had previously rested. Through the courtesy of those gentlemen, whose names are mentioned elsewhere in this book, I have been able to obtain some typical sections of the strata of the new mining fields.

Great changes have been made in the washing floor and in the smelting house since 1821. To Mr. A. Bolton, master of the smelting house at Nenthead, and Mr. James Atkinson, master of the Rampgill Low washing floor at the same place, I am indebted for much valuable information on the subjects of smelting and dressing.

To all who have assisted me to prepare this edition of the "Strata" for the press, I beg to tender my acknowledgments, and more especially to the many working miners who have kindly placed at my disposal the results of their own experience.

My thanks are due to Mr. W. B. Brown, Ivy House, Garrigill, and Mr. T. Forster Brown, Cardiff, for the loan of Westgarth Forster's Papers.

Alston, May, 1883.

PREFACE TO THE SECOND EDITION.

SINCE the First Edition of this work was offered to the public, the science of geology has been more assiduously cultivated in this country, than at any former period; and the exertions of many of our most eminent modern philosophers, have caused it to assume a highly imposing appearance. The science itself is intrinsically of a nature to excite the greatest interest in inquiring minds. All the different branches of human knowledge tend to make us better acquainted with the objects around us: the astronomer directs our attention to the heavenly bodies: the chemist investigates the changes that take place in the molecules of matter: and the natural historian arranges, classifies, and describes the objects on the surface of our globe. The philosophical cultivator of these branches is amply repaid for his labour, not only by the refined and delicate pleasure he experiences in his investigations, but by the consciousness that he is extending the boundaries of human knowledge, eliciting new objects of inquiry, and displaying new topics for discussion. These inducements to the prosecution of research are not wanting when applied to the science of geology. As far as regards the extension of our knowledge its importance is sufficiently established. It makes us acquainted with the internal structure of our globe, and enables us partially to explain some of the most recondite and tremendous natural phenomena.

The geologist, in the course of his enquiries, is frequently led to contemplate objects which inspire him with the most sublime thoughts. To him the rugged mountain and the trackless desert are alike objects of interest; and, amidst apparent chaos and confusion, he surveys the world in primeval ages. He traces vestiges of many tremendous convulsions which our globe has, at different periods, undergone; he distinguishes in these relics of devastation, the marks of awful omnipotence; and his mind is alternately overwhelmed with wonder, or filled with admiration.*

But the mere extension of our knowledge is of comparatively little importance, however sublime the truths developed, or the secrets disclosed, unless it promote the happiness of mankind. The philosopher who, after a life spent in refined speculation, sinks into the grave without leaving a monument of his usefulness, deserves but little gratitude from his surviving fellow creatures.

The science of geology is recommended to our notice, not only by the sublimity of the facts which it brings under our observation, but also by the service which it is capable of rendering to man, by enabling him to procure the more readily many of those substances without which polished society could not exist. This statement is so completely substantiated in the following pages that it is useless here to insist upon it at greater length.

The district, which it is the object of this treatise to describe, does not possess that sublimity of external appearance which characterises many other portions of the globe; but for rich and valuable deposits of lead ore the world cannot, at present, produce its parallel. It has for ages produced more of this valuable substance than all other parts of the kingdom taken together, and its mines invariably excite the astonishment of those mineralogists who have visited the reputed rich lead mines of other countries. The district has, however, been strangely neglected by scientific men. Before the publication of the First Edition of this work, little had been written upon it which was calculated to excite attention. That edition was therefore received with considerable avidity. It has, however, been for some time confined to the libraries of original subscribers. More recently Dr. Thompson and Mr. Winch have written upon the Northern mining field; but,

* [The belief that great changes have been wrought in the configuration of the earth's surface by tremendous physical convulsions—such as the sudden upheaval or depression of portions of the earth's crust—was generally prevalent in our author's time. Sir Charles Lyell was the first to propound the doctrine that the forces which elevate or depress the land, are regular and constant in their operation. Under the name of Uniformitarianism, Lyell's doctrine is now generally accepted by geologists.—ED.]

although each supplies us with some valuable information, yet, in what are denominated the lead measures, they have made many mistakes, for want of a correct local knowledge of the country. Under these circumstances it is presumed that the present edition of this work cannot be unacceptable to the geological world; and, that the additions it has experienced are of a nature to render it more worthy of their patronage than the first. In making these additions I have availed myself of several ·modern works, and particularly of the paper written by Mr. Winch. I have also received information from Messrs. John and Thomas Dickinson, of Lowbyer, near Alston, Mr. Isaac Hornsby, Nenthead, Mr. Thomas Fenwick, of Dipton, and Mr. Robert Hayton, of Grassfield, near Alston. I am indebted to Mr. James Mulcaster, of Langley Mill, one of the ablest metallurgists in the kingdom, for much valuable information in the smelting department, and to Mr. H. L. Pattinson, late of Alston, but now of Newcastle, for a revision of a great part of the work, and for several detached portions of original matter. To all these gentlemen, and to some others, whom I cannot enumerate, I beg leave to return my thanks for their friendly assistance.

With regard to the manner in which I have executed my task, as an author, a very few observations may suffice. I have not used the polished language which characterises the works of some elegant authors, who embellish with the beauties of composition whatever they describe. But, if I have not written the language of elegance, I have endeavoured to confine myself to the language of truth. I have been more solicitous to give plain, substantial, and solid practical information, than to indulge in flights of fancy, or excursions of imagination. Theory has hitherto been the bane of geological science. It has cramped the efforts of inquiry, and paralysed the exertions of research. Geologists have been too apt to spurn the drudgery of patient investigation; but it is the road that leads to truth, and the road which I have undeviatingly pursued.

Some practical miners have censured the first edition of this work because each individual stratum did not correspond, in respect of position and thickness, with that in the mining field where they were concerned. It may be observed, however, that it is impossible to make a single section correspond with every mining field, inasmuch as differences occur in the thickness of each stratum in very short distances. When local accuracy is required, the mine-master, or agent, would do well to construct, from actual admeasurement, a section for himself.

In preparing for the publication of this edition, I have met with the most liberal patronage from many gentlemen engaged in subterranean researches; and, in returning them my most grateful acknowledgments, I may be allowed to express a hope, that their endeavours will be finally crowned with success.

Garrigill Gate, June 26th, 1821.

INTRODUCTION.

NATURAL HISTORY is the name given to that branch of knowledge which has for its object the examination of the bodies of which the earth is composed. In its most comprehensive sense, it embraces all terrestrial phenomena, from the changes which take place in the atmosphere to those which take place upon and in the crust of the earth.

A subject so large could not be successfully treated as a whole : it is, therefore, divided by naturalists into several departments, or sciences, each science being again divided into several branches. The science which describes the configuration of the earth's surface, its oceans, seas, lakes, and rivers, its mountains, hills, valleys, and plains, is called geography: the science which describes the animal kingdom is called zoology: that which describes the vegetable kingdom, botany.

To investigate and describe the structure of the earth's crust, the rocks of which that crust is composed, and the changes which have taken place and are now progressing in it, is the province of geology: to classify and describe the mineral substances which are found in the earth's crust, to show in what manner they generally occur, and to explain their uses, is the province of mineralogy.

The constituents of rocks are:—(1) earths and stones, (2) the various kinds of salts, (3) the inflammable bodies, and (4) the metals. Of these, the earths and stones are by far the most abundant. They are easily distinguished from salts by their insolubility, and from the inflammable and metallic substances by the resistance which they offer to the action of fire. As rocks, they are either spread out in layers, or beds (Latin, *strata*); or else they occur in amorphous (shapeless) masses. The geologist, taking advantage of these circumstances, divides the rocks into two great classes, the *stratified* and the *unstratified*. Generally there is no difficulty in distinguishing the one class from the other, though there are cases in which even geologists of acknowledged standing do not readily recognise the distinction between them in consequence of the divisional lines of the stratified rocks having been either totally obliterated, or very much obscured by igneous agencies. Rocks thus changed are said to be metamorphosed, and are, therefore, called *metamorphic* rocks.

But the geologist has other names than these for the rocks. Having discovered, from an examination of their composition, that the stratified rocks were formed through the agency of water, and that, on the other hand, the unstratified rocks were formed through the agency of fire, he has called them respectively the *aqueous* and the *igneous* rocks. For reasons, which will presently appear, he also calls the former *sedimentary* rocks. The three terms stratified, aqueous, and sedimentary are thus applied to the same class of rocks; the other class being known as the unstratified or igneous.

According to the geological periods in which the rocks are supposed to have been formed, they are divided into the *primary*, *secondary*, and *tertiary;* according to the character of their fossils and predominant minerals, they are further divided into *systems* and *groups* (see ideal section on page 83).

The most distinctive and best known among these systems is the carboniferous (coal bearing). To the immense development of that system in the south of Scotland, northern and central England, Wales and Ireland, the United Kingdom is chiefly indebted for its present position among the nations of the earth. The carboniferous strata yield, in great abundance, the various metals of which our tools and machines are made, together with the mineral which supplies the motive power for conducting the operations in which these tools and machines are employed.

The principal object of the following treatise is to describe a section of these strata as they are developed in the northern counties of England, and to give an account of the mineral veins which traverse them.

The upper portion of the carboniferous system crops out to the day (in mining phraseology) in the low land near the mouth of the Tyne, whilst the lower portion crops out in the comparatively high land on the west side of Cross Fell, the whole of the seven groups into which the system has been subdivided being represented, some fully, others partially, in the district which lies between the east coast and the Vale of Eden.

The Relation of the Carboniferous System to the other Systems is shown by the ideal section on page 83. It is there represented as being overlaid by the lower new red of the Permian and underlaid by the yellow and red sandstones of the Devonian. It is generally, though not always, found in this position. There are districts where it is capped by the magnesian limestone, and there are others in which it rests upon the Silurian. The line of demarcation between the lowest members of the carboniferous and the topmost members of the old red is not, however, clearly defined. No one is able to say, with any degree of certainty, where the former end and the latter begin (see engraved section, page 103).

The relation of this system to the other systems may be shortly defined thus :—It generally occurs between the lower new red and the upper old red : in some districts it is capped by the magnesian limestone : in others it rests upon the silurian slates. It is never found above the new red, excepting in cases where the usual order of the formations has been inverted by igneous agencies ; nor is it ever found beneath the old red.

The *lie* of the strata in the northern district is explained on pages 3 and 54. Speaking generally, it may be said that from the summits of Cross Fell and Hartside the strata dip towards the north-east, whilst from the Cheviots they dip towards the south-east. The general dip is modified in many places by local circumstances.

The Formation of the System.—An inspection of the engraved section on pages 85–105, will show that the sandstones and shales greatly predominate over the other strata. The limestones are next to them in point of number and thickness, the coal seams being next to the limestones. There is one sheet of igneous rock, the whin sill. The sandstones and shales are simply solidified layers of sand and mud, which were originally spread out, in a position approaching more or less to the horizontal, in alternate and nearly parallel layers, upon the floor of an ancient sea. In treating of the formation of these rocks, it will be convenient to regard the thick sandstones which form the base of the carboniferous system (see Tuedian series on page 103) as being continuous with the upper portion of the old red. The floor upon which the deposition commenced may then be considered as consisting of the upper silurian slates (page 83). Over an area which was co-extensive with that now covered by the carboniferous system, inclusive of the districts from which the system was afterwards wholly or partially denuded, the deposition was continued until the accumulations of sand and mud, which are now represented by the old red and the Tuedian series, were formed. The sea was not rendered shallow by these accumulations, the loss in depth being more than counterbalanced by the continued subsidence of the floor.

In the comparatively deep water which existed after the deposition of the sandstones, and which was apparently deeper towards the south than in the north, coral reefs were formed and organic remains deposited in layers. Through a long period of time the reefs rose higher and higher, and the layers continued to be piled up, until those accumulations were formed which were afterwards consolidated into the scar limestone series (page 101).

After the deposition of this series, the accumulations of matter in the form (1) of alternating layers of sand, mud, and organic remains, (2) of thick layers of coarse sand, and (3) of thin layers of fine sand and mud, continued until (1) the lead measures, (2) the millstone grit, and (3) the coal measures, were formed.

The deposition did not proceed without interruptions. There were sub-aqueous eruptions when the lava spread itself out upon the floor of the sea and subsequently formed sheets of trap rock. The frequent alternations of sandstones, shales, and limestones, prove, beyond the possibility of doubt, that the floor of the sea oscillated greatly during the process. The presence of coal seams shows that when the floor rose above the water and became dry land, it was soon covered with rank vegetation.

The Upheaval and Partial Denudation of the Carboniferous Rocks.—At the close of the period an upward movement of the whole series commenced. The rate of upheaval was not equal over the whole area subject to it. It was most rapid (though actually very slow) over the Cheviot and the lake districts, and North

Wales. Over those places the recently formed strata were gradually brought within the sweep of the waves, and being exposed to the action of the breakers, were broken up and swept away. Layer after layer was stripped off, until at last the silurian floor was laid bare.

The force by which the strata were upheaved, rent them asunder and dislocated them. Hence, probably, the numerous faults, dykes, and vein-fissures, which are found in the carboniferous rocks, some of them the source of much gain to the miner, others the cause of much loss. The extent of the denudation at this period is a matter of conjecture. At the centres of upheaval which have been mentioned, the destruction of the carboniferous strata was complete. The whole mass, together with the silurian floor itself, was swept away. At places remote from these centres, where the strata were less exposed to breaker action, the denudation was partial.

The districts which are now known as our coal-fields were, in a great measure, exempt from the operation of the destructive agencies. The districts which were intermediate between the centres of elevation and the coal-fields were denuded of a great thickness of strata. Many thousand feet were probably stripped off the lead mining districts by breaker action and sub-aerial agencies before the commencement of the next period of submergence.

Their Submergence.—The carboniferous rocks, much shattered and denuded, again sank beneath the waves, and, in turn, formed the floor upon which the lower new red, the magnesian limestone, the upper new red, and probably the lias and the oolite were deposited. Portions of these more recent formations still overlie the coal measures, even in the mining districts; but the bulk of them was washed off during their upheaval. It was probably during this second upheaval that the district on the east of the Pennine chain was severed from the district on the west, and the great Pennine fault was thus formed. Since that upheaval sub-aerial agencies have been unceasingly at work, and have given to the northern district its present configuration (see page 143).

CONTENTS.

PART I.

PART II.

PART III.

WESTGARTH FORSTER.

WESTGARTH FORSTER, mining engineer, geologist, and mineralogist, was the eldest son of Westgarth and Lucy Forster, of Ivy House, Garrigill, Alston Moor, and of Jeffry's Rake, Hunstanworth. Whether he was born at Ivy House, or in the family residence at Jeffry's Rake, is a matter open to some doubt, there being no record of his baptism in either the Alston or the Hunstanworth parish registers. There is extant a document, dated May 2nd, 1771, which represents Westgarth Forster, the father, as then living at Garrigill. It designates him as Westgarth Forster, of Garrigill Gate, in the County of Cumberland, gentleman. There are also certain entries in the registers kept at Garrigill chapel, the particulars of which correspond, in respect of date, with the particulars in this document. One entry certifies that Susan, daughter of Westgarth Forster, of Garrigill, was born March, 1769, and baptised April 14th, 1771. Another certifies that Lucy Forster was baptised on the same day; but no mention is made of the brother of those two sisters. There is, however, a record of his death in the adjoining churchyard. On a large limestone slab, which is supported in the horizontal position by four sandstone pillars, are graven the following words :—" Westgarth Forster, son of the above Westgarth and Lucy Forster, of Unthank Hall, died Nov. 9th, 1835, aged 63 years." This inscription fixes the date of our author's birth within the year 1772.

Had the family removed from Ivy House to the old home at Jeffry's Rake during the interval between the baptism of the two daughters and the birth of the son? The absence from the Garrigill registers of any record of the child's baptism may be regarded as a proof that the family had left Ivy House before he was born, and this proof is corroborated by the fact that the child's two uncles, Thomas and George Forster, removed from Allendale to Ivy House either in 1772 or 1773. There is then a strong probability that the author of the "Strata" was born in the family mansion at

C

Jeffry's Rake, where, in 1738, his father was born, and where his grandfather, George, lived at the time of his marriage with Mary Westgarth.

A lengthened account of the Forster family would be foreign to the purpose of this memoir; but some reference to George Forster's relatives and connections is necessary, inasmuch as they exercised considerable influence over the fortunes of his son and grandson. George was a scion of the ancient Forster family of Etherstone, or Edderstone, and was, therefore, connected with that William Bacon of Staward and Newton Cap, who married Margaret, eldest daughter of Thomas Forster, Esq., of Etherstone, and who filled the office of High Sheriff of Northumberland in 1745. "On the extinction of the right line of the Forster family in the death of Thomas Forster, a minor, in 1764, the Etherstone estates descended to William Bacon's grandson, John William Bacon, who took the name of Forster." * These Bacons where extensive owners of mining property in the north. They held, with their connections, the Blacketts, thirty mines in the county of Durham ; they were the owners of the Allendale Smelting Works, and they were probably shareholders in the Allendale and Coalcleugh mines. The conjecture may, therefore, be hazarded that when, about the year 1774, a second agent was wanted to assist Mr. J. Dickinson in the management of the Allendale and Coalcleugh mines, it was mainly through the influence of the Bacon Forsters that Westgarth Forster, the father of our author, was appointed.

George Forster was not then alive, having died in 1754. The deed of administration which was granted to George's widow by Richard Trevor, the successor of Butler in the Bishopric of Durham, is still extant. By this deed Mary was constituted "administratrix of all and singular the goods, chattels, and credits of her deceased husband, George Forster, of Jeffrys, in the parish of Hunstanworth, gentleman." There is nothing on record to show that George was interested in mining, or that he displayed any capacity for those studies in which his son and grandson were destined to excel.

The duties upon which his son entered in 1774 were of a responsible character. He was required to superintend the inside works

* Mackenzie and Dent.

of the Allenheads mines, to set on levels and drifts, rises and sumps,
or, in other words, to explore the veins in any direction which might,
according to his judgment, lead to the discovery of ore.   He was
also paymaster for the Allendale and Coalcleugh Mining Company.
In this latter capacity he met the directors of the company at Newcastle, received from them the cash for the monthly lendings, or the
annual pays, and, with the assistance of the clerks, distributed it
among the workmen.   He died in 1797, in the 59th year of his
age, at Unthank Hall,* having removed thither in 1794, either from
Jeffry's Rake, or from a house at Allenheads which he seems to have
occupied for a short time.   Among the obituary notices which
appeared in the *Newcastle Chronicle* for February 6th, 1797, was
the following:—"On Wednesday, at Unthank, in his 59th year,
Westgarth Forster, esteemed for his general worth, and as one of
the best judges of lead-mines in the North of England."

He left eight children—four sons and four daughters—the eldest
of whom was Westgarth, the author of the "Strata."   Of young
Westgarth's early life little is known.   That period of it which
embraces childhood and youth was spent at Jeffry's Rake and
Allenheads; the period of early manhood was spent at Unthank
Hall.   Whether, as a boy, he was bright or dull; studious or idle;
what school he attended, who where his teachers, and who were his
school-mates, are points upon which no information can now be
obtained.

If one might judge of the boy from the man and of the man
from the tone of his letters, and the traditions of him which still
linger among the people in Allendale, Weardale, and Alston, the
conclusion arrived at would be that he was of a kind and gentle
disposition, of shy and retiring manners, and of studious habits.
That he was exact and painstaking in his lessons, and subsequently
in his professional engagements, is evident from the manner in
which a large copy-book, used by him, when a lad of about fourteen,

* The Westgarths were the owners of Unthank and the adjoining estate for
nearly 200 years.   John Westgarth, Esq., J.P., who died in 1781, left three daughters
—co-heiresses of the estate.   One of these daughters married the Rev. Henry
Hildyard, another married Francis Threepwood, Esq., the third, Mary, died in 1841.
—See "Stanhope and its Neighbourhood," by Mr. M. M. Egglestone.

in his lessons on surveying, has been kept, and also from the many well-executed sketches and plans, and well-written papers, which he has left.

On the death of her husband the duty of winding up his affairs devolved upon Mrs. Lucy Forster.* She was well qualified for the discharge of that duty. Her "Memorandum Book of Cash Paid and Received by her after the Death of her Husband in 1797, at Unthank and Garrigill," has been preserved. The accounts which it contains run up to some thousands of pounds, and are spread over eight years; yet they are kept in a neat and orderly manner. The first item is a statement of the amount of cash in the house on the 14th January, 1797, the day, apparently, on which Mr. Forster was taken seriously ill; the last item, dated May 3rd, 1806, is a notification of rent received for a portion of the Ivy estate. A full account is rendered of all moneys received and expended between those two dates.

Two short letters, written by Mrs. Forster on the 2nd July, 1797, have also been preserved. One is addressed to her brother-in-law, George Forster; the other to a more distant relative who was somewhat reluctant to settle an account which he had opened with her late husband. They are characteristic productions, and not unworthy of a place in this memoir :—

Dear Sir,—As I suppose you will attend the Stagshaw Fair, and may then have an opportunity of seeing Mr. Bell, the steward, I desire that you will, please, give him your determination concerning your withdrawal from the lease of Unthank, as I wish to have this matter settled in some way with the proprietor.—I am, with love to your sister, who I hope is better, yours truly,   LUCY FORSTER.

Mr. George Forster.

Sir,—Annexed is your account, and I desire that by the first conveyance you will send what you have against me. I confess that I was a little surprised at your telling me at Hexham that you owed me nothing, but on whichever side the balance lies, it is high time the account was adjusted. I am desirous of having my affairs settled as soon as possible, and therefore hope you will not fail to transmit me your account.—I am, Sir, your obedient servant,   LUCY FORSTER.

A strong sense of justice sometimes induces the best and most kind-hearted of people to use severe language. In this second letter

---

* Mrs. Lucy Forster's maiden name was Emerson. The Emersons were an old Weardale family, and many of their descendants live in the dale.

Lucy Forster does not spare her relative, yet there are abundant proofs of her large-heartedness and generosity as a woman, of her fondness as a mother, and of her kindness as a mistress, in her "Memorandum Book." On December 8th, 1797, she gave to her daughters £2 15s. for pocket money; on December 4th, 1798, she sent her son William to London with £18 in his pocket; in June, 1799, she gave her daughter Phœbe—the authoress of "Emma"— £4; in 1800 she erected a monument to the memory of her late husband at a cost of £18; and in 1801 she took her family to Tynemouth for a week—a somewhat expensive trip in those days. It appears from the first of those letters that Mrs. Forster surrendered the lease of the Unthank farms soon after the death of her husband. She continued, however, to live at the Hall until 1801, when she removed with her family to Ivy House, Garrigill, where she died in 1806. She was laid by the side of her husband in Garrigill churchyard.

Whilst the mother was thus engaged in the management of domestic affairs, the eldest son, Westgarth, had, at the request of the directors, taken his father's position as manager of the Allendale mines—a position which he held until 1807 or 1808. He was well qualified by previous training for that position, having for some years acted as assistant to his father. There is very little that is reliable to record with reference to this period of his life, though many traditions have gathered round it. It is said that he was a man of eccentric habits—absent-minded—somewhat reserved towards strangers—but affable towards people whom he knew. It is said also that he constructed elaborate plans of the Allendale mines, which have been of great use to his successors in the agency and that he then earned a reputation as a skilful miner. It was probably during this period that the following incident occurred. Whilst a party of gentlemen, from Newcastle, were on a visit to Alston Moor they met Forster, either accidentally or by appointment, at the Fox Inn, Garrigill. The conversation having turned to the subject of mining, one of the party asked "How far it might be necessary to *sink* from the surface, in Garrigill, before the uppermost coal seam could be reached?" Forster smilingly replied "that it would be necessary to *rise* and not to *sink*."

Not until 1809 does Forster really appear upon the scene, and then as the author of the "Strata." For some reason, the nature of which cannot now be satisfactorily ascertained, he had, previously to 1809, ceased to be agent for the Allendale Company. Great changes had taken place in the directorate of that company since the death of the elder Forster. Sir Thomas Blackett was dead, and his place as director-in-chief was filled by Colonel Beaumont. Whether or not these changes exercised any influence upon the fortunes of our author, there is no information to show. Probably they did not, since the Colonel seems to have been on the most friendly terms with the Forster family. In that portion of our author's correspondence which has been preserved, and which comprises between two and three hundred letters, many of them addressed to members of his own family, many more to his most intimate friends, and in which his most private affairs are freely discussed, not one word of complaint against Colonel Beaumont can be found. The belief, which is so generally prevalent among the dalesmen, that Forster resigned his situation in consequence of some misunderstanding with Mr. Beaumont receives no support from his letters. Neither does it receive support from the subsequent events of his life. When he brought out his "Strata," the Colonel was one of the best subscribers towards it; and when, in after years, he was in sore need of a situation, the Colonel's son, Thomas W. Beaumont, was the person to whom he applied for one.

Is Forster's resignation not fully accounted for by the changes which took place in his home and family soon after the death of his mother? Of the eight brothers and sisters who had stood round their mother's bier, two brothers and one sister were now married, two sisters were dead, and one brother had entered into business in London. Westgarth and Susan were thus left the sole occupants of Ivy House and of the Ivy Farm. Susan alone was not equal to the management of the house and farm; Westgarth could lend her no assistance because of the pressing nature of his own duties as mine agent; moreover, the distance of the mines rendered it necessary that he should be frequently from home. Either the agency, or the farm, could have been done without, for the income from either, supplemented by the income from other sources, was amply sufficient for the requirements of the brother and sister. The suggestion, then, that Forster resigned the agency because he preferred the farm, need excite no surprise, especially when it is remembered that the farm was his own property and had descended to him from his grandfather.

A temporary retirement from one branch of his profession allowed him more time for the study of another. He was now collecting materials for the first edition of his' "Strata," and in his search for them it was necessary that he should make long and frequent journeys to the places where they could be found. Much time was consumed in those expeditions—more, indeed, than he could have spared if he had retained the agency. Moreover, a great saving of time and labour was effected by making Garrigill the centre from whence those expeditions could be made. Access to the mountains and valleys of the Pennine district, in the very midst of which Garrigill is situated, was very difficult eighty years ago. Those splendid macadamised roads which now traverse that district were not then made. There were no railways. The produce of the mines was carried over the mountains on the backs of small galloways. The expenditure of time and labour which was then required for a journey from Newcastle to the top of Cross Fell would now suffice for a journey to the top of Ben Nevis. Hence the need of some central position in the heart of the mountains for the proper study of the science of geology. No position was more central than Forster's own house at Garrigill.

That village is most advantageously situated for the study of the mountain limestone formation. It stands on the Tyne-bottom shale and limestone, which are the lowest strata in the upper portion of that formation. The South Tyne flows through it in a deep channel which the river has worn out in the rock. Towards the east, south, and west the land rises rapidly until it culminates in the peaks of the Pennine Chain—Kilhope Law on the east, Yad Moss on the south, Cross Fell and Hartside on the west. The sides of the mountains are deeply scored by "gills," through which many streams rush downwards to the bottom of the valley, where, uniting their waters, they form the South Tyne. In the sides of those gills, and in the beds of the streams, many partial sections of the strata are exposed, which, when viewed in relation to each other, form a tolerably complete section of the rocks which lie between the millstone grit and the great whin sill. Similar sections may be seen in the lead mines. The mineral veins which traverse the rocks from east to west, and from north to south, have in many places been laid bare by the streams. They have also been cut through and explored in every direction in the mines. There is little doubt that all these advantages were present to the mind of Forster when, in 1807, he decided to resign his agency and devote his time and attention to his farm and his book.

The first edition of the "Strata" appeared in 1809. In the same year appeared the first geological map of England, by William Smith. These two productions—both the results of much patient investigation—conducted in two different portions of the same field of enquiry, laid the foundations of a sound knowledge of English geology. Previously to their appearance there had been much speculation as to the origin and the constitution of the earth—many ingenious theories had been started, discussed, and abandoned, but little real progress had been made in that science. Since their appearance the progress has been both real and rapid. The cause of the change is obvious. It is plainly indicated in the introduction to the "Strata":—"Theory," says the author, "has hitherto been the bane of geological science. It has cramped the efforts of enquiry, and paralysed the exertions of research. Geologists have been too apt to spurn the drudgery of patient investigation, but it is the road that leads to truth, and the road which I have undeviatingly pursued." Smith pursued the same road, but in advance of Forster.

The "Section of the Strata" was the first "Section" of any importance published in this country; many have been published since its appearance. It was well received by geologists and miners. In the preface to the second edition, Forster says that the "first was received with considerable avidity." Robert Bakewell, a geologist of some ability and the contemporary of Forster, wrote thus of the "Strata," in the "Philosophical Magazine":—"Much has already been done to elucidate the geology of part of the coal districts by Mr. Westgarth Forster, whose 'Section of the Strata,' taken in great part from actual admeasurement, comprises the coal districts

on the eastern and middle parts, and the metalliferous limestone
districts on the west, an extent of forty miles and an actual depth
of nearly 1,400 yards. This Section, perhaps the most important
and extensive that has ever been made, was taken by a person
educated as a practical miner, who had spent the early part of his
life in that district; as such I consider it particularly valuable."
This was written in 1815, that is, six years after the issue of the
" Strata."

Though the profits accruing from the sale of the "Strata" were
small, the author had good reasons for being satisfied with the success
it had met with. It brought his name prominently before the
mining community; he was henceforth recognised as an authority
on geological and mining questions. The owners of mining property,
the directors of mining companies, and mining agents sought his
assistance in their difficulties. A new career as a mining surveyor
was opened out to him, and it was opened, too, at a critical moment
in his history.

The great crisis of Forster's life occurred in 1809. He then lost
a considerable portion of his fortune. Hitherto he seems to have
lived pretty much at ease, and to have been little troubled with the
ordinary cares of life. He was about to experience some of the
hardships which fall to the lot of men who, together with a small
fortune, inherit a good name and a respectable position; he was now
under the necessity of turning to practical account those talents for
surveying and engineering which he possessed. The experience
which he had gained whilst acting as a mining agent under the
supervision of his father was now of great use to him; it qualified
him for entering at once upon the duties of a professional mine
surveyor. In this respect he was fortunate, and he soon found
abundance of employment. When the fact became generally
known that the author of the "Strata" was open to engagements,
owners of mining property were not slow in availing themselves of
his services. Forster gave up farming, let the Ivy House and estate
to his brother-in-law, Thomas Brown, and spent the remainder of
his active life in mining pursuits.

He may be said to have fully entered upon his duties as a mine
surveyor in 1810. In 1833 he retired into private life. His pro-

fessional career thus extended over twenty-three years, exclusive of
the time during which he acted as agent for Sir Thomas Blackett
and Colonel Beaumont. As compared with the average duration
of professional careers, his was a short one. But if measured by the
amount of work accomplished, it is justly entitled to be considered
a long one. During those twenty-three years he surveyed, mapped,
and reported upon, mining fields in Westmoreland, the North Riding
of Yorkshire, Derbyshire, Cheshire, Shropshire, North and South
Wales. He also visited Spain and North America for the purpose
of surveying mines in those countries. He had offers of employment in Ireland and Norway, but declined to accept them. Some
of his reports, and many of his plans, are now extant. The former
are remarkable for their clearness and a comprehensive grasp of the
subject with which they deal; the latter are remarkable for their
order and neatness; both the former and the latter appear to have
given satisfaction to W. Forster's employers, and to have inspired
them with the most implicit confidence in his ability.

One of the first and most distinguished of those employers
was the Duchess of Buccleuch. This lady was the owner of some
mining ground in North Yorkshire, the resources of which she was
desirous of developing. How, or when, Forster's name was first
brought under her Grace's notice is not known. Whether, indeed,
the Duchess herself ever had any direct communication with him
cannot now be ascertained, though it is probable that she had.
Like her contemporary, Lady Beaumont, she took great interest
in her mines. There is extant a report made by Forster on some
mining ground in the West Riding belonging to her Grace, which
shows that he must have been engaged in her service in the year
1813. That his survey gave satisfaction is evident from the fact
that her Grace sought his assistance again in 1814. On this latter
occasion, "Mr. Forster" was requested "to go over the ground at
Brennand and Whitendale for the purpose of ascertaining what
veins of lead-ore, or any other mineral, are likely to be found there,
and when he has sufficiently informed himself," he was further
requested "to report upon them, and divide the ground for letting
into such parcels as he thinks right." "Mr. Forster was also requested
to point out on what terms the takers of a vein are usually allowed

to smelt ore at the owner's mill, viz., what per ton for fuel, labourers' wages, the use of the mill, and through what processes the ore is carried for the benefit of the taker." The last enquiry was made "because the Duchess' agent had been informed that the owner of the metal has the first and second fire, and that the owner of the mine is by custom entitled to black slags, soot, and other things of inferior value, from which a profit is derived." So reads the memorandum which was delivered to Mr. Forster by her Grace's Yorkshire agent.

How long Forster continued in the Duchess' service cannot now be determined in consequence of the loss of the papers which relate to the years 1815–19. There is no doubt that he was actively engaged during the whole of that time, but no record of his labours has been preserved. He is next heard of in the year 1820, in connection with his book. Encouraged by the success of the first edition he had, for some time apparently, been collecting materials for a second and greatly enlarged edition. To the "Treatise on a Section of the Strata" he proposed now to add "A Treatise on the Discovery, the Opening, and the Working of Lead Mines, with Chapters on the Dressing and Smelting of Lead Ores." Few, if any, of his contemporaries were so well qualified as Forster to write on the subjects with which this latter treatise deals. His experience as a mining agent, and subsequently as a surveyor, who had, in the course of his engagements, seen many mining fields and super-intended the opening of many mines, and who had, moreover, devoted much time to the study of mineralogy and metallurgy, enabled him to speak with authority on these subjects. During the ten years which had elapsed since the issue of the first edition, geological science had made rapid progress. Forster says that it had "assumed a highly imposing appearance." Nowhere had it advanced at a more rapid pace than in the North of England, especially in the mining district in which our author lived. Geology was scarcely yet elevated to the dignity of a science before the attention of those who felt an interest in it became fixed upon that most remarkable of all geological phenomena—the great dislocation known as the "Pennine Fault." North-country lead miners had long been aware of the fact that many mineral veins dislocate the strata by throwing one cheek (side) up and the other down. They knew, for instance, that old Carr's vein dislocated the strata to the extent of 240 feet, and that the Burtreeford dyke dislocated it to twice that extent; but a dislocation of several thousand feet was a thing unknown to them; yet within an easy walking distance of Ivy House there is a dislocation which places the old red sandstone on a level with the new.

Forster, in common with all the geologists of the time, was ignorant of this fact when he published the first edition of the " Strata," and hence the error into which he fell with respect to the two great sandstone formations, which, to use the phraseology of miners, form the floor and the roof of the carboniferous formation. He was also ignorant of the true character of those rocks which are developed in such immense masses in the Cumbrian mountains. He supposed that they formed a portion of a dyke which ran down into Wales and up into Scotland :—" The most remarkable dyke," says he in the first edition, "that we find in the North of England is the great blue rock at Keswick, which in some places is ten or twelve miles wide, and may be traced into Wales to the southward and into Scotland northward." A careful examination of the Cumbrian and Pennine districts, made probably during his surveying expeditions in 1814 to 1820, showed him his errors. To correct these errors, and to furnish miners with a guide in their search for lead ore, and in the operations to which lead ore is subjected, were the objects Forster had in view when he began to prepare a second edition of his book for the press. A letter addressed to him in June, 1820, by Mr. J. W. Bell, of Newcastle, shows that he had then made considerable progress with his work :—" In your last letter you express a wish for me to colour you some of your Plates. This I shall be happy to do. I send you enclosed a first impression of Plate VII., which I hope will please. Mr. Bewick wants some more drawings from you to be going on with. I have no more of your sketches; if you think fit to forward any I will look them over. You will see by the enclosed that I had to make a different drawing from yours. If you send any Plates to colour, send a coloured one to go by. Pray have you gone to press yet; write me when you do go."

The second edition appeared in 1821. Its success was almost a foregone conclusion. Among the subscribers were Dr. Buckland, author of the Bridgewater Treatise on Geology; Sir Joseph Banks, President of the Royal Society; Count Breuner, of Vienna; the Duke of Devonshire; the Earls of Darlington and Strathmore; Dr. Shute-Barrington, Bishop of Durham; Professor Millington, of the Royal Institution of Great Britain; Dr. Thompson, Regius Professor of Chemistry, Glasgow; Colonel Prowse; and Colonel Beaumont. Eight hundred and fifty copies of this edition were printed, nearly all of which were sold. Writing to his friend, Mr. Douglas, in August, 1829, the author says:—"I still hope to have the pleasure of seeing you here," (Aberdovey, in Wales) "I should like to consult you respecting another edition of my book." In the following September he writes as follows to his sister Phœbe:—"I have some idea that I may soon want the plates and blocks which were used in the production of my book." The intention to bring out a third edition of the "Strata," which is clearly implied in these extracts, may reasonably be regarded as a proof that the second edition had been successful, for no man in his senses would waste his time and money in multiplying copies of a book which would not sell. Had circumstances permitted Forster to carry out his intention there would have been less need for the present re-issue, since copies of the "Strata," revised and corrected by the author himself, might still have been found upon the shelves of our booksellers.

In the same year in which the second edition of his book appeared, Forster went down to Somersetshire to survey some mining property there. This appears from a passage which occurs in a letter which he wrote in 1825:—"My friends in Somersetshire, where I was surveying in 1821, have been very successful in their search for coal at the new colliery"—a statement which leaves upon the mind the impression that he had "set on" that new colliery. This expedition to the West of England was destined to exercise great influence upon his after life. It was probably the first of many more expeditions which were undertaken by him during the years 1821 to 1825. Though there is nothing to show that Forster visited Wales in 1821, it may safely be assumed that he did. It

seems almost incredible that he should have returned to the North
without paying a visit to the great mining field of South Wales,
which possessed great attractions for him, both as a geologist and
a miner.

That great system of rocks to which the term carboniferous
(coal-bearing) has been applied, which rests upon the old red sandstone, and is overlaid by the new red, and of which the mountain
limestone forms the lower portion, is well developed in Wales.
Hence it is that the scenery in Wales presents so many points of
resemblance to the scenery in the North of England and South of
Scotland.   The mountains and hills of South Wales have the same
terraced sides, the same rounded shoulders, the same broad, flat, tops
as the mountains and hills of the Pennine districts of England, and
of the Lowland districts of Scotland.   The alternations of limestone,
sandstone, and slaty strata are as easily distinguished in the bed
of the Towey as in the bed of the Tyne, in the sides of the Brecknock-
shire mountains as in the sides of the Pennines.   The coal seams
which are found in Northumberland and Durham, South Yorkshire,
and South Lancashire, are also found in both North and South
Wales.   The county of Glamorgan is as rich in mineral wealth as
the county of Durham.   Coal, iron, lead, and copper are dug out of
its rocks.   In a letter, dated July 26th, 1825, and addressed to a friend
in Alston Moor, Westgarth Forster thus speaks of Glamorgan :—

If the company had proceeded you would probably have been employed as a
resident agent at a place called Lantrithid, belonging to Sir John Aubrey.   It is
situated in the county of Glamorgan, in a delightful district, which is called the
garden of Wales.   I do not know that there is a more fertile county in Great
Britain, or one richer in mineral wealth.   It contains the extensive basin of South
Wales, which abounds in ironstone and coal.   I have examined a great part of the
edge or lip of the basin, and have found that it contains a number of metalliferous
veins, which would, I think, produce lead ore and calamine in the limestone, which
here dips at an angle of 45 degrees into the basin.

Since that letter was written, the statements which it contains
have been abundantly verified by the development of the South
Wales mining field.   From a paper on the " South Wales Coal
field," which Mr. Thomas Forster Brown read before the Institute
of Mining and Mechanical Engineers, at Newcastle-on-Tyne, in

1881, it appears that whilst the number of tons of pig iron produced in Monmouthshire and South Wales in 1823 was 182,325, the number produced in 1872 was 1,002,623; and that whilst the number of tons of coal raised in South Wales during the period 1819 to 1830 was 7,123,395, the number raised during the one year 1872 was 15,047,250. These figures do not represent the whole of the mineral wealth produced in South Wales. In 1872, more than 250,000 tons of patent fuel and coke were sent out of the Principality. In a tract of country which, according to Mr. Brown, does not exceed 1,000 square miles in area, more wealth was found in the year 1872 than Cortes and Pizarro saw in the capitals of the Incas and Montezumas, or than Clive and Hastings saw in the palaces of the East Indian rajahs.

In addition to the natural desire which a man of his tastes would possess to see the coal seams and veins of a district which had long been famous for its mineral wealth, Forster had another motive for visiting the Principality. The identity of the strata in the west of our island with the similar strata in the north, was not clearly made out sixty years ago. That Forster believed in such identity and was on the look-out for proofs of its existence, is evident from some passages which occur in his reports and correspondence. In his report upon some mining ground near Cowbridge, belonging to Sir John Aubrey, the following passages occur :—

We found the whole of it in the lead measures, or limestone formation, similar to that which is found in Alston Moor; the veins we have seen are east and west veins. We had on Saturday observed two levels about seven miles north of Lantrithid, on the Marquess of Bute's property. This point seemed to be near the boundary of the limestone formation, where the coal overlaps it. All the rest of the district southward as far as we have surveyed is in the limestone formation. We saw numerous veins with calcareous spar in them. From the observations which I made on these veins I am led to think that the ore will be found in shakes, or cavities, and not in a continued regular rib as it usually occurs in the Grey-waucke formation in North Wales. The mines will, therefore, vary in their produce. I was informed that a belly of ore had been found by the parties who sank the shaft which yielded 40 tons.

The bellies of which Forster speaks are frequently found in our North-country lead mines, and more especially in the Allendale mines. There is an interesting account of them in the " Strata."

In a letter dated Cowbridge, May 31st, 1825, and addressed to Mr. Nichol, the London agent of the Northern and Welsh Mining Association, Forster returns to the subject of the strata :—

> I received yours of the 27th inst. by the coachman from Gloucester, just before leaving Chepstow.   On Friday evening I took a walk from the Beaufort Arms to view the cliffs on the opposite bank of the river Wye, and observed that the strata are nearly all limestone.   I take notice of what you say respecting the coal formation to the east of Chepstow, and from the fact of its being present there I infer that the above limestone belongs to the mountain limestone, or lead measure series.

Forster was too deeply interested in the self-imposed task of tracing the relation which the rock formations of the West bear to those of the North of England, to let slip the opportunity, presented by his journey to Somersetshire, of paying a visit to Wales. Assuming then that he did visit Wales for the first time in 1821, we may also assume that he then became acquainted with Sir George Alderson, a gentleman who possessed considerable property in Merioneth and Cardigan, and who, in subsequent years, proved himself to be one of Forster's best friends.   There is extant a letter written by George Douglas, Sir George Alderson's agent, and dated London, March, 1824, in which Forster and his sister are referred to as friends of some standing.   Douglas says :—

> I avail myself of the opportunity which now presents itself of enclosing a letter from Sir George, and of thanking you for the specimens and pamphlet you sent. The former arrived quite perfect, and the latter has entertained myself and some of my young friends.   I expect to have the pleasure of seeing you this spring, when I shall be glad to thank your sister in person.   I leave here next week with Sir George for Cardiganshire, and it will be very gratifying to me to meet you there again.   If you are so disengaged that you can join us in Wales, please, say as much in a letter directed to me at Devil's Bridge, or to Mr. Alderson (a relative of Sir George) in London as usual.

There is also extant a mining report, dated November 13th, 1823, made by Forster upon some mining ground in Cardigan which belonged to W. E. Powell, Esq., M.P., in which Sir George Alderson is spoken of as lessee.   Douglas' letter and this report prove that the friendship which existed for so many years between Sir George and Forster must have sprung up at some time previous to the autumn of 1823.   It probably began in 1821.

In the spring of 1824 Forster undertook the direction of some mines which Sir George possessed in Merionethshire and Cardiganshire. It does not appear that he was formally engaged by Sir George as his agent, but that he merely superintended the mining operations during his intervals of leisure, receiving from Sir George such remuneration as the latter thought proper to give him. The acceptance of this semi-agency marks the commencement of Forster's career in Wales—a career which was chequered by many vicissitudes of fortune. Towards the close of 1824 he was offered and accepted an agency which, in a letter to his friend George Burnett, he characterised as "valuable and permanent." He then determined to settle in Wales. He took rooms and wrote to his sister requesting her to come and live with him. After many wanderings he seemed at last to have reached a resting place. In a letter which he wrote in 1829, when all his plans seemed to have failed, when hope seemed to have abandoned him and ruin seemed to be near, he informed Mr. John Fulton, of Alston, that at the time when he accepted this agency his "prospects were very flattering and his promised income handsome." He was doomed to the most grievous disappointment. The agency was of very short duration, and most of the troubles which embittered the rest of his life arose out of his acceptance of it. Had he steadily adhered to that plan of life which he adopted in 1809, and which had hitherto proved to be so successful, he would probably have ended his days in peace and comfort. In an evil hour he departed from it and the departure was followed by serious consequences. The company that now engaged Forster's services, on terms which he considered liberal, was known as the Northern and Welsh Mining Association. The directors had taken the lease of an extensive mining property in North Wales belonging to a Mr. Corbet. Forster's description of the property is interesting, but much too long for quotation. One paragraph of it is here given :—

From the above considerations I conclude that Mr. Corbet's ground possesses great advantages, and I think that if it had been situated in the mining district of the North of England it would have been completely occupied long ago. It is as large as the whole manor of Alston, belonging to the Greenwich Hospital. That manor is now in the occupation of at least twenty different mining companies—the largest being the Quakers, or London Company, which has about two miles square. I know of no other company in the district which has so large a tract as two miles. It is a great advantage to have a large district. I observe that Sir Edward Watkin [whose property Forster had surveyed] confines his mining tenants to much smaller portions.

Notwithstanding the advantages which Mr. Corbet's property possessed, the company who took the lease of it soon came to grief. It was dissolved in the beginning of July, 1825. Forster received notice of the dissolution on the 9th of July. On the 10th he wrote this letter to his friend Mr. Hogg :—

> I cannot express how much I was surprised and disappointed at the information contained in Mr. Nichol's letter of last night. He tells me that the Northern and Welsh Mining Company is dissolved. I was quite unprepared for such an event. I take the liberty of addressing you, as my first friend and as my introducer to the concern, on the subject of this dissolution ; and I hope you will give me every information respecting the cause of this unfortunate business. I flatter myself that there can be no fault attached to my department, as I feel perfectly conscious of having exerted myself in every possible way to promote the interests of the company. I beg that you will write me candidly and without reserve.

The only satisfaction which he received for his disappointment was a grant of £60 for "the valuable information he had given to the directors." The impression produced on the mind by the perusal of Forster's correspondence with Mr. Nichol, the company's London agent, is that the directors had never really meant business—that the company was formed for speculative purposes—and that there never was any intention on the part of the directors to work the lease. That Forster was misled there can be no doubt ; the tone of his letters shows that this was the case. On the 29th June, a few days before the dissolution was publicly made known, he found it necessary to address Mr. Nichol in the following terms :—

> I am rather surprised not to have heard from you for some time, as I now wish to have some instructions how to proceed. I do not feel myself sufficiently authorised to order the mining materials which the workmen are in immediate want of. I therefore expect an immediate reply, or the works must stand still.

The company never really commenced mining operations. Forster might well feel disappointed at the turn which matters had taken. He had surrendered the direction of Sir George Alderson's mines and given up other engagements in order to accept one which promised to be permanent and lucrative, but which lasted only six months. He was not, however, long out of employment. On the 11th July he wrote this letter to Mr. Evans :—

I have this day received a letter from the directors of the Northern and Welsh Mining Company, in which I am informed that the company is dissolved, and that I am at liberty to engage myself in any way I please. I shall, therefore, be happy to meet you at Chester, at any time you may think most convenient. I shall be here for a week, or ten days, in order to arrange matters previous to my leaving altogether.

On the 12th July he wrote this to Mr. Nichol :—

I feel much obliged for your kind offer to recommend me to the Irish Mining Company, but I prefer to remain in England. I have had another letter from Mr. Acherley, of Bath, asking me to view some property of his in the neighbourhood of Chester. I propose going to Chester to-morrow morning to meet him.

These letters show that Forster could, without much difficulty, obtain that kind of employment which was most congenial to his tastes, and which was fairly remunerative. His charges for surveying were one guinea per day, during absence from home, and all expenses. One other letter of his should be read here ; it is dated Aberdovey, July 25th, 1825, and is addressed to Mr. Acherley, of Bath :—

I arrived here safely last night about 11 o'clock, having posted from Newport on account of the coaches only going a few days in the week. I found several letters which require immediate replies, one from the Honourable Mr. West, of Ruthvin Castle, requesting to know when I can meet him, in order to look over his estate, which he says is only about twenty miles from Chester. If I should pass through that city again whilst you are there, perhaps I shall have the pleasure of seeing you. I intend to make a fair copy of the report on your property, either this evening, or to-morrow morning, with a view to giving it publicity.

During the years 1825–6 Forster surveyed, sketched, and reported upon, mining properties in Cardiganshire, Merionethshire, Glamorganshire, Monmouthshire, Pembrokeshire, Montgomeryshire, Denbighshire, Shropshire, Cheshire, and the Isle of Man. Among the proprietors who availed themselves of his services were the Marquis of Bute, Lords Dynevor and Talbot, Sir Charles Morgan, Sir Watkin W. Wynne, Sir John Aubrey, Sir G. Alderson, W. E. Powell, Esq., Athelstane Corbet, Esq., and Pryse Pryse, Esq.

Some idea of the way in which Forster went about his work may
be formed from an extract taken from the report, already referred to
in this memoir, which he drew up in 1823 for the satisfaction of Sir
George Alderson :—

It is my opinion that a general survey should be made of the whole of the ground
belonging to Mr. Powell, that the courses of the rivers and brooks, and the position
of the hills should be noted, that the bearings of the veins should be taken, and the
appearances of lead-ore observed, and that a plan of the whole district should be
constructed, on which all these points should be indicated. Such a plan might be
the means of making valuable discoveries, and would, in any case, facilitate future
trials in this manor. I shall take the liberty of remarking that more attention must
be given to the dressing of the ores. I should advise the proprietors to employ an
English washing master, who is fully competent to conduct washing operations.
He should daily instruct the washers and examine the ore in order to see that it is
properly prepared for the smelter before it is sent away from the mines. In the smelting
operations great attention should be paid to the consumption of coal and lime, as
they are very expensive articles in this place. The coal not being sufficiently bituminous there is a great waste in coking, which might, in a great measure, be avoided
by the erection of two roasting furnaces. They would make as much coke as would
be sufficient for one slag-hearth, and thus effect a considerable saving. I am of the
opinion that the ore, when properly dressed, will yield 63 per cent.; but I think that
the lead will not be refineable, or, in other words, that it does not contain sufficient
silver to pay the expenses of refining. I have no doubt that there are some argen-
tiferous pieces of ore mixed among the other ores, but the silver they contain is lost
in the general mass. It is necessary that frequent assays of the ore be made in order
that the real produce of lead may be ascertained.

No one can doubt that the man who drew up the report, from
which this extract is taken, thoroughly understood mining in all
its branches, and that, moreover, he was anxious to promote the
interests of his employers. Above ground, or under ground, on the
washing floor, or in the smelting house, Forster appears to have been
equally at home. He knew what he was about, and he could make
others understand what he meant. His language is clear and to
the point. There are, in this extract, none of those vague generalities
which characterise the reports of men who are afraid to commit
themselves to precise and definite statements. Forster's report is as
honest and manly as it is clear. He gives his employers some
wholesome advice. Their washing master, a Welshman, was not
sufficiently competent; he advises them to dismiss him and employ

an Englishman in his stead, who could instruct the washer boys, examine the ores, and dress them properly. There was a waste of coal and lime going on in the smelting house; he points out how that waste might be avoided by the expenditure of a little capital on the erection of two roasting furnaces. His employers imagined that the ores contained sufficient silver to pay for the cost of its extraction; he tells them plainly that such is not the case.

Surveying excursions suited Forster exactly. He was an expert draughtsman and a ready penman, and was, moreover, fond of exercising both his hand and his brain on any subject worthy of his attention, as the plans and papers which he has left testify. He was also an earnest student of that youngest of the sciences—geology. These excursions were, therefore, a source of pleasure to him; and as they were also, as has already been stated, fairly remunerative, he would have acted wisely had he never entangled himself in the concerns of the Welsh mining companies. His income from all sources during the year 1825 was probably not less than £1,000— a sum which was sufficient to maintain himself and his sister in a state of comfort. He was now well known in the North of England, the South of Scotland, and Wales, as an accomplished surveyor— an able mining engineer—and one of the most eminent geologists of the day. He had already been employed by some of the largest landowners in the north and west of our island; some of his reports had appeared in the public prints and had attracted considerable attention; his fame had even extended beyond the shores of Britain; and his services were in request in Ireland and Spain. Notwithstanding the failure of his mining agency, his prospects were at this time very fair; yet soon after this time they began to grow dim, and those pecuniary troubles began to gather round him which saddened the remainder of his life.

The causes of those troubles are not far to seek. Forster's youth and early manhood were spent in the midst of plenty. Though there was no superabundance of wealth in his father's house, there was, on the other hand, no poverty. There was no need to practice that severe economy which is often the last resource of honest respectability. On the death of his father Forster inherited the Ivy estate, though a considerable portion of the income derived

from it was settled upon Mrs. Forster for her life. That Mrs.
Forster's income was quite sufficient for her wants is shown by
two documents found among her son's papers. One of them is, a
receipt for a legacy of £100, left by the will of Lucy Forster,
deceased, to her son Westgarth. The other is a receipt for a legacy
of £50, left by the said Lucy Forster to her daughter Phœbe.
Three sons and two daughters survived the death of their mother.
If each of the sons received £100, and each of the daughters £50,
by her will, she must have left £400 in all, which sum probably
represents the amount of her savings during the nine years she
outlived her husband. A person who is able to save £45 per
annum out of his income is not badly off.

If, then, Lucy Forster was left in such easy circumstances
by her husband, it is reasonable to infer from the fact that
her eldest son Westgarth inherited from his father a considerable property, into the full enjoyment of which he would come
on the death of his mother in 1806; and, notwithstanding the loss
which he incurred in 1809, there are good reasons for believing
that he was at this time, 1825, in the enjoyment of a comfortable
income. How then are we to account for the straitened circumstances of his after life, when his need was so great that he offered
his services to a small mining company for £60 per annum, and
was compelled to part with the books and minerals which he prized
so highly? The answer to this question will be found in the events
which are now to be narrated.

Soon after the dissolution of the Northern and Welsh Mining
Association, a new company was formed in London, which
took up the forfeited leases. Forster was offered and accepted
the agency. The salary was to be £150 per annum until the
mines became productive, when it was to be raised to a higher
figure. His relation to the new company is clearly defined in
a letter which he wrote to his friend Mr. Hogg, some time
before he accepted the agency:—"The plan I now mean to
adopt is to survey and report upon mining ground for private
gentlemen and public companies, and to direct the mining operations
of this company, through under-agents, if required. With respect
to salary, I hope the company will not think £150 too much for

the first year." In a letter addressed to the Honourable Mr. West, dated September 30th, 1825, he says:—"Part of Mr. Corbet's mines are likely to be engaged by a London company. I have an offer to take the direction of them, but my engagement will not be of such a nature as to prevent my surveying or taking the direction of mines belonging to other companies."

He entered upon his new agency on the 1st January, 1826. The company's London agent was a gentleman of the name of Nugent. To prevent any future misunderstandings with respect to the conditions of his engagement, Forster wrote to Mr. Hogg, who was in communication with Mr. Nugent, in the following terms:—"I suppose that Mr. Nugent perfectly understands that my engagement is such that I am at liberty to survey and report upon mines which belong to other concerns than this. I shall not, however, leave home so as to neglect the company's affairs." Such an arrangement could not possibly last long. No company could allow its chief agent to spend the main portion of his time away from their mines. Forster left Aberdovey on the 23rd January to survey some mines in Shropshire, and did not return until the middle of February. No one will be surprised to learn that his management did not give satisfaction to the directors, that another agent of the name of Marshall was sent down from London in the autumn, and that Forster threw up the agency in the spring of 1827. His reasons for resigning are fully stated in a letter to Mr. Hogg, dated August 9th:—

I sent in my resignation of this agency in May last, forwarding it to Messrs. Nugent and Mayhew at their office in London. They accepted it only a few days ago, having kept me three months in suspense. My reasons for resigning were:—1st. The action taken by the company in sending down people here only a few months after I had commenced operations, which led me to think that they did not place that confidence in me which is necessary for the proper management of such a concern. Mr. Marshall came down without any letter of introduction from the directors, but said he was in the concern. He assumed authority and took the management of the works. I wrote to Mr. Nugent to learn whether I was to continue to have the sole direction of the mining operations, and whether Mr. Marshall was officially employed, but he returned me no answer. Mr. Marshall knows nothing about mining, and he is a person with whom I want to have little connection. A mine which I recommended to the company in March last has turned out well. In the level there is a rib of ore 12 inches wide, and four men can raise nearly a ton per day.

On the same day, August 9th, Forster wrote to the Messrs. Mayhew:—"Gentlemen,—I have received your letter accepting my resignation. The books and papers in my possession, which belong to the company, are ready whenever Mr. Marshall can make it convenient to settle accounts. I have great pleasure in informing you that since I sent in my resignation the mine at Uddy-ny-Bryddell, which I recommended to you in March, is now exceedingly productive." His resignation was followed by consequences which no one could have foreseen.

When the question of remuneration for the services rendered by Forster to the company came before the directors in August, 1827, they found that they were not in a position to make him an adequate return for the discovery of the valuable mine at Uddy-ny-Bryddell. They had had the greatest difficulty in meeting the ordinary expenses of their mines. In the month of March, Forster, writing to his friend Hogg, said that he very much feared the company had not capital enough to prosecute the mines in a systematic manner. On more than one occasion he had been obliged to pay the workmen out of his own pocket, and then wait until the directors were able to refund the money. His own salary was in arrears. How then were the directors to raise, in a short time, a sum sufficient to compensate their agent for his services? They seem to have readily recognised his claims; but they were never able to satisfy them in the only way that could be satisfactory both to themselves and to him, that is, by a ready-money payment. When the mines were closed in January, 1828, Forster had received nothing from the company; but the directors then made him all the compensation they were able to make by putting him in possession of the lead-ore deposit which he had discovered. The transaction proved to be an unfortunate one for Forster. The mine was productive, but lead was then selling at a very low price— much lower than that at which it is now selling. In 1828-9-30, £12 per ton was gladly accepted for lead. When prices are ruling so low as this none but the very richest mines are remunerative. Uddy-ny-Bryddell was not one of the richest, and therefore could not, even under the skilful management of Forster, be made to pay. In accepting the offer of the directors, he had accepted also the responsibility of working the lease which they had surrendered —a responsibility to which he was unequal under the circumstances of the time.

But this was not the only responsibility under which he was placed. In a letter which he addressed to his friend Mr. Hogg, in September, 1827, there occurs the following passage:— " The mine that I am concerned with in Cardiganshire is not yet profitable. I have already engaged some ground which I think is promising, and I purpose placing two miners on it to make a trial. I have likewise other two places in view which I shall inform you of as soon as I have secured them." The mania for speculation in mining seems to have seized upon the imagination of Forster soon after the resignation of the last agency in 1827.

Before the spring of the year 1829 he had spent nearly all that he possessed upon abortive trials. He could not now fall back upon mine-surveying as a means of gaining a livelihood, for no one wanted his services. The lead trade was in a most depressed condition. Forster had at this time some tons of lead ore lying at Uddy-ny-Bryddell which he could scarcely dispose of at any price. When at last he did succeed in selling it he lost £70 by the transaction. Without money and without employment, a man verging upon his sixtieth year, and living among comparative strangers, is not in an enviable position. Such was Forster's position during the summer of 1829. All the property he now possessed was at Garrigill, and consisted of his furniture, plate, pictures, books, and minerals. The three first were family heirlooms, and, as such, were highly prized by him; the two latter were almost as dear to him. He could not part with any of them without a pang; yet it seemed probable that he would soon be obliged to part with all. That Forster felt his position most keenly is clear from the following letters to his cousin, George Forster, his sister Phœbe, and his friend John Fulton:—

Aberdovey, 19*th July,* 1829.

Dear Cousin,—It is so long since we had any correspondence that I scarcely know how to address you. I hope you will excuse my long silence. I regret that it should be necessary to tell you that I have met with many disappointments here; one disappointment has followed another so closely that I cannot now see my way through the difficulties by which I am surrounded. I am very well in health, and for this blessing I thank God. I am at present conducting a copper mine for Mr. Corbet, the Lord of the manor, who allows me a small salary, but it is so small that, unless something else turns up, I do not know what we shall do. I must not, however, despair, but hope for the best. If your son, Thomas, who, I am informed, has now the management of Hebburn Colliery, could find a place suitable for me I should be glad to accept it. I shall be happy to hear from you. My sister joins me in kind regards to Hannah and family, and I am, your affectionate cousin,

W. FORSTER.

September 30th, 1829.

Dear Sister,—Yours of the 8th inst. was duly received. I should have answered it before now, but have been waiting a week or two in the hope that I might have some better news to communicate. When I wrote to you last I told you that I had a little engagement with Mr. Corbet, but was afraid it would only be temporary. Such it has turned out to be ; Mr. Corbet has stopped the mine. I shall be quite out of employment in a few days. I cannot see my way at present. I do not, however, despair, but hope that, through God's providence, something will turn up. If Thomas will give Mr. Dickinson a note I shall allow goods to the value of the amount advanced, with interest, to remain with you, but I object to anything being taken out of the house. If times do not turn better soon I shall be obliged to return to the north, when I shall settle with Mr. Dickinson. If I cannot make any better arrangement, I shall dispose of as many articles as will be necessary to raise a sum sufficient to settle his account. My sister must, in that case, seek a situation in London. My sister joins me in kindest regards to Thomas and the lads.—I am, your affectionate brother, W. FORSTER.

July 27th, 1829.

Dear Friend,—I was duly favoured with your letter of the 21st ult. through Mr. Leathart, with whom I should have sent back an answer had their (Mr. Leathart's and Mr. Jacob Walton's) stay here not been so short. My situation here is, at present, so precarious that every nerve requires to be strained in order to keep the wheel going. The place where I am living is pleasantly situated. It commands a good view of the sea and of the river Dovey, which is navigable for eight miles up stream. The sands are beautiful and the scenery fine ; the situation is also healthy and, if I could only see a way out of my present difficulties, I should have no desire to leave ; but my prospects are very gloomy. I should feel obliged if you would give my respects to Mr. H. Lee Pattinson and urge him to let me know the result of the analysis of the copper and lead ores which I sent with Mr. Leathart. My sister joins me in best respects to your wife and family.—I am, yours, &c., W. FORSTER.

To Mr. John Fulton.

On the 9th September Forster wrote a letter to the Messrs. Aldersons which contains the following passage :—"From accounts which have come to me, I hear that mining concerns in the North are in as bad a state as they are here." Forster was now in his 58th year, and had probably lost some portion of his wonted energy. He felt that he was scarcely equal to the difficulties of his position; hence his tone of despondency, and his misgivings with regard to the future. The son of a gentleman, and the descendant of an ancient family; brought up in the midst of plenty; the recipient of an excellent education; the possessor of an honourable name and of a high character; and endowed with talents by the exercise of which he had created for himself a considerable reputation, Forster might well shrink from the fate which seemed to await his old age.

His state of despondency was intensified when he thought of Susan; she had been his constant companion for many years—the partner of his joys and his sorrows—the trusty friend who was always by his side in the hour of need—the prudent counsellor whose advice he had been accustomed to seek in every difficulty—the affectionate sister whose admiration for her brother could not be diminished by any failures on his part; yet she must now leave him and seek a situation in the great metropolis. Such was the prospect which Forster was compelled to look in the face. There is little doubt that the contemplation of it seriously affected his naturally robust health, and brought his life to a premature end. Whilst waiting in the midst of his difficulties for whatever Providence might send, his friend Thomas Alderson, the brother of Sir George, came to his aid with an offer which Forster was fain to accept. The nature of that offer will appear on reading the following letters:—

Aberdovey, March 2nd, 1830.

Dear Sir,—I was duly favoured yesterday with a letter from your friend, Mr. Lambert, saying that he wished to see me in London as soon as possible. I intend to take the first coach, which will leave here on Wednesday morning. The coaches only run from here on two days in the week. I expect to be in town either on Thursday night, or Friday morning, when I shall call upon you according to Mr. Lambert's request.—I am, dear Sir, with best respects to Mr. Douglas, yours, etc.,·

Thos. Alderson, Esq.,   W. FORSTER.

     16, Great Marlborough Street, London.

April 5th, 1830.

Dear Sister,—I suppose you think that I am lost or dead, so long is it since I wrote to you. I have pleasure in saying that such is not the case, although I have had many difficulties to contend with during these hard times. I am just returned from London, where I have been engaging with a gentleman to go out to North America to view some mining ground there. I received the offer through the recommendation of the Aldersons. We sail about the 20th inst. If, therefore, you desire to write to me before that date, you must do so on the receipt of this. I shall leave my sister here until I return, when I shall come down to the north and settle with Mr. Dickinson. I hope you will take care of my furniture, etc., until I return. Hoping that you are well, I am, your affectionate brother,   W. FORSTER.

To Mrs. Thos. Brown.

Aberdovey, April 7th, 1830.

Sir,—I beg to inform you that I arrived here safely on Saturday last after experiencing some very cold weather. I took an inside passage from London to Shrewsbury. I shall take the Machynlleth coach for Liverpool on Friday week. When you see Mr. Alderson and Mr. Douglas please to remember me to them.—I am, Sir, yours, etc.,   W. FORSTER.

Francis Lambert, Esq.

April 20th, 1830.

Sir,—I am sorry that I have not had an opportunity of saying good-bye to you before starting for America. I had a letter yesterday morning from Mr. Lambert requesting me to meet him at Liverpool on Thursday next. I am obliged, therefore, to go by way of Dolgelly on account of the coach. It would give me pleasure if I could render you any service respecting your mines. I did name your mines to Mr. Alderson when in town, and you will in all probability see Mr. Douglas in the course of the summer. The plans of Aberdovey and Millinlynpair are left in my sister's charge. You can have them whenever you want them.—I am, Sir, yours, etc.,

Athelstane Corbet, Esq.   W. FORSTER.

The next letter is dated Aberdovey, January 5th, 1831 :—

Sir,—I have duly received yours of the 26th ult., and have now enclosed in a packet my report, with a plan and some sections and sketches, which I hope you will receive, and I hope they will meet with your approbation. I shall also forward a box of minerals in the course of a few days. The week before we sailed for England we went up Hudson's River as far as Albany, and saw Professor L. C. Beck and W. Webster, Esq., at the Institute. They were very polite, and presented me with some specimens of minerals. They would also have given me a letter of introduction to Professor Easton, who lives in Coventry—two miles above Troy—but I declined it on account of time, as we had to sail in a few days. I obtained some sections, of which I send you copies. Enclosed you will find a statement of my account, which I hope will meet with your approval. I feel much obliged for your kind offer of reference ; I shall certainly avail myself of it if I should require it. I had no opportunity of seeing either Patterson or Dr. James, but I saw your brother at New York a few days before we sailed. He was very well, and gave me a letter for you which was sent on from Liverpool. All the advice I can at present give you is contained in the report, but if you find that I have omitted anything upon which you want information, I beg you will let me know, and I shall be happy to attend to it. A day or two previous to my departure from New York, I was requested by the Phœnix Copper Mine Co. to take a commission to get them partners, and provided I could not succeed in doing so, I was requested to dispose of their concern. I undertook the business on the understanding that I should first be allowed to consult you with reference to it. If you would kindly give me your advice, I should then put you in possession of the particulars.—I am, Sir, your obliged servant,

Francis Lambert, Esq.,   W. FORSTER.

11 and 12, Coventry Street, London.

In the next letter Forster gives an account of his travels in America :—

February 25th, 1831.

Dear Fulton,—I was only favoured with yours of the 23rd ult. on the 6th inst. I should have replied to it ere this had I not been so much engaged since my return from America. I now take the opportunity of giving you a sketch of my travels on that continent. We sailed from Liverpool in the fine packet-ship " Napoleon," of New York, on Monday, the 26th of April, 1830, and had a fairly good voyage of thirty-two days across the Atlantic, arriving at New York on Friday, the 28th May. The entrance from Sandy Nook commands the finest and most extensive prospect I ever before beheld. The water scenery is grand, Long Island being on one side of the harbour, and Staten Island on the other, there being many small islets scattered about in various directions. New York is a pretty large place, admirably situated for trade and commerce, being on a point between Hudson River and Long Island Sound. The Hudson is navigable for nearly 200 miles, and since the introduction of steam-boats by your ingenious namesake, Fulton, travelling is rendered both commodious and cheap. The boats travel at the rate of twelve miles an hour. When we arrived at New York we stopped a few days in that city, and then proceeded by the Union Line Steam-boat to New Brunswick—a distance of 45 miles—the scenery being fine for the whole of the way. Thence we proceeded another 11 miles by coach to Somerville, in the county of Somerset, and the State of New Jersey, which was to be the place of our residence when we were not travelling. After staying there about a fortnight, and viewing some copper mines in the neighbourhood, we journeyed by stage to Trenton, on the river Delaware, and thence by steam-boat down to the city of Philadelphia, which is a fine place, situated between the Delaware and the Schuylkill rivers. Most of the public buildings are of white marble, a stone which is found not far from the city. We stopped here a few days, and then proceeded by stage upwards of ninety miles to view the coal mines at Pottsville, which were only discovered about eight years ago. At that time there were only two houses at the place ; now it is a considerable town, and still continues to increase. The coal-field is of immense extent, and contains numerous seams, which vary in thickness from 14 inches to 6 feet, and it is so situated that the miners drive the level in the coal. The proprietors can open a mine for £10. I could tell you a great deal more about this coal-field, but I must curtail my description at present. There is a canal running along the banks of the Schuylkill, by which the coal is brought down to Philadelphia. From Pottsville I went to Mauch Chunk, on the Lehigh river, a tributary of the Delaware. This also is an immense coal-field. The mine, or quarry (for such it really is), opens upon the road by means of three passages, each eight or ten feet deep. The upper seam of anthracite is of great thickness, and has only about 3 feet of soil resting upon it. A boring of 20 feet through the slate has reached another seam of coal. From the mines there is a railway, on an inclined plane, running down to the bank of the canal, a distance of 9 miles. The waggons are impelled forward by the force of gravity, at the rate of 8 miles an hour, and are brought back again, when emptied of the coal, by mules. The mules themselves are carried down the incline in empty waggons, four in each waggon. The arrangement is a very curious one. There are passenger waggons for the use of visitors, which are drawn up by ponies.

I returned from Mauch Chunk by way of Easton, on the Delaware, to Somerville. After the lapse of a week or so I had to return to New York, from whence I proceeded by steamboat to Connecticut, in order to view the Phœnix Copper Mines, which are distant from New York about 150 miles. The scenery on the Connecticut river is beautiful. I am not at liberty to give you an account of the copper mines, though I may tell you that the copper is of good quality. Before I embarked for Britain I had a sail up the Hudson's river as far as Albany, a distance of 145 miles, for the purpose of visiting some scientific gentlemen who live there. I cannot give you here a detailed account of this visit, as I must now conclude this letter. I notice what you say about the low price of land in England, but the price is still lower in America. An American would say, "I guess you are (at Alston) in a bad way." Please to give my respects to Mr. and Mrs. Shaw.—Yours truly,

To John Fulton, Alston.   W. FORSTER.

One other letter, which was written by Forster soon after his return from America, may be given here. It was addressed to a Mr. George Bacon, who is supposed to have been the son of Charles Edward Bacon, and the grandson of John Bacon Forster:—

Aberdovey, May 3rd, 1831.

Dear Sir,—I was favoured with yours of the 24th March on the 29th ult. I am glad to hear that you have disposed of that portion of the mine you wished to sell. I have not been fortunate enough to find any person here willing to purchase. I shall be happy to see the gentleman to whom you have sold our interest in the mine, when he arrives in this country. I should have no objections to settle in America, provided I could obtain a permanent situation there. I should thank you for some specimens of gold, and especially for the one we saw in a shop window. I should feel obliged if you could procure it for me. I am happy to say that my sister and I are quite well: she joins me in best respects to your family, to Mr. and Mrs Stodart, and to your brother.—Yours truly,

To Mr. G. Bacon,   W. FORSTER.
    167, Broadway, New York.

Among Forster's "American Sketches" are views of the Wooden Bridge over the Delaware, at Trenton; the Wooden Bridge over the Schuylkill, at Philadelphia; the Coal Mines at Pottsville, Pennsylvania; the Single-arch Wooden Bridge over the Schuylkill, taken from the water-works at Philadelphia; the Hotel at Mauch Chunk, Pennsylvania; Scene in front of the Hotel; the Chimney Rock and the Butter-milk Stream, New Jersey; the South-west aspect of the Bridgewater Mountain; the Tallcott Mountain, as seen from the Phœnix Copper Mine, Connecticut; the Mountain which is seen from Plainfield, New Jersey; the Wooden Bridge over the Bariton, near Somerville; the Mill Pond, near Pluckemin; Fox Hill, as seen from the Vanausdales Mine; and of New Jersey. There are also ground-plan sketches of Pottsville and Mauch Chunk,—a Section of the Strata at the Pottsville Coal Mines, and a sketch of the Great Coal Seam at Mauch Chunk.

This narrative must here leap over an interval of two years and three months. On the 3rd May, 1831, Forster wrote to George Bacon from Aberdovey; on the 5th August, 1833, he wrote his cousin George and Mr. Wm. Crawhall, from Garrigill. The papers which relate to the period between those two dates are lost. There is no reliable information to show where, or how, he spent that portion of his life. There is a probability that he then visited Ireland. He had the offer of an engagement in that country in 1825, but declined it; if it were renewed in 1831, he might probably have accepted it. There is a probability, amounting almost to a certainty, that he visited Spain. When the Northern and Welsh Mining Association was dissolved, the directors recommended him to a situation in Spain, which he then declined because of his ignorance of the Spanish and French languages, and because he did not desire to sever his connections with the English and Welsh mining proprietors. Those connections having been severed by circumstances over which he had no control, and there being little prospect of their renewal, he might, if the offer was again made, reconsider his former decision, and go to Spain. Mrs. W. B. Brown, of Ivy House, informs the writer, that not many years ago she saw and read a portion of the diary which Forster kept whilst in Spain, and that she particularly remembers his account of a visit to Madrid.

That diary was not written before May, 1831; neither was it written after April, 1833. It must then have been written during the interval. If Forster went to Spain, he had returned to Wales before April, 1833, for he says in his letter to his cousin George, "yours of the 17th April was duly received at Aberdovey. Since that time I have been kept in suspense by two parties." Up to that time he had apparently been employed somewhere, probably in Spain. Forster sailed from Aberdovey, for the last time, on the 25th July, 1833, in the ship "Alliance," landed at Liverpool on the 27th, arrived at Penrith on the 28th, and at Garrigill on the 29th. He tells us in his diary that his sister's family "were busy in the hay-field when he walked into the village, but that they were all glad to see him after his long absence." His arrival soon became known throughout Alston Moor, and many were the "callers" at Ivy House during the following week. Among the first were Mr. T. Dickinson, father-in-law of the late Mr. Thomas Sopwith, and "a young gentleman named Grey, son of the new receiver for Greenwich Hospital." On the 31st, Forster took his first walk, since his arrival, through the village. He "saw many people whom he knew by sight, but could not recollect their names." He found the village much improved :—" Several new houses had been built, the bridges had been repaired, and the plantations had grown." But Forster thought of the dead as well as the living. Many of his old friends were now sleeping in the village churchyard. Thither, then, he wended his way on Sunday, the 4th August, and spent some time in meditation amongst the tombs. Near the angle which is formed by the east and south walls of the church are situated the graves of his parents and of four of his brothers and sisters. Though he makes no special mention of them, there can be little doubt that he visited them on that Sunday morning, and as little doubt that, whilst he stood by them, recollections of the past thronged upon him. Few men can look back upon the past with complete satisfaction; most men see in it many causes of regret, many mistakes which they would be glad to rectify if they had the power to do so. Such was the case with Forster. He had begun life under favourable circumstances; he had had the advantages of a good education, and a good start in a profession for which he was eminently qualified, and to which, if the choice had lain with himself, he would have given the preference over every other. In that profession he had distinguished himself so much that his name had become a household word in the mining districts of the North of England, the South of Scotland, and Wales. Yet now, in the sixtieth year of his age, when all his powers, physical and mental, were failing, he stood by the graves of his parents a poor man. The causes of his misfortunes have already been pointed out in this memoir. His thoughts at this time seem to have distressed him, and stimulated him to make new efforts to obtain a situation, for on the morrow of that Sunday he wrote these two letters :—

August 5th, 1833.

Dear Cousin,—I hear that there is a vacancy in the second agency at Coalcleugh. If you have any influence with Cuthbert Rippon, Esq., M.P., I should esteem it a favour if you would get him to speak to T. W. Beaumont, Esq., in my behalf. If you know of anything else that would suit me, I should feel obliged if you would let me know.—I am, your affectionate cousin, W. FORSTER.

Mr. George Forster, Hebburn.

Dear Sir,—I arrived here a few days ago from Wales. As I am at present out of employment, I should feel obliged if you would recommend me to a situation. I have been informed that there is a vacancy at Coalcleugh. I should feel happy to take your advice with respect to writing to Mr. Beaumont on the subject.—I am, yours, etc., W. FORSTER.

Wm. Crawhall, Esq.

In reply to these letters he was informed that there was no vacancy at Coalcleugh. Just when the gloom was thickest and when every ray of hope seemed to be intercepted by the dark clouds which had gathered over his head, there fell upon him a momentary gleam of sunshine in the form of a letter from Mr. Francis Lambert, which informed him that he had been recommended to an important agency by Mr. Lambert. Forster wrote the following letter in reply :—

November 29th, 1833.

Dear Sir,—I received your favour of the 15th inst., enclosed in a packet, on the 23rd inst., for which I beg to return you my thanks.

I have written to Richard Salter, Esq., under the cover sent here, enclosing a letter to the directors of the Alten Mining Association, stating my qualifications, &c.

E

I have named the Messrs. Aldersons and yourself as gentlemen to whom they can refer. I could refer them to several others, if necessary. I should esteem it a favour if you would kindly inform me of the time the directors would require my services, and of the salary they offer. I should prefer to go out to Norway as a surveyor and inspector, but should not object to assist in drawing up the bargains.

From Mr. Petherick's report I judge that it is very good mining ground. There is now more spirit among the miners in this neighbourhood, the price of lead having gone up.—Yours truly,   W. FORSTER.

Francis Lambert, Esq.

He was again doomed to disappointment. On the 6th of December he received a reply from the directors of the Alten Mining Association, in which he was told that "there were no vacancies in their establishment." The receipt of this reply marks the close of Forster's professional career. During the winter of 1833–4 he became conscious that his health was failing and that he was no longer equal to the discharge of any active duties. He, therefore, ceased to think of another situation. In the month of February, 1834, he disposed of his furniture, books, plate, pictures, and minerals,* realising by the sale of them a sum which was sufficient to maintain him in comfort during the short remainder of his life. He seems to have recovered, in a measure, his habitual cheerfulness, soon after his retirement from active life, for early in March he is found taking great interest in the affairs of the village, visiting his friends, and attending to his correspondence. Among his correspondents at this time were Professor Sedgwick and Hugh Lee Pattinson. When the weather was favourable, he spent a portion of his time in open air sketching and planning; when unfavourable, he amused himself within doors by colouring the plates in some volumes of the "Strata" which remained unsold. Forster was a regular attender on the divine service—at church, when service was held there—at chapel, when there was no service in the church. He very seldom stayed away from service when well enough to go.

On Monday, the 6th July, 1835, he was seized with the illness which terminated his life. He died at Ivy House on the 9th of November.

* The minerals were sold to Richard Cust, Esq., of Carlisle; the pictures were sent to London.

Though nearly half a century has elapsed since the grave closed over Westgarth Forster's remains, his name still continues a household word amongst the people of Alston Moor; he lives in their minds as a clever, though somewhat eccentric man, different in many respects from the ordinary run of men. But it is not only among the Alstonians that his name lives ; it is frequently heard in Weardale and Allendale. Local mining agents and local geologists are familiar with it; mining agents and geologists, who have a reputation which is more than local, still continue to quote him as an authority on mining and geological questions. His "Section of the Strata" is still the standard work on the geology of the two northern counties. It was never more highly prized by miners than it is now. Though the book was written when the science of geology was in its initial stage; when even people of education recognised no distinction between one kind of rock and another ; when such terms as stratified and unstratified, aqueous and igneous, seldom appeared in print, and were scarcely ever heard ; when the great works of Buckland, De la Beche, Philips, Lyell, Murchison, Sedgwick, and other geologists had not yet appeared, the classification of the strata, which it contains, is the one still in use. Forster rendered valuable service to the sciences of mining and geology, and for that service, if for no other reason, his name will continue to be remembered for a long time to come.

The letters and extracts quoted in this memoir show how upright and honourable he was in his dealings. The following short extracts show him as a relation and a friend. In the autumn of 1825, Mr. G. Forster, his brother, who was then living at Carlisle, was taken ill, together with some members of his family. Westgarth wrote him as follows :—

I received James' letter in due time. I am sorry to hear of the severe affliction of yourself and family, but hope that before this time you are quite recovered. I shall be happy to hear that you are able to go about again. Keep up your spirit, and there is no fear but that you will do well with William's assistance, who, I am glad to hear, is quite recovered. It gives me great pleasure to learn that he conducts himself with great propriety. I have no doubt but that he will be a comfort to you.

To Mr. John Leathart :—

I yesterday received a letter from James McLaurin, Esq., of Dalkeith, near Edinburgh, wishing me to recommend an agent to conduct some mines in Ireland. If you are not better engaged, I think this might be a desirable situation for you. I must, therefore, beg that you will write Mr. McLaurin on the subject as soon as you have made up your mind whether you will accept it or not. I have not forgot my old friends in the north, and must beg you will remember me to them all, particularly to Mr. John Dickinson, Mr. Hugh Lee Pattinson, and Mr. John Fulton.

The sense of humour was not very strong in Forster, though it was not entirely wanting. In a letter to his sister at Garrigill, dated 29th May, 1826, there occurs this passage:—"As the names of our mines may perhaps be curious and a little puzzling to some of your grammarians, allow me to insert them here—Melin-llyn-pair, Uyddy-ny-bryddell, Panteidial, Gwyn-fryn." In his diary there occur the following entries :—

August 10th, 1833.—There is a set of comedians at Alston exhibiting the wild scenery of Garrigill in the olden times.

August 13th.—We went to hear the ventriloquists and spent an amusing evening.

September 15th.—In the afternoon I went down to the Flatt with some bride-cake for Mr. and Mrs. Morrison.

A

TREATISE ON A SECTION OF THE STRATA

FROM

NEWCASTLE-ON-TYNE TO CROSS FELL.

===

PART I.

1.—OF THE STRATIFICATION OF COAL, &c.

THE terms STRATUM (singular), and STRATA (plural), in geology signify one or more of the several beds, or layers, of stone, or of other substances, whereof the solid parts of the earth are composed. These strata consist of various kinds of matter, as freestone, lime-stone, indurated clay, coal, &c. (to be specified in the sequel), which are disposed in beds, the under surface of one bearing against, or lying upon, the upper surface of the inferior stratum, which last lies upon the next below in a similar manner.

Strata differ considerably from each other in thickness. Some of them are from sixty to upwards of one hundred feet from their upper to their under surface, while others are so thin as scarcely to be discernible.

Strata are divided, or parted, from each other by nearly parallel smooth separations, with occasionally a thin lamina of soft dusty matter between them, called the *parting;* at other times the two contiguous surfaces are closely joined together without the inter-position of any visible matter, though the respective substance of each stratum is quite distinct. In the latter case they are exceedingly difficult to separate, and are technically said to have a *bad parting.* Besides their principal divisions, or nearly parallel partings, there are, in some strata, secondary divisions, or partings, separating the same stratum into parts of different thickness, nearly parallel to each other, just as the principal partings divide the different strata from each other. But these secondary partings are neither so strong nor so visible to the eye, nor do they make so effectual a parting as the principal partings. They are only met with in the strata that are not of an uniform hardness, texture, or colour from their upper to their under surface.*

There are other divisions called *backs*, or *slines*, in almost every stratum, which cross the former horizontal ones transversely, and cut the whole stratum through its two surfaces, into long rhomboidal masses. These, again, are crossed by others, called *cutters*, or end joints, running either in an oblique, or perpendicular direction to the before-mentioned backs, and also cutting the stratum across through its two surfaces. Both these kinds of joints, the backs and cutters, generally extend from the upper or superior stratum down through several of the lower ones; so that, together with the horizontal partings, they divide measures of the strata into innumerable nearly cubical, prismatical, or rhomboidal figures, according to the thickness of the stratum and the position and number of the joints. These joints have, sometimes, a kind of soft dusty matter within them, like the first-mentioned horizontal partings. There are more backs and cutters in soft strata than in those that are hard. Limestone strata have usually the most open vertical joints; freestone of the siliceous or sandstone kind have also many open joints in some situations.†

A seam, or bed of coal, is a real stratum, which is found to be quite as regular as any of the concomitant strata found in the coalfield, lying above, or below the coal; or, indeed, as any other of the various strata which compose the crust of our globe.

---

* [Secondary partings. These are now known as planes of cleavage; they are met with only in rocks of sedimentary origin.—ED.]

† [Joints are lines of fracture; they are seldom parallel with each other.—ED.]

There are, sometimes, in coal-fields, a considerable number of strata of coal of various qualities and thicknesses, placed *stratum super stratum*, with other strata interposed between them; and sometimes different strata are so near to one another that two, three, or more of them, are cut through and worked in one pit.

Every stratum of coal has some degree of declivity or slope, together with a longitudinal, or horizontal, bearing; and stretches as far every way as the strata which accompany it. The conclusion, therefore, appears reasonable, that coal is not an adventitious recent production, but that every stratum of it bears its proportion in composing the superficies of our globe.

The strata are seldom found to lie in a truly horizontal position, but have generally an inclination or descent, called the *dip*, to some particular part of the horizon. If this inclination be to the east-ward, it is called an east dip and a west rise; if to the north, it is called a north dip and a south rise. This inclination, or dip, of the strata is found to prevail almost everywhere. In some places it varies very little from the level; in others, very considerably; and in some so much as to be nearly vertical. But whatever be the degree of inclination which the strata have to the horizon, they are always found to dip in the same regular and uniform manner throughout their whole extent, if not intercepted by a ridge, or a trough, or disordered by dykes, hitches, and troubles. If the strata have an east dip, they may, by the intervention of a dyke, or a trough, have on the other side an east rise, which is a west dip; but any considerable alteration in the dip is never met with, unless occasioned by circumstances similar to the last mentioned.

Every stratum in a whole range, or coal-field, is spread out to a vast extent in an inclined plane. A dead level line drawn across, or upon, this inclined plane is called the bearing of the strata; and another line drawn at right angles to the dead level line is called the declivity of the strata, or the dip and rise of the strata. In general we can see on the surface but a very little way from the rise to the dip, or along the line of declivity of the strata; because they soon dip down beneath the other strata which lie upon them;

but we can sometimes trace the same individual stratum, or number
of strata, along the surface or dead level line for several miles ;* and,
therefore, we may properly call this the longitudinal line of
bearing.

It seems very probable that in many places the strata stretch
as far upon the latitudinal line of declivity as they do upon
the longitudinal line of bearing, although we are unable to trace
them in this direction to any great distance. We often see the
edges of the strata bursting out in different places upon the
lines of bearing, such as the banks of rivers and rivulets, in
cliffs, scars, &c., and we frequently work quarries, and especially
beds of coal, to a considerable length upon the stretch of this
line.

From these observations it appears that every individual stratum
in the whole section has its own position, and that, in general, it
spreads as wide and stretches as far as any of those that are placed
above or below it, which may, perhaps, be for several miles in every
direction. Now a seam of coal being a regular stratum, when the
crop, or outburst, is once discovered, we may generally take it for
granted that it will spread as wide every way as any of the other
strata which are found to accompany it above, or below.†

The stratum which is placed immediately above the seam of coal
is properly called the roof of the coal; and the stratum which is
placed immediately below the seam of coal is, with equal propriety,
called the pavement, or floor, of the coal. Now these three, namely,
the seam of coal, its roof, and its pavement, with the other concomitant strata lying above and below them, generally preserve
their positions with respect to each other, and have the same lines
of bearing and declivity.

* Mr. Wm. Smith, of Milford, near Bath, was the first to extensively verify and
apply this very important geological fact, by having, prior to the year 1795, actually
traced and mapped the course of the beds of several of the thicker strata of the south-
east of England, across the island, from the west to the east sea, in his Geological
Map of England, sold by Carey, London. [Smith's map was published in 1809, the
year in which the first edition of this book appeared.—ED.]

† [In extensive areas strata sometimes thin out and disappear.—ED.]

We shall give an account here of the several strata of stone and other matters which are usually associated with coal, arranging them in six classes, which shall include all the varieties of strata that have been found to accompany coal in the coal-fields of England and Scotland.

I.—OF WHINSTONE.*

The strata of what is denominated whinstone are the hardest of all others. The angular pieces will sometimes cut glass. Whinstone is often of a very coarse texture, and, when broken across the grain, exhibits the appearance of large particles of sand in a semi-vitrified state. Each stratum is commonly homogeneous in substance and colour, and is often cracked from the surface downwards. These strata are generally black or dark blue; yet there are others of an ashen colour and light brown. Their thickness is inconsiderable, varying from five, or six feet, down to a few inches; and it is only in a few places that they are found to attain the maximum we have stated. In the air whinstone decays a little, leaving a brown powder; and in the fire it cracks and becomes reddish brown in colour.

II.—LIMESTONE.

Limestone, or what is called bastard limestone, is sometimes, though rarely, met with in collieries. It is a well-known stone; but, from its resemblance in hardness and colour, it is often mistaken for a kind of whin.

III.—POSTSTONE, OR GRITSTONE.

This is a sandstone of the firmest kind, and is next to the limestone in point of hardness and of solidity. It is of a very fine texture; and, when broken, appears as if composed of the finest sand. It is commonly found in a homogeneous mass, though variegated in colour; and is not very liable to perish on being exposed to the weather. Of this kind of stone there are four

* This is not a true whinstone, but a hard sandstone.

varieties, which may be distinguished by their colour. The most common is white post, which is sometimes variegated with streaks or spots, of brown, red, or black.

Grey post is also very common : it appears like a mixture of fine black and white sand, and is often variegated with brown and black streaks, which resemble small clouds. These spots are sometimes caused by particles of coal.

Brown or yellow post is often met with of different shades of colour, but most commonly of light ochre, or yellow. It is as hard as the others, and is also variegated occasionally with white and black streaks. Red post is generally of a dull red colour. It is rarely met with in collieries and is often streaked with white, or black.

All these poststones occur in strata of different thickness, being generally thicker than any other strata. They are separated from each other, and from other strata, by partings of plate, or shiver, coal, sand, or other soft matters of various colours.

IV.—SANDSTONE, OR STONEBIND.

This is an imperfect freestone of a coarser texture than post, and not so hard. Its pores are so open as to render it very pervious to water. When broken, it is apparently of a coarse, friable nature ; it moulders into sand when exposed to the wind and rain. It has frequently white shining spangles, pebbles, or nodules, and other small stones, enclosed in its mass.

This sandstone is most generally found in strata of considerable thickness, with few secondary partings, but where these do occur, they are generally sandy and soft. It is also occasionally found subdivided into layers, as thin as grey slates.

Two varieties of this stratum are met with, distinguished by their colours, grey and brown, which are of different shades, lighter, or darker, in proportion to the colouring matter contained in the stone.

V.—OF METAL-STONE, BIND, OR CLUNCH.[*]

This is a tolerably hard stratum, being, in point of hardness, next to sandstone, generally solid, compact, of considerable weight,

---

[*] A species of shale.

and of an argillaceous nature, containing, in many places, nodules, or balls of iron ore, and sometimes yellow, or white, pyrites. The surfaces of these strata are clean, polished, and frequently as smooth as glass. It is internally of a fine texture, and when broken has a dusky appearance, resembling that of dried clay mixed with particles of coal. It is hard in the mine, or quarry, but when exposed to the fresh air, it falls into very small pieces, and at length into clay. The most usual colour of this stone is blackish; but there are several other lighter colours, down to light brown, or grey. Metal-stone is easily distinguished from freestone by its texture and colour, as well as by its other characteristics. It occurs in strata of various thickness, though seldom so thick as the two last-mentioned kinds of stone.

VI.—OF SHIVER, SHALE, OR PLATE.

This stratum is met with more frequently than any other in collieries. There are many varieties of it, which differ from each other both in hardness and colour, but they all agree in their principal characteristics.

The black shiver is by far the most common, and is called by the miners *black metal*, or *bleas*. It is softer than metal-stone, and, in the mine, is a tough rather than a hard substance. It is not, however, of a solid, or compact nature, but seems to be a sort of indurated clay, which is rendered easily separable by the multitude of its partings into very thin pieces, or laminæ, of unequal thickness. These laminæ break again into irregular rhomboidal fragments when struck with a slight force, and they have the property of rapidly absorbing water.

Each of these small pieces has a polished, glassy surface, and when broken across the grain appears of a dry, laminated texture, like exceedingly fine clay.

Shale is very friable, feels to the touch like an unctuous substance, and falls in air, or water, into a fine pinguid black clay. Nodules of iron, called catheads, are often found in it.

An accurate knowledge of the strata is indispensably necessary
to the coal master; and to obtain this knowledge he should himself
enter the pits, and levels which are sunk, or driven, in the coal-field.
In these he will see a great number of the different strata of stone, and
of the other coal metals,* thick and thin, hard and soft. An accurate
coal master will make himself well acquainted with the quality,
colour, and thickness of each of these, and will ascertain how far each
of them is above, or below, such and such a seam of coal. He will
carefully consider the order of the different strata, as they lie *stratum
super stratum*, with respect to one another, so that when he sees
any one of them he will know what others are to be found next to
it, either above, or below. This knowledge is often of great use
to him ; as, for instance, when the coal is thrown either up, or down,
by one of those faults, or slips, which will be presently described.
In this case the coal appears to be lost. Well, what is he to do in
this difficulty ? The coal is of too much consequence to be given
up. What method then is to be adopted in order to recover it ?
This the master cannot determine properly until he first knows how
far it is thrown out of its course, up, or down. The readiest way
to ascertain the position of the coal is to pierce the stratum, which
faces the workmen where the coal is cut off and lost; and if he
knows it with certainty he is encouraged to proceed, as he is
thereby made tolerably sure how far the coal is thrown off its
ordinary level, either up, or down; and, he can then decide as to
the most proper method to recover it with the least expenditure of
time and money. The coal is sometimes thrown a great way out
of its former position by faults, dykes,† or slips, which frequently
make it necessary to search for it on the other side of such troubles ;
it is sometimes prudent to quit the former station altogether,
and sink new pits. When this is the case an intimate acquaintance
with the strata, which, in that particular district, accompany the

---

* By coal metals, or coal measures, in treating of coal, are meant such strata as
are commonly found accompanying coal, without reference to metallic fossils.

† A dyke is a natural crack, fissure, or chasm in the strata, which is commonly
filled up with heterogeneous matter.

coal, becomes indispensably necessary; inasmuch as the want of it often leads masters to commit serious blunders, and thus waste both money and time.*

An expert coal master will, therefore, be careful to observe the order, disposition, and appearance of each stratum wherever it is seen cropping out, or basetting, in the edges of rivulets, or other places; he will examine, investigate, and compare all that he sees from time to time, and by this means he will ultimately become acquainted with the nature and internal position of the strata in the district, or coal-field, of which he has the management.

It is difficult to explain all the phenomena of faults, or slips, which are met with in working coal, because they all differ from one another in some manner, or degree. They will be more fully explained in Part II.

The different coal seams, with their concomitants, near New-castle-upon-Tyne rise and crop out regularly, one after another, upon the general rise or acclivity of the strata, considerably to the east of the river Derwent, or indeed, east of Healy-field lead mine.

EXPLANATION OF THE SECTION.

PART I.—COAL MEASURES.

The first part of the section commences with the highest stratum sunk through at St. Anthony's colliery, about two miles east of Newcastle-upon-Tyne. Before we proceed to describe it in detail, it may be proper to observe, that although it is presumed to commence with the uppermost stratum, which occurs in the coal measures, yet the stratum with which it really does commence, is supposed, in order of super-position, to be overlaid by the magnesian limestone, which bounds the eastern extremity of this part of our island. Mr. Winch has described the position and extent of this limestone with great accuracy, in the Transactions of the Geological

[* Colliery viewers now undergo a special training; their competency being tested by examination before they are appointed.—ED.]

Society, Vol. IV, page 3, from which we extract the following account.
In the south-eastern part of the county of Durham, a fine-grained
red sandstone* is stated to predominate, after describing which, Mr.
Winch proceeds, as follows :—

"To the north-west of the red sandstone, the Magnesian or
Sunderland limestone is found.   In the cliffs at Cullercoats, in
Northumberland, a dyke, well known by the name of the *Ninety
Fathom Dyke*, is seen dislocating the coal measures, and passing
into the sea.   Here is the northern extremity, of the western boundary, of the magnesian limestone.   A few masses again occur, among
the rocks of sandstone and slate clay, upon which Tynemouth
Castle stands ; but it is on the coast, in the neighbourhood of South
Shields, in the county of Durham, that this formation first becomes
extensive.   From this point it swells into a range of low round-
topped hills, and is seen stretching towards the south-west,
protending into the coal-field, and forming an undulating line, by
Cleadon, Boldon, Clacksheugh, upon the Wear near Hilton Castle,
Painshaw, Houghton-le-Spring, Sherburn, Coxhoe, Ferryhill, on
the turnpike road leading from Durham to Darlington, Merrington,
Eldon, Brussleton, Morton, Langton, and Sellaby, till it reaches
the Tees below Whinston Bridge, thirty miles west-south-west of
that river's junction with the sea, and forty-four miles from the
Tyne at South Shields.

"The sea coast forms its eastern boundary for twenty-seven miles
and a half, from the Tyne to the rocks of Hartlepool, and the red
sandstone already mentioned, from Hartlepool to the termination
of that rock. west of Croft-bridge.   The same bed is afterwards
continued through Yorkshire, Derbyshire, and Nottinghamshire, to
the neighbourhood of Nottingham, where it suddenly terminates.

"The quarry at Whitley, near Cullercoats, affords the geologist
an opportunity of ascertaining that the magnesian limestone overlies the coal measures, and that the latter were consolidated before
the limestone was deposited upon them.   I shall therefore describe
that curious spot.   A hollow space, formed like a basin or trough,
is filled with the limestone.   The length of this, from east to

* Now well known as the New Red Sandstone.

west, is about a mile, the breadth, from north to south, four hundred yards, the depth, seventy feet. The beds pass over the Ninety Fathom Dyke, which has occasioned in them no confusion or dislocation, so that there can be little hazard in stating that the beds of the magnesian limestone belong to a more recent formation than those of the coal-field. The limestone has been quarried across its whole breadth, and a numerous set of thin strata are thus exhibited to view. At the surface loose blocks of bluish grey coralloid limestone, the produce of the lead mine district, are found embedded in the soil. Three or four of the uppermost strata of the quarry are of white slaty limestone, which, being nearly free from iron, burns into a pure white lime. Below these, an ash-grey fine-grained stratum is met with, which strongly resembles a sandstone, and seems to contain nearly as much iron as the ferri-calcite of Kirwan, becoming magnetic by the action of the blow-pipe: it produces a brownish-yellow lime, less esteemed for agricultural purposes than the former. The beds next in succession are of an ash-grey colour, compact in texture, and conchoidal in fracture: these afford a buff-coloured lime, which sells for nearly the same price as the white. Near the bottom of the quarry the limestone alternates with shale, the whole rests upon a stratum of shale upon the southern side, and upon a thick bed of sandstone upon the northern. The shale has been cut through to a considerable distance from the kilns, in the direction of North Shields, for the purpose of laying a railway to the Tyne. The thickness of the limestone strata varies from three or four inches to as many feet. Small strings of galena have been found here, and, in one of the strata that was walled up when I visited the quarry, a few organic remains have been noticed.

" It is well ascertained that the magnesian limestone of this district, as is the case with that of Derbyshire and Yorkshire, rests upon the coal measures. No coal mine has yet been won, in Northumberland or Durham, by sinking a shaft through the lime-stone, although the workings of collieries, situated on its western boundary, have been carried underneath it. It is therefore a matter of great importance to those who have royalties within its limits, to know under what thickness of limestone the coal measures are buried, whether, after passing under the limestone, they continue to dip at the same angle as before, and whether the quality or thickness of the coal seam is then altered.

"Along the coast of Durham, from Shields to Hartlepool, the limestone strata dip to the south-east. At Chapter Main, near South Shields, the coal measures, although approaching the limestone, rise towards the sea, in conformity to their direction on the north side of the Tyne; but at Painshaw, Newbottle, Rainton, &c., they dip to the south-east, the limestone being there protruded into the coal-field beyond the prolongation of that line from which the coal measures, that are without covering, begin to rise in an eastern direction. It appears, therefore, that their dip is not affected by the limestone. It is a circumstance, however, too well ascertained to admit of a doubt, though difficult to be accounted for, that the coal is deteriorated in quality when covered by the limestone."*

* [Since the above was written the coal measures, underneath the magnesian limestone, have been proven over the greater part of the area capped by it. The beds of coal have been found *in situ* quite unaffected by the overlying limestone, and not in the least degree deteriorated in quality.

The thickness of the limestone, as proven by the several pits sunk through it, varies throughout the district. It attained its greatest thickness at the following collieries:—

					Fathoms.
Monkwearmouth, with the alluvial above it	...		...	...	67
Ryhope	,,	,,	...	...	37½
Seaton	,,	,,	...	...	—
Murton	,,	,,	...	...	72
South Hetton	...	...	...	...	...	57½
Haswell, with the alluvial above it	...	...	...	50½
Thornley	,,	,,	...	...	...	25
Castle Eden	,,	,,	...	...	...	103

These collieries are more particularly on the line of the sea-board. As the limestone recedes from the coast it is found to gradually thin off and to form the bold escarpments seen at Ferryhill, Quarrington Hill, Sherburn Hill, and Boldon on the north side of the Wear.

The section of the Haswell colliery (see sections), which was sunk by the late Mr. Thomas Emerson Forster, in 1833, is a typical account of the strata met with in the collieries worked underneath the magnesian limestone, and shows the whole of the seams hitherto met with in that district.—Ed.]

We have before given a general description of whinstone, bastard limestone, poststone, sandstone, metal-stone, &c., all of which, with their several varieties, may be seen in the first part of the section. It would be tedious and unnecessary to describe all the different alternations in succession, as many of them closely resemble each other, and, perhaps, the whole are comprised in the varieties we have enumerated.

Of the coal itself three distinct kinds are found, the common, or slate coal, cannel coal, called *splint*, or *parrot coal*, and *coarse* coal, also called splint.

The texture of fine splint is compact, the cross fracture conchoidal, and the fragments are cubical. Coarse coal is slaty in its texture, and it seems to be intermediate between common and cannel coal.

These varieties are not found to occupy separate and peculiar seams of the coal formation, but alternate irregularly with one another, as layers of the same bed.

Though the same kinds of strata are found to occur in almost every colliery, yet they frequently differ considerably in thickness. They also vary in other respects. In some places they are mostly of the hard, in others mostly of the soft kind, and it rarely happens that in any one district all the various kinds are found. Some may, perhaps, occur once, or twice only, while others are met with ten, or twenty times before we reach the principal stratum of coal. Hence, in forming an individual section of an extensive district, it is impossible to enumerate all the irregularities that are found at different places, or to define the precise thickness of each stratum, for any considerable distance, either on the acclivity of the strata or the horizontal line of bearing. Anomalies of this nature also frequently occur in the lead measures, which cannot be explained;* but these irregularities are not of much consequence when regarded from the geologist's point of view, since they do not generally affect the aggregate depth of the strata, the deficiency in the thickness of one stratum being supplied by the redundancy of another.

The order, position, and thickness of the strata alter so considerably in different parts of the Northumberland coal-field that it is

[* See the Greenhurth Section.—ED.]

F

sometimes very difficult to identify even the various coal seams. Sometimes two of the coal seams on the river Tyne form only one on the river Wear, as particularly mentioned in the section.

Mr. Winch's paper, in the Geological Transactions, to which we have before alluded, contains so much valuable information on the Newcastle coal-field, and elucidates in so clear a manner what we have already stated, that we beg to present the following extract to our readers:—

"The coal seams and the rocky strata, which together constitute the coal formation of Newcastle and Sunderland, are, in part, covered by the magnesian limestone and rest upon the lead mine measures. They occupy a hollow or trough, of which the extreme length, from the Acklington colliery, near the Coquet, in the north, to Cockfield, in the neighbourhood of West Auckland, is fifty-eight miles; and the breadth from Bywell-on-the-Tyne to the sea-shore is twenty-four miles. This formation first makes its appearance on the south bank of the Coquet, near that river's junction with the sea, and bounds the coast of Northumberland in a south-south-eastern direction for twenty-three miles. It then crosses the mouth of the Tyne, after which the magnesian limestone begins to cover a part of it, and continues to intrude more and more upon it until both approach the Tees. The distance from South Shields to Cockfield is thirty-two miles in a south-westerly direction. The western side of this district cannot be so easily defined, since many of the lead mine measures strongly resemble those of the coal-field, but when the *millstone grit* (a coarse-grained sandstone so called) and the *blue encrinal limestone* (or *fell top limestone*, numbered in the section 121) are seen cropping out, one may then be sure that the boundary of the coal formation is passed. However, if a line be drawn from the vicinity of Acklington, on the Coquet, to cross the Tyne at Bywell, the Derwent near Allensford, and the Wear below Wolsingham, and to terminate at Cockfield, a tolerably correct idea may be formed of its western limits.

"This district is characterised by low round-topped hills, which rise gently from the sea and increase in height towards the west. Pontop Pike, situated on the Derwent, not far from the western boundary of the coal-field, is reckoned by Mr. Fenwick, of Dipton, to be one thousand feet high, and by Colonel Mudge, one thousand and eighteen; and a pit sunk near the summit proves that it cannot be much less. That part of Newcastle Leazes which lies close to Spring Gardens and the western turnpike gate, is ascertained to be one hundred and ninety feet above the level of the Tyne and two hundred and five above the sea. Benwell hills to the west and Gateshead Fell to the south are somewhat higher.

"The inequality of the surface does not affect the dip, or inclination of the coal measures, and when they are interrupted, or cut off by the intervention of a valley, they will be found on the sides of the opposite hills, at the same levels as if the beds had been continuous. Thus the *grindstone bed* may be seen on Byker Hill, Gateshead Fell, and Whickham Banks, though nowhere in the vales of the Tyne and the Team, which severally intersect those elevated portions of land. The conclusion is obvious, that the present irregularity of hill and dale has been occasioned by the partial destruction and dispersion of the uppermost rocky masses which constitute the coal formation.

"That part of the trough in which the greatest thickness of the coal measures is found seems to lie in the vicinity of Jarrow, and from this point the beds appear to rise to some considerable distance on each side, particularly in a western direction. The average dip of the coal measures is one inch in twenty, but this inclination is by no means uniform in every part of the district. Thus that seam of coal called the High Main, which lies buried at Jarrow under one hundred and sixty fathoms of beds of stone, soon rises to the day in a north-east direction, and bassets out in the cliffs between Cullercoats and Tynemouth. In its north-westerly range it reaches Benwell hills, and at Pontop, nearly eighteen miles due west of the sea shore at Sunderland, it is met with at thirty-eight fathoms and a half from the surface. In a southerly direction it is found at fifty-two fathoms on Gateshead Fell, but bassets out before it reaches the Wear.

"The principal substances, besides coal, which constitute the coal formation, are shale and sandstone, which, as they vary in hardness or colour, receive different provincial names from the miners. It is not possible to discover, in the coal measures, any regular order of succession, which will apply to the whole coal-field, and it is even with difficulty that, in limited portions of it, the continuity of particular seams can be traced. This arises from the variable thickness, and the rapid enlargement and contraction of the different beds, that which in one section is scarcely perceptible, having attained, in a neighbouring pit, the thickness of several fathoms. It is thus that the Five-Quarter Coal Seam, of the mines on the Wear, is divided into the Metal and Stone Coal Seams of Sheriff Hill. Thus also in Brandling and Hebburn collieries, a parting of stone first divides, and afterwards usurps the place of, the High Main Coal Seam; and thus the two upper coal seams that are well worth working (see the section of Montague colliery north) at Kenton, are no longer so in the neighbouring colliery of Killingworth.

"The following is an account of a similar occurrence in Montague colliery, abridged from an unpublished memoir by Mr. Thomas, of Denton, on the dykes found in that mine :—

"Within the Newbiggen Stone Coal Seam, at twenty inches from the floor, there is a band of soft clayey substance one inch and a half thick, but the band increasing in thickness towards the east, the coal is divided into two distinct seams, whose aggregate thickness is less than that of the original seam. At the distances of one thousand yards to the east, and three hundred yards north of the main dyke (the ninety fathom dyke described before) the band is twenty-four feet thick, the upper coal seam six inches, and the lower sixteen inches. The band decreases towards the north, at the rate of something more than one inch per yard, and the coal at the same time increasing, the upper and lower parts are so nearly united, at the distance of one hundred and sixty yards, as to form again a workable seam. The upper coal then measures twenty-one inches, the lower twenty-four, and the band fifteen.

"The most valuable seam in the whole coal-field, in point of thickness and quality, is that called the High Main, of the mines situated between Newcastle and Shields. It there averages above six feet from the roof to the floor, contains a large proportion of bitumen, and is sufficiently hard to bear carriage without breaking into very small fragments. I have already described, in part, the basseting of this coal seam, along the course of an oval line, of which Jarrow is the centre, from which some idea may be formed of the extent of country which it underlies, south of the Ninety Fathom

Dyke. At a land-sale pit, a little above the Ouseburn Bridge, near Newcastle, this seam was found at fourteen fathoms, but on the Town Moor, from the numerous vestiges of ancient pits, it appears to be exhausted.

"Wallis, in the history of Northumberland, gives an account of a fire happening in the High Main coal, about a hundred and forty years ago, on the Town Moor and Fenham estates, which continued to burn for thirty years. It began at Benwell, about a quarter of a mile north of the Tyne, and at last extended itself northward into the grounds of Fenham, nearly a mile from where it first appeared. There were eruptions at Fenham in nearly twenty places, sulphur and sal-ammoniac being sublimed from the apertures, but no stones of magnitude ejected. Red ashes and burnt clay, the relics of this pseudo-volcano, are still to be seen on the western declivity of Benwell Hill, and it is credibly reported that the soil, in some parts of the Fenham estate, has been rendered unproductive by the action of the fire.

"At Byker, St. Anthony's, and at an adjoining colliery, the Low Main coal is found at fifty-nine fathoms below the High Main, but though the seam proved to be six feet and a half thick, the workings of it were, for a time, abandoned as unprofitable, the coal being extremely fragile and the mines very subject to the fire-damp. On the south side of the Tyne at Felling, Tyne Main, and Gateshead Fell, the quality of this coal is very much improved, and, under the name of the Hutton Main, it forms one of the most valuable seams on the Wear."

CO-ORDINATION OF THE COAL SEAMS ON THE TYNE
AND THE WEAR.

The High Main Coal of the Tyne extends to the Wear, but is there known as the Three-Quarters Coal; in the Tanfield district it is known as the Shield Row Seam.

The Metal and Stone Coals form the Five-Quarter Seam on the Wear and the Grey Seam of Northumberland.

The Yard Coal of the Sheriff Hill district is the Main Coal Seam of the Wear and the Brass Thill of the Tanfield district.

The Bensham Seam is the Maudlin Seam of the Wear.

The Five-Quarter Seam of the Tyne is the Low Main of the Wear.

The Low Main is the Hutton Seam of the Wear.

The Beaumont Seam of the Tyne becomes divided into the Harvey and Townley Seams of the Wear.

The Top Busty of Sheriff Hill is the Stone Coal of the Walbottle and Blaydon districts.

The Bottom Busty is the Five-Quarter Seam of these districts.

The Top and Bottom Busty Seams form one seam at Marley Hill and other places. The outcrop of this seam is at Busty Bank, hence the reason why it is called Busty. It has been sunk into on the Tyne, but has not been much worked. In the western portion of the coal-field the Busty and Brockwell have been, and are, extensively worked, the coal therefrom being largely used in the making of coke.

The Three-Quarter Seam is called in the Auckland district, the Top Coal of the Brockwell.

The Brockwell.—This seam is the lowest, of any value, in the series. It is known as the Splint Seam at Walbottle, and as the Horsleywood Seam at Wylam. It outcrops in the Derwent Valley and many other places in West Durham.—ED.

SECTION OF THE STRATA BORED THROUGH AT THE FRANCIS PIT AT MONTAGUE MAIN COLLIERY, ON THE NORTH SIDE OF THE NINETY FATHOM DYKE.

	Fms.	Ft.	In.
Soil and clay ... ... ' ...	1	1	6
Grey metal stone	3	3	0
Strong grey post	1	3	0
Grey metal stone, with girdles	4	1	6
Grey post, with metal partings	6	2	6
Whin*	0	0	9
Blue metal stone	5	5	0
COAL—Waste of the Seven-Quarter coal, or Kenton Main, worked out in 1690	0	0	9
Blue grey metal	0	1	0
Grey metal stone...	2	2	0
Grey post	1	3	0
Grey metal stone, with girdles	2	1	0
White post	3	0	6
Metal stone	1	5	0
Blue grey metal	0	2	6
Stone COAL ...	...	0	0	3
Black metal stone	Two Five-Quarter, ...	0	0	2
COAL ...	or Newbiggen ...	0	1	9
Black metal stone	Stone Coal ...	0	0	2
COAL ...	...	0	2	1
Grey metal stone...	0	4	0
Strong white post	1	4	0
Strong grey metal stone	0	4	0
Strong white post	0	2	0
Grey metal stone...	2	3	0
COAL	0	0	6
Grey stone, with post girdles	3	1	6
Mixture whin	0	1	3

* The author of the article "Mine" in Brewster's Encyclopedia says, "in the sections which have been made of the Newcastle coal-field, the term *Whin* is applied to many of the strata; these strata, so named, are, however, not whin, but are sandstones of the hardest kind. The mis-application of the name whin (or greenstone) has led mineralogists to wrong conclusions as to the coal formation of that district."

	Fms.	Ft.	In.
Grey post	1	0	0
Grey metal stone...	0	5	10
COAL	0	0	6
Grey metal stone...	0	0	2
COAL	0	0	8
Grey metal stone...	1	0	0
Strong white post	1	0	4
COAL	0	0	8
Grey metal stone...	0	1	0
Grey post	0	1	6
Strong white post	1	0	0
Dark grey metal	0	1	11
COAL	0	0	4
Grey metal stone...	2	4	4
COAL	0	0	4
Grey metal stone	0	1	3
Black slaty metal, mixed with **COAL**	0	1	0
Strong grey metal stone	5	2	11
Strong white post, with whin	12	3	0
Grey metal stone, with black skamy partings	2	5	0
Strong white post	1	3	0
COAL	0	1	0
Grey metal stone...	0	2	0
Grey metal stone, with girdles	2	0	0
Strong white post, with whin girdles and skamy partings	5	1	7
COAL ... ⎰ Benwell Main ⎱	0	2	5
Black slaty metal... ⎱ Coal ⎰	0	0	3
COAL (foul) ... ⎱ ⎰	0	1	0
Grey metal	1	3	0
Strong white post	5	0	9
Black grey stone	2	0	0
COAL	0	0	9
Blue grey metal	0	0	5
COAL	0	0	4
Blue grey metal	0	3	6
Strong white post	0	4	7
Grey metal stone, with girdles	0	4	8
Grey metal, with skames of coal	0	1	3
Grey metal stone...	3	3	c
Grey metal, with a mixture of **COAL**	0	2	0
Grey metal stone...	1	3	6
Grey metal, with whin	0	1	6

	Fms.	Ft.	In.
Grey metal stone...	0	2	2
COAL	0	0	10
Grey metal	0	0	6
White post	0	1	6
Grey metal	0	2	6
Whin	0	0	4
Strong white post, with partings	0	3	0
Whin	0	1	0
Strong white post	0	2	0
Grey metal stone, with girdles and partings	1	3	6
COAL	0	0	8
Grey metal stone...	0	0	4
Strong grey and white post	0	1	6
Grey metal stone, with hard girdles	0	5	6
Strong white post	0	5	0
Whin	0	4	2
Strong white post, mixed with whin	1	2	6
Blue metal	0	3	0
Mixed whin, girdles, or lumps	0	0	4
Blue metal	0	0	10
COAL—Beaumont seam	0	3	10
Grey metal stone...	1	0	0
Strong post with whin	2	4	0
Whin	0	0	8
COAL	0	0	6
Black slate, with coal	0	1	2
Grey metal	0	1	6
Strong white post	0	2	6
Grey skamy post...	0	2	0
Strong white, post with whin	2	1	10
COAL	0	0	10
Grey metal stone...	0	1	1
Total	118	4	0

SECTION OF STRATA SUNK THROUGH IN THE CAROLINE PIT, MONTAGUE MAIN COLLIERY, ON THE SOUTH SIDE OF NINETY FATHOM DYKE.

[*I am indebted to Mr. Thomas Benson, Allerwash, for this Section.*—ED.]

	Fms.	Ft.	In.
Walling	2	2	0
Mild freestone	6	2	0
Shelly post, mixed with coal-pipes	0	1	8
Post	2	4	8
Mild black metal	0	1	1
Post	4	3	7
Grey metal	0	4	6
Blue „	0	3	6
COAL (burns to white ash)	0	1	6
Fire clay, soft	0	4	0
Goaf, Benwell Main, walled up, broken strata	2	3	9
Fire clay on to wood wedging crib	0	4	9
Grey metal and whin girdles	2	2	3
Post, mixed with whin	2	3	1
Grey metal, with whin girdles	0	4	5
Post, with gullets and water, originally wedged off	2	3	3
COAL	0	0	3
Fire clay	0	2	0
Grey metal and iron girdles	1	2	7
Post	1	5	8
COAL	0	0	4
Fire clay, mixed with iron balls	0	1	3
Strong grey metal	3	5	8
COAL	0	0	3
Coarse fire clay	0	2	0
Grey metal	0	4	11
COAL—Tyne Level Coal Seam	0	1	1
Fire clay	0	0	4
Post and coarse strong metal	0	5	4
Whin	0	1	4
Grey metal, with iron girdles	4	0	0
Blue metal, with iron girdles	0	5	5
Post, with whin	2	3	0
Blue metal and post girdles	1	0	0

	Fms.	Ft.	In.
Beaumont Seam goaf	4	2	0
Thill stone to metal wedging crib laid on post ...	0	5	0
Strong white post (no partings)	2	4	1
Hodge **COAL**	0	0	5
Grey metal, mixed with iron	0	4	8
Grey post, with metal partings, very strong	5	4	2
Metal troubly	1	1	8
COAL	0	0	3
Fire clay	0	0	10
Grey metal	1	5	1
Brown post	4	0	0
COAL—Stone Coal Seam	0	1	6
Fire clay, good	0	1	7
Coal pipe (this coal much thicker than the Engine Pit)	0	0	4
Coarse fire clay, or metal	1	4	5
Post, mixed with whin	3	5	5
Grey metal and post girdles	0	4	0
COAL—Top Coal, Low Main Seam	0	0	4
Black band, or badger	0	0	4
COAL, good	0	2	8
Fire clay, good, very mild	0	1	0
Coarse coal, very brassy	0	0	4
Grey metal and black stone, with iron girdles ...	2	3	2
COAL—Three-Quarter Seam	0	1	5
Dark fire clay band	0	0	3
Bottom **COAL**	0	0	6
Grey metal	0	5	1
Dark grey post	2	4	9
Dark grey metal with girdles	2	5	0
White post	2	0	10
COAL—Low Low Main, or Brockwell Seam ...	0	3	0
Splint	0	0	2
Fire clay	0	1	3
Grey metal	0	5	0
COAL	0	0	7
Post, with metal partings	3	4	5
Total	95	2	11

STRATA SUNK THROUGH IN THE *B* PIT, HEBBURN COLLIERY.

	Fms.	Ft.	In.
Clay	9	5	0
Grey metal stone	1	1	0
Post, with metal partings	8	4	0
Blue metal	0	2	0
COAL*	0	3	0
Blue metal	1	2	0
Grey metal stone	2	3	0
Post, with metal partings	1	4	0
Blue metal stone	0	5	6
Grey metal, with post girdles	2	4	6
Blue metal stone	1	5	0
Grey metal, with post girdles	5	2	0
Hard white post	1	4	0
Grey metal, with post girdles	4	4	0
Grey metal, with open partings	0	3	0
Blue metal	6	5	6
Black and blue metal	1	1	6
COAL	0	0	1½
Black metal	0	0	6
White thil	0	4	10½
White post	0	2	5
Blue metal	0	0	1
Grey post	0	0	6
Grey metal, mixed with post	0	1	0
Strong white post	2	3	6
White post, with grey metal partings	0	4	6
Strong white post	8	0	0
COAL	0	0	1½
Grey thil	0	3	10½
Grey metal, mixed with thil	1	5	0
Grey metal	0	1	0
Post, with metal partings	0	3	0
Strong white post, mixed with whin	0	3	0
Grey and blue metal	0	4	0

* This seam lies all through Hebburn and Jarrow collieries.

	Fms.	Ft.	In.
Black stone	0	3	0
COAL	0	0	4
Black stone	0	1	4
COAL	0	1	0
Strong grey thil	0	2	6
Strong grey post	0	0	10
White post girdles, with metal partings	1	3	0
White post	0	3	0
Thin post girdles, with metal partings	0	1	0
Whin	0	3	0
White post, with metal partings	0	5	6
Grey metal	0	1	0
White post	0	4	9
Blue and grey metal	4	5	9
White post	0	4	0
Blue and grey metal	2	3	6
COAL	0	0	5½
Blue and grey metal	2	5	6
COAL	0	0	2
Grey thil	0	2	4
Blue and grey metal	3	1	2
COAL (called the Seventy Fathom Coal)	0	1	2
Grey thil	0	4	6
COAL	0	0	2
Grey metal and post girdles	2	0	0
Black and grey metal	2	5	6
Post	1	1	2
COAL	0	0	4
Grey thil	1	0	0
Blue and grey metal, with post girdles	3	0	6
Strong white post	4	4	6
Brown post, with blue metal partings	1	1	10
Strong white post	4	2	2
Blue metal	1	0	0
Post	0	1	6
Black stone	0	5	0
White post	0	2	6
Blue and grey metal	1	5	0
Black stone	2	0	0
COAL	0	0	6
Grey thil	0	4	0
Blue and grey metal	0	5	0

						Fms.	Ft.	In.
Post	...	...	...	...	...	10	2	0
High Main **COAL**		...	...	...	...	1	0	0
White thil	...	...	...	...	...	0	1	8
Slaty **COAL**	...	...	...	...	...	0	2	4
Blue metal	...	...	...	...	...	0	1	0
		Total	...	...	...	131	3	11½

[*This continuation of Coal Seams at Hebburn Colliery, below the High Main, is supplied by Mr. G. B. Forster.*—ED.]

				Fathoms from Surface.		Thickness.	
						Ft.	In.
Metal **COAL**	...	...	...	120	...	2	6
Stone **COAL**	...	...	...	127	...	0	7
Yard **COAL**	...	...	...	135	...	1	5
Bensham Seam	...	...	...	149	...	5	5
Five-Quarter	...	...	...	160	...	2	3
Low Main	...	...	...	172	...	5	5

SECTION OF THE STRATA AT SHERIFF HILL, ON GATESHEAD FELL.

					Fms.	Ft.	In.
Shiver and blue slate sill	...	...	...	...	3	0	0
White flag post	...	...	...	...	2	0	0
Grindstone sill	...	...	...	...	11	0	0
White post plate	...	...	...	...	1	3	0
Blue plate	...	...	...	...	1	0	0
Grey post plate	...	...	...	...	1	3	0
Blue plate	...	...	...	...	1	0	0
Whin plate	...	...	...	...	1	3	0
Blue sill	...	...	...	...	1	0	0
White post sill	...	...	...	...	3	3	0
Three-Quarter **COAL**	...	...	...	...	0	2	3
White post sill	...	...	...	...	5	3	0
Grey post	...	...	...	...	1	0	0
Dun post sill	...	...	...	...	6	0	0
Blue plate	...	...	...	...	1	0	9

	Fms.	Ft.	In.
Eleven fathoms white post...	11	0	0
High Main **COAL**	1	0	0
Grey post sill	6	0	0
Metal plate	1	0	0
Metal **COAL**	0	1	2
White post	4	1	10
Stone **COAL***	0	3	0
Black stone sill	1	3	0
Bandy **COAL** Seam	0	0	6
White post sill	4	3	6
Blue plate	2	3	0
Black plate	0	1	6
Little **COAL** Seam	0	0	6
Grey sill	2	0	0
Yard **COAL**	0	3	0
White post sill	11	3	0
BENSHAM SEAM†	0	3	3
Blue plate	2	0	0
Bandy **COAL** Seam	0	0	9
White post sill	5	2	0
Blue plate	0	3	0
Six-Quarter **COAL**	1	0	3
Grey whin post	1	5	7
Five-Quarter **COAL** ‡	0	3	2
Grey post	1	5	3
Bandy **COAL** Seam	0	0	9
White post	5	0	0
Low Main **COAL**§	1	0	6
Dark white sill	0	1	0
White post	3	5	6
Two-Quarter **COAL**	0	1	6
White post sill	21	0	6
Harvey's Main **COAL**, or Whickham Stone Coal ...	0	3	0

* This and the metal coal form the Five-Quarter Coal on the Wear and the Grey Seam in Northumberland.

† Maudlin Seam on the Wear.

‡ The Five-Quarter Coal Seam is the Low Main Coal on the Wear.

§ Hutton Seam on the Wear.

[*I am indebted to Mr. G. B. Forster for this continuation of the Strata comprising the Sheriff Hill series, as shown in Redheugh sinking, below the Harvey.*—ED.]

					Fms.	Ft.	In.
Sagger, or fire clay	...	...	...	...	o	2	6
Strong grey metal	...	...	...	...	o	3	o
Strong white post	...	...	...	...	2	o	o
Grey metal	...	...	...	...	o	3	o
COAL	...	...	...	...	o	o	9
Strong grey metal	...	...	...	...	o	2	6
COAL	...	...	...	...	o	o	9
Strong grey metal	...	...	...	...	o	2	6
COAL	...	...	...	...	o	o	9
Strong grey metal	...	...	...	...	1	1	o
White post	...	...	...	...	7	o	9
Blue metal	...	...	...	...	o	1	6
COAL—Top portion of Busty	...	...	...	o	2	8
Fire clay	...	...	...	...	o	3	o
Strong grey metal and post girdles	...	...	...	2	5	8
Splint and black stone	...	...	...	...	o	o	5
COAL—Bottom Busty	...	...	...	...	o	1	7
Fire clay	...	...	...	...	o	3	o
Strong white post	...	...	...	...	8	3	o
Strong grey metal	...	...	...	...	o	4	o
COAL—Three-Quarter Seam	...	...	...	o	2	o
Fire clay	...	...	...	...	o	2	6
Strong grey metal	...	...	...	...	1	3	o
Strong white post	...	...	...	...	2	2	o
Strong grey metal	...	...	...	...	o	5	o
Blue metal	...	...	...	...	o	3	4
COAL ⎫	...	...	...	o	1	5
Band* ⎬ Brockwell Seam	...	...	...	o	2	4
COAL ⎭	...	...	...	o	3	1
Fire clay	...	...	...	...	o	2	8
Total	...	...	...	168	3	8

* A bore-hole which was put down to the depth of 44½ fathoms below the Brockwell Seam discovered some thin beds of coal, one of them being about 14 inches in thickness.

STRATA AT PONTOP PIKE COLLIERY, SITUATED ON LANCHESTER COMMON.

	Fms.	Ft.	In.
Soil and clay	1	0	0
Brown post	1	5	9
Grey metal stone...	3	3	0
COAL	0	0	10
Grey metal stone...	2	4	0
COAL	0	2	0
Grey metal stone, mixed	8	1	6
COAL	0	0	8
Grey metal stone, mixed with coal	0	4	9
Grey metal stone...	2	0	0
Grey post	1	0	6
Grey metal stone, the top mixed with girdles... ...	4	0	3
White post, Shield Row post (the main post) ...	13	0	10
Shield Row **COAL** (High Main at Sheriff Hill) ...	0	5	3
Whitish grey metal stone, with post girdles	6	3	0
Grey post	2	3	5
Grey metal stone...	0	3	0
White post	1	3	0
Grey metal stone...	3	2	0
Black grey metal stone	0	1	4
COAL—The Hard Coal Seam (Stone Coal at Sheriff Hill)	0	4	9
Dark grey metal stone, mixed with coal	0	1	9
COAL—The Brass Coal Seam (Yard Coal at Sheriff Hill)	0	5	3
White post	1	2	2
Grey metal stone, with girdles	0	4	0
Black grey metal stone	0	1	3
Grey metal stone, with post girdles	3	0	2
Dark grey metal stone, with post girdles	4	1	0
Brown post	0	3	0
Grey metal stone...	0	3	2
Brown post	0	3	1
Grey post	0	3	1
White post	1	5	2
Black metal stone	0	1	3
Strong white post	3	0	6

G

	Fms.	Ft.	In.
Grey metal stone	0	4	6
Strong grey post	1	3	7
Whin	0	3	0
Strong grey post...	2	1	6
Whin	0	3	8
Grey and white post, mixed with whin	6	5	6
Blue grey metal stone, with whin girdles	1	1	0
COAL—Hutton Seam, Five-Quarter Coal, at Sheriff Hill	1	1	0
White post	0	5	10
COAL—Twenty-inch Seam	0	1	8
Blue metal stone	1	3	9
Grey post, mixed with whin	3	0	0
Blue metal stone	1	5	0
Main **COAL**—Low Main at Sheriff Hill	0	3	6
Total	96	2	2

AN ACCOUNT OF THE STRATA SUNK THROUGH AT HASWELL COLLIERY, JULY, 1833.

*[I am indebted to Mr. G. B. Forster for this Section.—*ED.*]*

	Fms.	Ft.	In.
Outset	—	—	—
Soil	0	1	0
Brown sandy clay	0	1	2
Blue clay	0	5	10
Sand, gravel, and water	0	1	2
Sandy blue clay	1	3	5
Limestone marl, soft	0	5	0
White limestone, mild	2	3	5
„ (got first water here)	6	0	6
„ strong	5	2	11
Limestone, mild, and runs a great deal	1	0	6
Brown limestone, mild	6	0	7
„ strong	0	2	8
Light brown limestone	5	4	0

	Fms.	Ft.	In.
Strong yellow limestone, mixed with strong balls ...	2	0	4
White limestone, mild	0	5	0
„ strong with water	8	3	0
Brown limestone, mild	1	1	0
„ strong with water...	2	3	0
Blue limestone, strong	4	0	8
Dark blue metal	0	1	2
Strong grey post	1	5	4
Grey metal	0	0	8
Red freestone, with a little water	0	0	8
Strong white post (two wedging cribs laid here) ...	0	3	2
Strong red post	1	2	0
Purple and blue metal, with red post girdles, soft ...	2	1	0
Red and white post mixed	3	0	0
Grey metal, very soft	0	2	0
Strong red and white post	4	4	0
Blue metal	2	0	0
White post, with scores of blue and grey metal ...	0	5	0
Strong grey post (a little water wedging crib here) ...	2	3	0
Grey metal, with scores of coal and post girdles ...	0	4	0
Post girdles, with metal partings and water	1	5	0
Strong post, with metal partings	3	2	0
„ with coal pipes and thin partings ...	3	2	0
Light blue metal	1	4	0
Black stone parting	0	0	6
Light blue metal	0	3	8
Black stone and iron girdles	0	0	9
Splint **COAL**	0	2	5
Black stone	0	0	4
Light blue metal and ironstone	1	5	7
Black stone	0	2	3
Light blue metal and ironstone girdles	1	0	0
Black metal stone	0	0	7
Blue metal	2	4	8
Black metal stone	0	2	10
COAL, good ...	0	1	8
Band ... Three-Quarter	0	0	4
COAL ... Coal.	0	0	2
Band ...	0	0	2
COAL, good ...	0	1	8
Dark thil stone, with ironstone girdles	1	2	1
COAL—Five-Quarter Seam	0	3	6
Thil stone	0	0	6

	Fms.	Ft.	In.
Blue metal	3	5	6
Post girdles, with metal partings and water	1	4	9
White post with water	1	2	0
Grey metal, with strong post girdles	2	0	0
White post	0	2	3
Strong grey post, with metal balls and partings ...	3	1	0
White post, with whin and balls of metal	3	2	0
COAL—Main Coal	0	2	1
Dark thil stone	0	1	0
Grey metal stone	0	1	0
White post and partings	0	5	10
Blue metal	0	4	0
COAL	0	0	1
Thil stone, soft	0	4	0
Blue metal	1	1	0
COAL	0	0	$0\frac{1}{2}$
Blue metal, strong	1	4	0
Strong grey post girdles	1	1	0
Blue metal	3	3	0
Grey metal and post girdles	5	2	0
Strong white post, with metal partings	1	3	6
Blue metal	0	0	6
Strong white post	2	0	0
Post much mixed with metal	1	1	0
Strong post, trouble in pit	5	0	0
COAL—Low Main	0	3	7
Dark thil stone	0	4	0
Grey metal	0	1	6
Grey post	0	5	0
Blue metal, mixed with post girdles	0	3	0
Grey post, mixed with grey metal	1	1	0
Blue metal	0	5	0
COAL—Splint Coal	0	0	10
Black stone	0	1	3
Blue metal	0	4	0
White post	0	1	3
Blue metal	0	4	0
COAL	0	0	4
Black stone	0	1	0
COAL	0	0	8
Strong grey Thil stone	0	2	6
White post, very strong	2	2	0
Grey metal and post girdles	0	1	8

					Fms.	Ft.	In.
Blue metal					o	4	o
Grey metal, with post girdles					3	3	7½
Strong white post, much whin at top					5	1	o
COAL, good ...				...	o	4	1
COAL, coarse and brassy				...	o	o	2½
COAL, not so coarse	Hutton Seam			...	o	o	5½
Splint **COAL** ...				...	o	o	4½
Bottom **COAL** ...				...	o	o	3½

April, 1840, *bored :—*

					Fms.	Ft.	In.
Black stone					o	o	8½
Thil stone					o	4	o
Blue metal					2	o	2
Black stone					o	o	9
COAL					o	o	6
Thil stone					o	3	o
Blue metal					1	2	o
Grey post					o	3	8
Black metal					o	1	4
Grey metal and post girdles					o	1	o
Grey post					o	o	11
White post, very strong					o	o	5
Blue metal					o	o	7
Post					o	1	4
Grey metal					o	2	4
„ and post girdles					o	2	10
Blue metal					o	2	o
White post					o	o	11
Blue metal and coal pipes					o	5	11
Dark blue metal					o	1	o½
Black metal					o	o	6
Post					o	o	3
Black metal, soft					o	1	7
Grey metal and post girdles					o	o	5
Grey metal					o	1	5
Post, very strong...					o	1	5
Black metal					o	1	7
Grey post					o	o	3
Black metal					o	3	10
Blue metal, soft					o	3	8
Grey metal and post girdles					o	4	11

					Fms.	Ft.	In.
Post, strong					0	0	4
Black metal					0	2	8
Blue metal					0	0	11
Grey metal					0	1	1
Grey metal and post girdles					0	2	9
Black metal					0	3	3
Blue metal					0	3	6
Grey metal					0	2	4
Post					0	0	4
Grey metal and post girdles					0	2	9
Grey metal					0	1	5
Grey metal and post girdles					0	5	2
Blue metal					0	2	7
Post					0	0	5
Blue metal					0	3	5
„ dark					1	1	5
White post, strong					0	0	9
Grey metal					1	0	11
Blue metal					0	0	9
Grey metal					0	1	1
Black metal					0	0	7
COAL—Beaumont Seam					0	1	6
Total					176	0	2

SECTION OF THE STRATA IN BIRTLEY COLLIERY.

	Fms.	Ft.	In.
Brown Post			
Grey metal stone...			
Brown stone			
White post	32	0	0
Blue metal stone			
Grey post			
Blue and grey metal stone...			
Five-Quarter **COAL**	0	3	9
Grey post	10	2	3
Grey metal stone, with whin girdles... ...			
Main **COAL**	0	5	6
White and brown post	11	0	6
Grey metal stone, with whin near the bottom...			
Maudlin **COAL** Seam	0	4	6
Blue post	12	1	6
Blue and grey metal stone...			
Low Main **COAL**	0	3	3
Blue metal stone	7	2	9
White post and whin			
Hutton **COAL** Seam	0	4	6
	76	4	6

[*I am indebted to Mr. G. B. Forster for this continuation of Strata below Hutton Seam, at Birtley, as shown in the sinking of Ouston B Pit.*—ED.]

	Fms.	Ft.	In.
Sagger, or fire clay	0	2	10
Strong white post	2	1	1
Blue metal	0	0	4
COAL	0	0	2
Fire clay	0	5	0
Blue metal	0	2	10
Grey metal, with post girdles	2	3	8
COAL, coarse	0	0	7
Grey metal	0	4	3
Hard white post	0	2	3
Grey post	0	2	0
Soft blue metal	0	3	3
COAL	0	0	10
Strong fire clay	0	2	9

					Fms.	Ft.	In.
Hard white post ...	...	...	...	...	0	1	5
Grey leafy post ...	...	...	...	...	1	4	6
White post ...	...	...	...	...	1	4	10
Dark blue metal ...	...	...	...	...	2	3	10
COAL ...	...	...	...	...	0	0	2
Sagger ...	...	...	...	...	0	2	0
Grey stone, with iron balls...	...	...	...	1	0	0
Blue metal ...	...	...	...	...	1	0	5
Whin girdle ...	...	...	...	...	0	0	6
Blue metal ...	...	...	...	...	1	0	0
COAL ...	...	...	...	...	0	0	4
Shale band ...	...	...	...	...	0	0	4
COAL ...	...	...	...	...	0	0	1
Thil stone ...	...	...	...	...	0	0	5
Fire clay ...	...	...	...	...	0	1	0
Hard white post ...	...	...	...	...	0	1	8
Grey metal ...	...	...	...	...	0	4	6
COAL ...	...	...	...	...	0	0	10
Fire clay ...	...	...	...	...	0	4	0
Grey post ...	...	...	...	...	1	0	4
Blue metal and sagger ...	...	...	...	0	2	3
Grey metal ...	...	...	...	...	2	0	9
COAL ...	...	...	...	...	0	0	2
Strong post ...	...	...	...	...	0	3	4
White post and metal partings	...	...	...	2	4	8
COAL ...	...	...	...	...	0	0	10
Fire clay, posty ...	...	...	...	...	0	3	0
Grey metal and post girdles	...	...	...	0	4	0
COAL—Beaumont Seam ...	...	...	...	0	1	7
Sagger ...	...	...	...	...	0	3	0
Hard, white post ...	...	...	...	...	0	1	6
Sagger and grey metal ...	...	...	...	0	3	0
Grey post ...	...	...	...	...	0	1	0
White post ...	...	...	...	...	2	0	11
COAL ...	...	...	...	...	0	0	4
Dark sagger, mixed with coal pipes ...	...	...	0	5	8
Grey metal and post girdles	...	...	...	1	5	6
White post ...	...	...	...	...	1	5	6
Grey metal ...	...	...	...	...	0	1	8
BUSTY SEAM ...	...	...	...	..	0	5	10
	Total below Hutton Seam		...	39	3	6
	Total	...	...	...	115	8	0

SECTION OF STRATA AT HARTLEY BURN COLLIERY ON THE NORTH SIDE OF THE GREAT STUBLICK DYKE.*

[*I am indebted to Mr. John Cruddas, Haltwhistle, for this Section.*—ED.]

					Fms.	Ft.	In.
Clay	...	...	...	...	...	4	0	0
Freestone	...	...	...	...	...	4	2	0
Combe	...	...	...	...	...	1	1	3
Plate	...	...	...	...	...	1	1	6
Grey beds	...	...	...	...	...	0	2	1
Black metal	...	...	...	...	...	0	4	1
COAL	...	...	...	...	...	0	0	8
Grey beds	...	...	...	...	...	0	4	2
Black metal	...	...	...	...	...	0	0	7
Ironstone	...	...	...	...	...	0	0	2
Grey beds	...	...	...	...	...	1	0	8
Black splint	...	...	...	...	...	0	3	10
Grey beds	...	...	...	...	...	0	3	1
Freestone	...	...	...	...	...	0	3	4
Plate	...	...	...	...	...	0	1	10
Freestone	...	...	...	...	...	0	5	2
Grey beds	...	...	...	...	...	0	4	4
Ironstone	...	...	...	...	...	0	0	2
Grey beds	...	...	...	...	...	0	2	6
Post girdles	...	...	...	...	...	0	0	8
Grey beds	...	...	...	...	...	0	1	10
Black metal	...	...	...	...	...	0	1	0
Total		...	...	...	18	2	11

* The great Stublick Dyke runs in a direction nearly east and west, and may be traced for a considerable distance on its line of bearing, viz., from Stublick Dyke westward to Cupola Bridge, where it crosses the Allen Water, from thence over Whitfield ridge to the river Tyne, a little below Eals Bridge, thence to the south of Hartley Burn and Tindale Fell collieries. It has an immense throw down to the northward, but the precise distance cannot be exactly ascertained; it must, however, be very considerable, as it throws down the lower part of the Newcastle coal series in the districts through which it passes. There is some reason to suppose it identical with the Ninety Fathom Dyke, which dislocates the coal measures near Tynemouth castle.

					Fms.	Ft.	In.
Post girdles	...	...	...	...	...	0	0	6
Grey beds	...	...	...	...	...	0	2	2
Hazel	...	...	...	...	...	0	3	4
Grey beds, hard	...	...	...	...	...	0	1	10
Whin	...	...	...	...	...	0	1	1
Freestone	...	...	...	...	...	0	1	5
Grey beds	...	...	...	...	...	0	1	10
Hazel	...	...	...	...	...	0	2	8
Grey beds	...	...	...	...	...	0	2	10
Post girdles	...	...	...	...	...	0	0	10
Grey beds, hard	...	...	...	...	...	0	1	6
Grey beds, soft	...	...	...	...	...	0	3	10
Ironstone	...	...	...	...	...	0	0	3
Black splint	...	...	...	...	...	0	5	8
Grey beds	...	...	...	...	...	2	0	6
COAL	...	...	...	...	...	0	0	9
Blue metal	...	...	...	...	...	0	5	9
Black metal	...	...	...	...	...	0	2	9
Grey beds	...	...	...	...	...	2	4	0
Freestone	...	...	...	...	...	7	5	8
COAL*	...	...	...	...	...	0	4	0
	Total	...	...	...	38	2	1

* NOTE.—The strata on the north side of the Great Stublick Dyke have a great acclivity to the north, or north-east, from the vale of south Tyne at Haydon Bridge and Newbrough, which causes the lead measures to crop out from beneath the lower series of the coal measures.

[*I am indebted to Mr. G. B. Forster for the following Tables of Coal Seams.*—ED.]

The following seams of coal are met with below the main coal at East Tanfield Colliery. They are a type of what are also met with throughout the west district. In places the Busty is found divided into two seams. The Brockwell becomes much thinner towards the west:—

				Fathoms from Surface.	Thickness. Ft.	In.
Harvey Seam	...	...	...	21	2	0
Seam ...	...	...	...	41	2	0
Busty Seam	...	...	...	45	4	10
Three-Quarter	...	...	...	56	1	4
Brockwell ...	...	...	...	60	3	10

Seams met with at Walbottle Colliery, Wellington Pit :—

Grove Seam	...	...	...	16	2	11
Engine Seam	...	...	...	50	3	10
Hodge Seam	...	...	...	53	1	8
Three-Quarter	...	...	...	$67\frac{1}{2}$	1	11
Splint Seam	...	...	...	86	4	0

Seams met with at Throckley Colliery :—

Engine Seam	...	...	...	$36\frac{1}{2}$	4	0
COAL ...	...	...	...	48	2	2
Main COAL	...	...	...	51	2	11
Splint Seam	...	...	...	$61\frac{1}{2}$	2	10

Seams met with at Wylam Colliery :—

High Main Seam	...	...	...	6	5	7
Five-Quarter	...	...	...	21	3	$4\frac{1}{2}$
Six-Quarter	...	...	...	26	3	4
Yard COAL	...	...	...	32	1	2
Horsley Wood Seam		...	...	38	0	$11\frac{1}{2}$

DEPTHS TO THE SEAMS OF COAL.

*[I am indebted to Messrs. James Joicey & Co. for the following Tables of depths.—*ED.*]*

A.—CHESTER-LE-STREET DISTRICT.

Alma Pit :—

					Fms.	Ft.	In.
Five-Quarter	...	...	...	...	12	1	0
High Main	...	...	...	...	21	2	0
Maudlin ...	...	...	...	...	46	4	0
Low Main	...	...	...	...	51	0	0
Hutton ...	...	...	...	...	59	2	0

Handen Hold Pit :—

Five-Quarter	...	...	...	...	19	1	0
Main **COAL**	...	...	...	...	25	5	0
Maudlin ...	...	...	...	...	50	0	0
Low Main	...	...	...	...	54	3	0
Hutton ...	...	...	...	...	62	5	0

Twizell Colliery:—

Main **COAL**	...	...	...	...	19	1	0
Maudlin ...	...	...	...	...	45	0	0
Low Main	...	...	...	...	49	5	0
Hutton ...	...	...	...	...	55	4	0

Second Pit:—

Shield Row	...	...	...	...	10	4	0
Five-Quarter	...	...	...	...	19	2	0
Main **COAL**	...	...	...	...	27	5	0
Low Main	...	...	...	...	57	3	0
Hutton ...	...	...	...	...	63	1	0

Air Pit:—

Shield Row	...	...	...	...	20	2	0
Five-Quarter	...	...	...	...	33	4	0
High Main	...	...	...	...	42	2	0
Maudlin ...	...	...	...	...	67	4	0
Low Main	...	...	...	...	74	5	0
Hutton ...	...	...	...	...	87	3	0

Stanley Pit:—

					Fms.	Ft.	In.
Crow **COAL**	...	...	...	...	17	3	0
Shield Row	...	...	...	...	32	5	0
Five-Quarter	...	...	...	...	46	0	0
High Main	...	...	...	...	55	5	0
Maudlin ...	...	...	...	...	81	1	0
Low Main	...	...	...	...	87	0	0
Hutton ...	...	...	...	...	92	4	0

B.—TANFIELD DISTRICT.

South Tanfield Colliery:—

Shield Row	...	...	...	...	26	0	0
Five-Quarter	...	...	...	...	42	2	0
Brass Thil...	...	...	...	...	48	2	0
Hutton ...	...	...	...	...	78	0	0
Main **COAL**	...	...	...	...	82	0	0
Hodge ...	...	...	...	...	111	0	0
Top Busty	...	...	...	...	121	4	0
Bottom Busty	...	...	...	...	127	0	0
Three-Quarters	...	...	...	...	129	4	0

Tanfield Moor :—

Shield Row	...	...	...	...	37	1	0
Five-Quarter	...	...	...	...	48	1	0
Brass Thil...	...	...	...	...	55	0	0
Hutton ...	...	...	...	...	85	1	0
Main **COAL**	...	...	...	...	91	2	0
Busty Bank	...	...	...	...	135	3	0

Tanfield Lea :—

Shield Row	...	...	...	...	14	2	0
Five-Quarter	...	...	...	...	21	4	0
Brass Thil...	...	...	...	...	31	4	0
Hutton ...	...	...	...	...	64	4	0
Main **COAL**	...	...	...	...	69	0	0

East Tanfield:—

Hutton ...	...	...	...	...	12	1	0
Main **COAL**	...	...	...	...	16	3	0
Busty Bank	...	...	...	...	59	1	0
Three-Quarter	...	...	...	...	70	3	0
Brockwell ...	...	...	...	...	75	4	0

DEPTHS CONTINUED.—SEAHAM DISTRICT.

[I am indebted to Mr. Vincent W. Corbett, Londonderry Offices, Seaham Harbour, for this Table.—ED.]

Seams.	Seaham Colliery.			RAINTON COLLIERIES.								
				Adventure Pit.			Alexandrina Pit.			Nicholson's Pit.		
	Fms.	Ft.	In.	Fms.	Ft.	In.	Fms.	Ft.	In.	Fms.	Ft.	In.
Five-Quarter	190	3	4	14	2	10	34	2	10	43	5	7
Main Coal ...	218	1	4	22	4	9	43	2	6	53	5	8
Maudlin ...	226	5	2	35	1	6	56	5	4	63	5	6
Low Main ...	237	5	8	.43	3	8	65	0	2	73	5	5
Hutton ...	254	3	11	54	5	10	81	0	1	86	5	10
Harvey ...	281	2	0	—			—			—		
Busty ...	299	3	10	—			—			—		

A LIST OF THE COLLIERIES NEAR CHILCOMPTON,

In the County of Somersetshire, about Twelve Miles S.W.

of the City of Bath,

WITH THE DEPTH OF EACH COLLIERY IN YARDS,

Commencing at the Mountain Limestone, or Lead Measures,

near Nettle Bridge.   April 12th, 1821.

						Yards.
Embrow ...	...	...	...	...	...	45
Moor Wood ...	...	...	...	...	...	140
Bentar Works	...	...	...	...	...	120
Nettle Bridge	...	...	...	...	...	50
Adford Works	...	...	...	...	...	120
Edford Marsh	...	...	...	...	...	100
Leacham ...	...	...	...	...	...	100
Bobstar ...	...	...	...	...	...	100
Breach ...	...	...	...	...	...	70
Vobstar ...	...	...	...	...	...	80
Tor ...	...	...	...	...	...	45

The above abut against the Mountain Limestone to the westward, near Nettle Bridge, the coal measures turning up nearly vertical in the basset.

	Yards.
South-hill	200
Old Rock	250
Pit Cot	150
Bar Lake	240
Holkcombe	150
Coal Barton	120
Good Avaise...	120
Newbury	150
Fobster Tear	90
New Rock	150
Farrington	150
King's Chilcompton	60
Salisbury	120
Welton	200
Bromley	100
Wick	120
Sutton	200
Clutton	250
High Grove	200
Mearnes	300
Woody High Grove	100
Amesbury	300
Allens-paddock	100
Old Grove	250
Tening Work	300
New Grove	250
Hay's Wood...	290
Puilton Works	300
Buttons	250
Hamwork	150
Upper Hamwork	150
Radford, near the Canal	400
Withy Mills	120
Clandown (the deepest colliery in England, in 1821) ...	403
Radstock, Old Pit	300
„ Middle Pit	250
Ludlow	200
Withlay	250
Camerton (six miles south-west of Bath)	270
Dunkerton	230

The sections which are here inserted will, it is hoped, be found exceedingly useful in giving a general view of the Northumberland and Durham coal-fields.

I have before remarked upon the impossibility of giving in one section all the information that might be required; and, indeed, it is only by a comparison of the stratification in different parts of the district that a correct idea of its conformation can be obtained. The discrepancies, which will be found by comparing one section with another, are, in many instances, very difficult to account for, yet, it will be perceived, that the general order and disposition of the strata remain the same over the whole tract of country where the coal formation occurs.

Before proceeding to describe that part of the section which comprises the lead measures, it will not be improper to insert Tables of the strata which are found to accompany coal in other parts of the kingdom, as information of this sort is sometimes particularly useful to practical men.

TABLE I.

ACCOUNT OF THE STRATA AT CROFT PIT, AT PRESTON HOWS, ABOUT A MILE AND A HALF TO THE SOUTH-WEST OF WHITEHAVEN; THE DEPTH OF 108 FATHOMS.

From Dr. Miller's edition of William's Mineral Kingdom.

	Fms.	Ft.	In.
Soil	0	1	3
Soil and clay, mixed	0	4	9
Black soil	0	1	0
Brown soft limestone, resembling stone marl in irregular strata	1	3	0
Dark-coloured limestone, harder	1	0	0
Yellowish limestone, mixed with spar	0	4	0
Reddish hard limestone	0	2	0
Reddish hard limestone, but with finer particles ...	0	1	6
Hard dark-coloured limestone	0	1	4
Yellowish limestone, mixed with spar	0	4	0

	Fms.	Ft.	In.
Soft brown limestone	0	4	2
Soft brown and yellow limestone, mixed with freestone...	0	2	6
Limestone, mixed with yellow freestone	0	2	0
Reddish soft freestone	0	1	6
Red slate, striated with freestone in thin layers	0	2	6
Red freestone	7	0	6
Soft red slate	0	0	6
Red slate, striated with red freestone in thin layers	4	1	0
Red slate, striated with freestone	4	3	0
Strong red freestone, rather greyish...	4	5	9
Lumpy red freestone, speckled with white freestone	0	0	9
Blue argillaceous schistus, speckled with **COAL**	0	0	9
Red soapy slate ...	2	1	0
Black slate with a small appearance of **COAL** under it	0	1	0
Ash-coloured friable argillaceous schistus	0	4	6
Purple-coloured slate, striated with freestone ...	3	5	3
The same, and under it black slate ...	0	4	0
COAL	0	1	0
Soft whitish freestone	1	4	2
Blackish slate, a little inclined to brown	0	4	11
COAL	0	1	10
Blackish shale, intermixed with **COAL**	0	2	6
Whitish freestone	1	2	6
Strong bluish slate, mixed with grey freestone	0	3	0
White iron stone	0	1	0
Freestone, striated with blue slate ...	0	1	8
Freestone, striated with slate in thin layers	1	3	3
Dark blue slate ...	2	1	6
COAL	0	0	9
Dark grey slate ...	2	3	8
COAL, with slate one inch thick ...	0	2	0
Grey freestone, mixed with iron stone	1	2	0
Hard white freestone	2	3	6
COAL	0	1	0
Shale, mixed with freestone	1	2	0
Olive-coloured slate adhering to black	0	2	4
COAL	0	1	1
Black shale, mixed with freestone	1	2	8
White freestone, mixed with slate	1	2	0
Dark blue slate ...	3	4	4
COAL	0	1	3
Black shale, mixed with freestone	1	1	6
Strong white freestone	1	0	0

H

	Fms.	Ft.	In.
Brown iron stone...	0	3	0
Dark grey slate	1	0	0
Dark grey shale, with an intermixture of **COAL** about five inches thick	0	5	6
Light-coloured slate, mixed with freestone	0	5	6
Blue slate, striated with freestone	1	4	0
Strong white freestone, a little tinged with iron ...	0	2	6
Very black shivery slate	1	4	3
COAL, strong, and of a good quality	0	0	4
Soft grey slate	0	0	3
COAL, very black, burns well	0	0	8
Hard black shale	0	1	7
COAL, mixed with pyrites	0	1	2
Argillaceous schistus, grey and brittle	0	3	0
Blue rough argillaceous schistus	0	4	6
Fine blue slate	0	3	0
Freestone, mixed with iron stone	0	3	0
Black shivery slate	1	0	0
Dark blue slate, very fine	0	5	6
Dark blue slate, very brittle	0	0	6
COAL	0	2	6
Soft grey argillaceous schistus	0	0	6
Argillaceous schistus, mixed with freestone	0	2	0
White freestone, with fine particles	1	1	0
Blue slate, striated with white freestone	0	4	7
Light blue slate, very fine	0	3	0
Blue slate, a little mixed with iron stone	2	0	0
Black shivery slate	0	1	0
COAL	0	0	6
Brownish hard slate	1	3	0
Strong blue slate, tinged with iron stone	4	4	6
Dark blue slate, rather inclined to brown, and brittle ...	0	1	6
Blue soft brittle slate	0	0	6
COAL	0	1	0
Lightish grey argillaceous schistus, brittle and soapy ...	0	4	0
Freestone, striated with blue slate	1	1	0
Fine blue argillaceous schistus, striated with white freestone	0	4	0
Black slate, with hard, sharp, and fine particles ...	0	3	0
Blue slate, light and fine	4	3	0
COAL	0	5	4
Soft grey argillaceous schistus	0	4	3
Black shivery slate	0	2	2

	Fms.	Ft.	In.
COAL	o	1	3
Strong lightish-coloured shale	o	3	4
Blue slate, striated with white freestone	o	3	4
Iron stone	o	o	4
Grey slate	o	3	9
Strong white freestone	o	5	6
Freestone, striated with blue slate	o	o	10
White freestone	o	1	3
Freestone, striated with blue slate	o	3	11
Black slate	o	o	5
Freestone, striated with blue slate	o	1	4½
Strong white freestone	o	o	4
Freestone, mixed with blue slate in thin layers ...	o	2	4
Strong white freestone	o	o	5
Greyish slate, of a shivery nature	1	o	o
Freestone, mixed with blue slate in thin layers ...	o	4	o
Very strong, with freestone	o	5	3
Fine blue slate	o	2	3
White freestone, striated with blue slate	o	o	7½
Fine blue slate	o	o	4
White freestone, striated with blue slate	o	2	1
Freestone, striated with blue slate, in fine particles ...	o	o	10
White freestone, in thin layers	o	o	4
The same, but more friable	o	o	5
Fine blue slate	o	2	1
COAL	1	1	10

TABLE II.

EXHIBITS THE STRATA MET WITH IN SINKING A PIT AT
ILKESTON, IN DERBYSHIRE, THIRTY-ONE FATHOMS
AND A QUARTER.

From Dr. Miller's edition of "Williams' Mineral Kingdom."

	Fms.	Ft.	In.
Soil and yellow clay	1	o	6
Black shale	o	4	o
Iron stone	o	1	6
COAL	o	1	3
Clunch	1	o	6
Grey stone	1	3	o
Blue stone	1	1	o
Black shale	o	1	6

	Fms.	Ft.	In.
Brown iron stone	0	1	0
Black shale	1	0	0
Light blue bind	1	0	6
Burning shale	0	2	6
Light blue clunch	0	4	0
Light blue stone	1	3	0
Blue bind	0	2	3
COAL	0	1	6
Black clunch	0	0	4
Black jet, a kind of cannel **COAL**	0	0	9
Lightish blue clunch	0	2	5
Broad bind	1	1	6
Light-coloured stone	0	4	0
Greyish blue cank (a hard substance)	1	0	6
Very light-coloured stone	2	2	0
Strong broad bind	0	4	0
Grey stone	1	1	0
Blue bind	0	4	0
COAL, soft quality	0	2	6
Black bind	1	0	6
COAL, soft	0	4	0
Black clunch	0	3	0
Light-coloured clunch	0	3	0
Broad bind	1	5	6
Black clunch	0	3	0
Clunch and bind	4	1	6
COAL	1	0	3
Clunch	0	3	9

SEAMS OF COAL MET WITH AT THE MANNERS COLLIERY, DERBYSHIRE.

[*I am indebted to Mr. T. F. Brown, Cardiff, for this Table.*—ED.]

	Yards from Surface.	Thickness. Ft.	In.
Waterloo **COAL**	33	1	5
Deep soft **COAL**	110	9	0
Deep hard **COAL**	129	2	0
Piper **COAL**	144	4	8
Furnace **COAL**	182	3	5
Black shale **COAL**	252	1	9
Kilburn **COAL**	381	4	2

SECTION OF THE STRATA FROM BRANXTON PIT, AT BORE-
LAND, BY DYSART, FIFESHIRE, SCOTLAND.

*[I am indebted to Mr. James McLay, the Earl of Rosslyn's Collieries,
Dysart, for this Section.—*ED.*]*

	Fms.	Ft.	In.
Soft white sandstone, with occasional black seams through it	7	3	7
Alternate beds of light-coloured blaes and sandstone ...	1	4	o$\frac{1}{2}$
Soft sandstone	o	2	6
Hard sandstone	o	4	1o$\frac{3}{4}$
Soft grey faikes	o	o	1o
Soft blue blaes	o	3	5
COAL—More	o	1	9
Light-coloured blaes, with some thin bands	2	1	6$\frac{1}{4}$
Soft white sandstone	1	o	11$\frac{1}{2}$
Hard sandstone	1	o	5$\frac{1}{2}$
Soft white sandstone	o	3	8
Hard sandstone	o	4	4
Soft white sandstone	o	1	8
Dark-coloured blaes	o	1	8
COAL	o	o	4
Blaes, with bands...	o	3	o
Soft sandstone	o	4	8
Blae	1	4	9$\frac{1}{2}$
Hard grey sandstone	o	3	6$\frac{1}{4}$
Blaes	o	3	9$\frac{1}{2}$
COAL—Mangey	o	2	4
Light-coloured blaes	o	5	7
Grey sandstone	1	o	4
Hard sandstone	o	1	8$\frac{3}{4}$
Softer sandstone	o	1	6
Black sclaty blaes	o	4	2
Light-coloured blaes	o	3	o
Sandwell **COAL**	o	1	3
Light-coloured soft blaes	2	5	9
Soft sandstone	o	3	9
Hard sandstone	1	o	4
Light-coloured blaes	o	2	9
Hard sandstone	2	5	4$\frac{3}{4}$
Blaes and bands	2	2	6

	Fms.	Ft.	In.
Blaes	0	3	9
COAL	0	0	8
Blaes and bands	0	5	0
Soft sandstone, with thin beds of blae	0	3	9
Sandstone containing hard portions	5	1	10
Black slaty blae	0	3	6
A very hard band	0	0	9
Light-coloured blae	0	4	0
Hard band	0	0	10
Blue blaes	0	2	10
Hard band	0	0	3
Blaes	1	3	6
Grey sandstone	0	2	0
Very hard sandstone	0	3	9
Softer sandstone	0	2	7
Sandstone	1	5	2
Grey blaes, with hard bands	0	4	3
Bluish coloured blaes	1	3	2
Hard white sandstone	0	1	9
Very hard sandstone	1	1	2
Grey faikes	0	3	8
Very hard sandstone	0	3	0
Soft grey faikes	0	3	0
Hard sandstone	0	4	2
Softer sandstone	1	0	3
Hard sandstone	0	2	9
Softer sandstone	0	2	7
Light-coloured blaes	1	0	0
COAL, left for a roof ... ... ⎫	0	4	3
Stone ... ... ⎪	0	0	3
Uppermost **COAL** wrought ... ⎪ Dysart	0	4	0
Stone, with a thin seam of **COAL** ... ⎬ Main	0	1	6
COAL, with a dalk near the bottom ⎪ **COAL**	1	0	0
Stone ... ... ⎪	0	1	3
COAL theif, a black sootre coal, not generally wrought at Dysart ... ⎭	0	2	9
Total	63	3	8¼

"In the preceding tables the local names are retained. Many of these, it must be acknowledged, are extremely arbitrary; but it will not be difficult to understand them by a comparison of the strata in the different tables. It may be just noticed, that the grey stone and blue stone of table 2 are sandstones; clunch is a bituminous shale, and bind is an indurated clay. The blaes, of table 3 is also a bituminous shale, and the grey faikes is a shivery, foliated sandstone.

"It is no unusual circumstance, to find the remains of animals and vegetables, particularly the latter, on the strata, which accompany coal. Impressions of fishes, or of river shells, as muscles and land-snails are sometimes met with on the shale; but those of plants, of the fern and grass tribes, are most common. The sandstone, also, not unfrequently contains similar impressions, as well as the entire mass of the roots, trunks, or branches of trees, sometimes in a horizontal position, and compressed as if with great force into a flattened form; and sometimes in a vertical position, seemingly the same in which they existed in the living state. Such trees, it may be added, are entirely converted into the matter of the sandstone, excepting the bark, which is often changed into a substance of the nature of coal, and in many cases possesses all the properties of true coal. But, although the remains of organized bodies appear both on the common and bituminous shale, the latter of which is almost in immediate contact with the coal, yet the coal itself rarely exhibits any vestiges either of vegetable or animal impressions. This is, undoubtedly, a very singular and unaccountable fact, and seems not very favourable to the opinion of the vegetable origin of coal, unless it be admitted by those who support that opinion, that the vegetable structure has been entirely destroyed during the process of nature in the formation of coal. It must not, however, pass unnoticed, that all coal is not destitute of vegetable remains. When the coal is of a laminated or slaty structure, as in the cannel or parrot coal, the impressions of plants, of the grass or reed kinds, are very common on the surface of the stratum of coal; and the organized structure is often so entire, that the fibres, of which the plant has been composed, may be separated into very fine filaments of a glossy or silky appearance. Sea shells are very rarely found in the strata which accompany coal, a circumstance, which must be considered as rather adverse to the opinion, of coal having been formed, by deposition, at the bottom of the ocean."—*Williams' Mineral Kingdom.*

In the Midlothian coal-field, in the counties of Edinburgh, Haddington, and Peebles, in Scotland, Mr. Farey, senior, in the year 1816, enumerated three hundred and thirty-seven principal alternations of strata, between the surface (in the town of Fisher Row, on the banks of the Frith of Forth, where the highest of these strata occurs) and the commencement of the Basaltic rocks, forming the general floor and border of this important coal-field. These strata lie internally in the form of a lengthened basin, and consist of sandstone, shale (or blae), fireclay, coal, limestone, ironstone, &c.

In the general section containing the above-mentioned particulars, which Mr. Farey prepared for the late Duke of Buccleugh, sixty-six seams of coal (without reckoning double or treble coals at more than one each) and seven limestones are seen separated by seventy-two assemblages of barren, or stone sinkings, forming an aggregate thickness of above five thousand feet.

In all, eighty-four seams of coal, and eight intervening limestones, appear in this general section of the Midlothian coal measures,—a greater number of such strata than were supposed, by geologists, to exist in any one place.

PART II.—LEAD MEASURES.

The strata, which I shall now proceed to describe, form that portion of the mountain limestone series which is developed in the mining districts of Derwent, East and West Allendale, and Haydon Bridge, in the county of Northumberland ; of Weardale and Teesdale, in the county of Durham ; of Alston Moor, in the county of Cumberland ; of Kirby Stephen, in Westmorland ; of Lunedale, Wensleydale, Swaledale, and Nidderdale, in the North Riding.

This tract of country differs considerably, in external appearance, from that in which coal occurs. The easy undulations of the surface in the neighbourhood of Newcastle, rise into more rugged and alpine elevations; the fertile valleys of the Tees, the Wear, and the Tyne, are greatly contracted in breadth, and separated by sterile and desolate mountains, whose summits, for a great part of the year, are covered with snow.

Among these mountains are situated the valuable lead mines, which constitute so large a part of the mineral treasures of Great Britain, and which equal, if not excel, in productiveness, any yet discovered in the world.

The stratification of this part of our island has been ascertained with the greatest precision, the multitude of shafts and workings of the lead mines, and the numerous bassets of the strata on the sides of the mountains, affording ample means for observation over an extensive district; and, it must be observed that, although some irregularities, in order and thickness, are found to occur,* yet, the general agreement of sections from different mining fields is much more striking, than in that part of the series I have just described. In working the lead mines, each individual bed is anticipated and calculated upon with the greatest confidence, by practical miners, by whom it is received as a general rule, that what is lost in thickness in one stratum, is, very often, gained in another; that is to say, what is lost in the plate beds is generally gained in the limestones and hazles; so that the same aggregate thickness is maintained throughout the section.

I have observed, on page 9, that the different coal strata crop out, or basset, to the east of Healy-field Lead Mine, and that the uppermost strata of the lead measures are presumed to basset from beneath the lower coal seams. It must be confessed, that the continuity of any individual bed has never yet been actually traced below the lower series of coal measures, in such a manner as to connect the lead measures accurately with them, and, it is therefore probable, that a few thin beds intervene between the Brockwell coal seam, No. 90 in the section, and the slate sill, No. 91; but they are too inconsiderable to deserve much notice, and do not at all affect the general accuracy of the section.

---

* See Greenhurth section.

The dip of the strata on the east of the Pennine fault is towards the north-east. In Crossgill Burn, in Alston Moor, Cumberland, it makes 2 degrees 15 minutes with the horizon, or nearly a yard in twenty-seven: the bearing with the true meridian is S. 35 W.

Grey Beds.—These consist of several beds of sandstone, of a siliceous nature, seldom above an inch in thickness, which alternate with thin beds of plate.

They occur pretty frequently in the lead measures, and are numbered in the section 99, 100, 101, 102, 103, 107, 115, 116, 189, and 205.

Slate Sills.—These strata are of a siliceous nature, will strike fire with steel, and frequently contain small particles of mica. The common grey roofing slates are obtained from the slate sills.

They are numbered in the section 91, 129, and 131.

Girdle Beds.—These are harder strata than grey slate, of a closer texture in the stronger posts, and strike fire plentifully with steel.

They are numbered in the section 93, 141, and 236.

Freestones are sandstones of a softer nature than the last-mentioned, being also more porous and open; but they are harder than the sandstone described on page 6. They are generally divided into posts, with partings between them, and will strike fire with steel, but not so plentifully as the strata called grey beds.

They are numbered in the section 95, 108, 219, 222, 224, 226, 228, 231, 235, and 237.

Millstone Grit, or Grey Millstone.*—This stratum, No. 104 in the section, is of a coarser grain, and considerably more porous than freestone. In some places it is quarried for millstones for grinding corn, and is commonly called the grey-stone. Mr. Farey supposes that the famous peak millstones of Derbyshire are of a similar kind of stone. This stratum may be seen upon the mountains between Stanhope and Wolsingham, in the county of Durham.

---

* [The term Millstone Grit, here applied by Forster to a single stratum in the lead measures, is now generally used to designate the series of strata which lie between the lower coal measures and the lead measures. "Sandstones differ from grits in being finer in structure than the latter, and in their component grains being usually less completely incorporated with the cementing medium."—*Trans. Geo. Society*, Vol. XXXVII, page 6.—ED.]

Hazle is a sandstone, harder than freestone, but softer than girdle bed. It does not readily strike fire with steel.

The stone to which this term is applied occurs very frequently in the section.

Grindstone Sill.—This stratum, numbered in the section 117, is less porous, but harder than the millstone grit. It is in some places hewn into grindstones, from which circumstance it has derived its name. It is the uppermost stratum in the rich mining fields of Allenheads and Coalcleugh, in the county of Northumberland, and at Rampgill-head, near Nenthead, in the county of Cumberland. It is also nearly the uppermost stratum upon the summit of Cross Fell.

Immediately below the grindstone sill is a pretty thick plate bed, No. 118, and below the plate bed a stratum of hazle, No. 119. Underneath the hazle we find another plate bed, No. 120, which overlies a thin stratum of limestone, commonly called the Fell Top limestone. This is the first limestone that occurs in the lead measures (see page 14), and the uppermost that we find either in Weardale, Allendale, Derwent Dale, or Alston Moor.

Underneath the fell top limestone is a thin coal seam, about six or eight inches in thickness. It is of that species of coal called by the country people crow coal, and emits, while burning, effluvia of a suffocating and sulphureous nature. In Alston Moor it is mixed up with clay, and formed into round balls, commonly called *cats*, for fuel. All the other coal seams in this part of the section are of this species.

The next stratum below is a hazle, No. 123, about four yards thick, commonly called the upper coal sill.

Below the stratum of plate which underlies the upper coal sill, is a hazle, No. 125, of a pretty close texture. It is sometimes used for sharpening scythes, &c., and has from this circumstance been called the whetstone sill.

Underneath this is a plate bed, and again another hazle, or whetstone bed, of a similar nature, No. 127.

We now arrive at the upper slate sill, eight yards, and the lower slate sill, seven yards in thickness; divided from each other by the stratum of plate, No. 130.

These sills have been very productive of lead ore at Coalcleugh,
and Rampgill lead mines, and, indeed, in most of the mines in
Teesdale, Allendale, Weardale, and Alston Moor. Underneath the
lower slate sill, we meet with a hazle, which is occasionally found
united to the lower slate sill, without the intervening stratum of
plate, No. 132, forming with it a thick stratum, which is called the
low great sill.

Below the plate bed, No. 134, we meet with a thin bed of
sulphureous coal, No. 135 (similar to that we have already
mentioned), which overlies the stratum of ironstone, No. 136, so
called from its containing a quantity of iron in its composition.
This latter is a close, hard stone, varying much in thickness. At
Coalcleugh, it is only about a foot thick, at Middlecleugh Moss,
near Nenthead, it is above a yard in thickness, whilst in other
places it is scarcely perceptible.

Firestone Sill.—This stratum, No. 137, is of various thickness.
At Allenheads, it is about six fathoms; at Coalcleugh only about
three. At Wolfcleugh, in Rookhope, in the county of Durham, the
white tuft or white sill, No. 139, and the firestone, almost unite and
form one stratum. The firestone strikes fire with steel plentifully,
and is micaceous. It is sometimes used as hearth-stones for fire-
places, whence, probably, its name.

The plate bed, No. 140, girdle bed, No. 141, and plate bed,
No. 142, in some places form one stratum, commonly called the
eleven fathom plate.

Pattinson's Sill.—This stratum, No. 143, is a hazle, four yards
in thickness, and is so called from the person who first sunk into it
at Rampgill vein. It has been very productive of lead ore in several
mining fields.

Little Limestone is the next stratum of limestone, No. 145,
under the Fell Top limestone, and the second which occurs in the
lead measures. It is tolerably hard, and has been very productive
of lead ore, in Alston Moor, and other places.

From the last-mentioned limestone, downwards, we have a plate
bed, which immediately overlies the high coal, No. 147. This coal
seam rests upon the high coal sill,* which, in turn, rests upon the

* The upper coal sill, No. 123, is 58 fathoms above the high coal sill, No. 148.

plate bed, 149. Upon the low coal sill, rests another seam of sulphureous coal, numbered in the section 150. In some places we find three coal sills, all of which are tolerably hard, and emit sparks freely with steel.*

The plate bed, No. 152, beneath the lower coal sill, rests upon the great limestone. This plate is tolerably hard, and frequently contains a number of balls, or nodules, of iron pyrites, commonly called cat-heads. Some of these are very curious when cut and polished, being veined and streaked with different colours. This plate bed frequently bursts down in large masses, after a current of air has circulated freely through levels driven in it. A great deal of timber is then required to secure the roofs and sides of the workings.

Tumbler Beds and Great Limestone.—This is the most predominant stratum of limestone that we find throughout the whole section, and has yielded nearly as much lead ore as all the other strata together, in the extensive mines of Weardale and Teesdale, East and West Allendales, and Alston Moor. About sixteen feet of the upper part of this stratum is called the tumbler beds, which, in some places contain *entrochi* and other organic remains. Between the tumbler beds and the body of the limestone is a soft, argillaceous substance, about a foot in thickness, commonly called the black bed. From the black bed to the high flat, is generally about four feet, and from thence to the middle flat, ten feet, or thereabouts ; from the middle flat to the low flat is about thirteen feet. What are here called flats will be more fully explained in Part II., where the subject of flats, or dilated veins, is discussed. This stratum is pretty uniform in thickness.

It bassets at a little distance to the south of Dun Fell lead mine, and occurs also upon Meldon Fell, in the county of Westmorland. It is the uppermost stratum at Hartside Cross, on the Penrith and Alston road. A thin seam of crow coal occurs under it, about one mile south of Cross Fell mines, where it bassets on the north bank of the river Tees, and also at Meldon Fell.

---

* At Cross Fell lead mine the plate bed, under the little limestone, is about **five** feet in thickness ; then comes a coal about six inches ; underneath that is a white hazle three and a half fathoms. There is a famp bed, about a foot in thickness, six or seven feet from the bottom of the hazle.

It may be seen, too, dipping below the bed of the river Wear, between Wolsingham and Frosterly, in the county of Durham, where it has been quarried for marble.

Tuft, or Water Sill.—This stratum, No. 154, is a friable gritstone, considerably softer than the generality of hazles. It has a sandy appearance, will strike fire with steel, and is pervious to water: it lies close to the bottom of the great limestone, and has been very productive of lead ore in many mining fields.

Underneath the tuft is a plate bed which divides it from the

Quarry Hazle.—This stratum, No. 157, is of various thickness, being, in some places, about six fathoms, in others only about three or four, and being sometimes divided by a famp bed. Its upper part is occasionally of a somewhat calcareous nature, and is then called the limestone post, 156. The quarry hazle is called, in Weardale, Hewitson's sill; it strikes fire with steel pretty freely, and has been very productive of lead ore in the mines at Allenheads. It is underlaid by a firm plate bed, No. 158. The lower part of this plate is considerably harder than the upper, and is of a somewhat cherty* nature, generally forming a distinct stratum, called the till bed, No. 159.

Four Fathom Limestone.—This is a strong, compact stratum of limestone, No. 160, which is pretty regular in thickness. Below this limestone, at Nattrass Gill, in Alston Moor, there occurs a thin seam of coal. It may be observed that limestones, in general, are more uniform in thickness than the other strata.

Nattras Gill Hazle.—This stratum, No. 161, frequently lies close to the bottom of the four fathom limestone, but at some places a thin coal seam is found between them, as at Nattrass Gill. Occasionally about two feet, or a yard, of plate occurs between the limestone and the coal, as at the lead mine called Grass-field, in Alston Moor.

---

* Chert is found among the limestone strata in Derbyshire. It is of a flinty nature, nodulous in form, like flint in chalk, and sometimes a little stratified. Some of it abounds with the impressions of *entrochi*, which have manifestly been enclosed in the solid substance of the chert, though not the least fragment of them is now remaining. Its colour is similar to that of other flints, but when stratified it is generally a good black. It is sometimes so like the limestone in which it is enclosed, as to be only distinguished from it by its not effervescing with acid.

This hazle is of a somewhat coarser nature than the others, and strikes fire with steel.

The Three Yards Limestone is the next stratum. It varies a little in thickness, sometimes not being more than a fathom.

Six Fathom Hazle.—This stratum, No. 164, is commonly called, in Alston Moor, Arthur's Pit Hazle. It is a siliceous substance, pretty hard, strikes fire with steel like most of the other hazles, and lies close to the bottom of the last-mentioned limestone.

The Five Yards Limestone.—This is the next limestone that we find under the three yards limestone. It is in some places underlaid by a small coal seam, of a sulphureous nature.

Slaty Hazle.—This stratum, No. 167, lies close to the bottom of the last-mentioned limestone, wherever the seam of sulphureous coal does not occur. It is of a close texture, and strikes fire with steel.

Scar Limestone.—This limestone is next to the great limestone in thickness, and is similar to it in having three flats, called the high, middle, and low flats. The great áqueduct level, called Nentforce level,* which is now (1821) being driven by the Commissioners and Governors of Greenwich Hospital, commences under this limestone, near the town of Alston, in Cumberland. At the same place the river Nent is precipitated over the basset of this stratum, forming a romantic waterfall several yards in height, called Nentforce. The stupendous level of Nentforce was begun in the year 1776, for the double purpose of discovering metallic veins and draining several rich mines in the neighbourhood of Nenthead. It has now (1821) proceeded upwards of three miles, and, as it is driven in the direction of the rise or acclivity of the strata, it will reach a great depth before its termination. Its forehead at present stands in the upper part of the Tyne-bottom plate, 189.

Underneath the scar limestone there are several thin strata of hazle, plate, &c. (which appear in the section), before we arrive at a limestone, commonly called the *cockleshell* limestone. It has entrochi, anomia, ostrea, and other organic remains imbedded in it.

* [The Nentforce level has been driven forward, under the scar limestone, to Welgill; from thence it has been driven upon the scar lime to the deep shaft in Rampgill level. The total length is nearly five miles.—Ed.]

It may be seen in Garrigill, Eshgill, and Crossgill Burns, in Alston Moor, Cumberland.

Below the cockleshell limestone there are two thin plate beds and two small hazles, and then the single post, or Garrigill Burn limestone. From thence to the Tyne-bottom limestone we find a considerable thickness of plate, alternating with grey beds, No. 189, which is so very hard and compact that it can scarcely be wrought without blasting. In some places it can be divided into very thin pieces, which are used as slates for roofs, &c. This stratum is generally distinguished by the name of Tyne-bottom plate.

Tyne-bottom Limestone.—This is the lowest stratum of limestone in Alston Moor. The river South Tyne runs nearly all the way from Tynehead to Garrigill Gate upon it, a distance of about four miles, the dip of the strata being equal to the fall of the river. It is the uppermost stratum at Dufton Fell, in the county of Westmorland. Like the Great and the Scar limestones, it has three flats, which are always recognisable.* This circumstance will be discussed more fully in the section on dilated veins. The Tyne-bottom limestone may be traced from the smelting house at Tyne head to the southward over to the banks of the river Tees, in the county of Westmorland, and from thence to the lead mines at Netherhurth and Dun Fell. It crops out at Birkdale, on the banks of the Maze-beck (a stream which divides the counties of Westmorland and Yorkshire), and again at High Cup Nick, from whence it may be traced to Lunehead, in the county of Yorkshire.

	Ft.	In.
* From the top of the limestone to the high flat	2	6
From the top of the high flat to the sole	4	6
From the sole to the middle flat	5	0
From the middle flat to the sole	4	0
To the bottom of the limestone	5	0
Total	21	0

Whetstone Bed.—This is a thin, soft stratum of argillaceous earth, No. 191. Underneath it is a very hard post of basalt, called the

*Great Whin Sill.**—This rock, No. 192, varies greatly in respect of thickness. At Caldron Snout, a waterfall on the river Tees, it is nearly thirty fathoms; at Dufton Fell it is only about seven or eight fathoms; and at Hilton (a lead mine in Westmorland) it is little more than four fathoms in thickness. The whin occurs at the smelting house, near Tynehead, and also at Kesh Burn Force, a waterfall in Alston Moor. It may be traced down the river Tees to Caldron Snout, and up Maze Beck to High Cup Nick, where it

* [The occurrence of this sheet of basalt in the mountain limestone series has been the cause of some controversy among geologists. By some it is considered a volcanic rock, contemporaneous in its origin with the series in which it occurs; by others it is regarded as an intrusive mass which has been injected among the strata since their consolidation.

The former adduce the following proofs in support of their view: (1) The whin sill generally lies in one position, *i.e.*, immediately underneath the Tyne-bottom limestone. (2) It rests conformably upon the other strata, dipping when they dip and rising when they rise. (3) It is cut through by the east and west mineral veins, whereas in Derbyshire those veins are themselves cut off by the intrusive toadstones. (4) The strata which lie upon the whin sill are not changed either in appearance or structure. They are as compact as the other strata, and their lines of stratification and cleavage are quite distinct; whereas strata which are in contact with eruptive rocks exhibit many signs of change, their lines of stratification being obliterated, and their general aspect being greatly altered.

The latter contend: (1) That the whin does not always occur in the same position, but that in some places it is found far below, and, in others, far above the Tyne-bottom limestone. (2) That the strata above it are metamorphosed and broken up, in places, by the intruding whin. (3) That instances are known of the inter-stratification of sedimentary rocks with the whin sill.

Without presuming to express any decided opinion upon the question at issue between the vulcanists and the intrusionists, I may venture to observe that, with rare exceptions, the miners, who, on a point of this kind, are the most reliable authorities, maintain that the whin has never yet been found either above, or far below, the Tyne-bottom limestone. Forster, who, as a native of Northumberland and a mine agent, had abundant opportunities for observing the whin sill both in the mine and at the outcrop, seems to have entertained no doubt with respect to its position when he penned the above paragraph. He had then before him a paper by Robert Bakewell, which contains this statement:—"An intelligent gentleman, well skilled in mineralogy, who has resided long in the county (Northumberland), and paid particular attention to the subject, informed me that he did not consider the great whin sill as a regular stratum, but as a wedged-shaped mass of basalt, probably formed by the expansion of basalt from one of the great basalt dykes which intersect

I

bassets. It occurs in Lunehead, in the county of Yorkshire, and to the north of Lune, at Holwick, in the same county. At Tyne-bottom mine, near Garrigill, the whin is sunk into to the depth of nearly twenty fathoms; at Settlingstones lead mine, two miles and a half north-east of Haydon Bridge, in Northumberland, it occurs at the surface, and is penetrated to the depth of twenty-two fathoms; it also bassets at Sewnshields Crag, a little north of the great Picts wall, in the same neighbourhood, and forms the bed of the river Wear at Unthank Bridge, near Stanhope, in the county of Durham.

that district." Yet for reasons, which, no doubt, seemed to him sufficient, Forster did not think the opinion of Mr. Bakewell's informant worthy of serious notice. The late Thomas Sopwith, in his little book on the "Mining Districts," after fully endorsing Forster's account, adds to it this statement:—"The volcanic origin of the whin sill of Alston Moor, Teesdale, &c., is now (1833) generally considered as an established geological fact."

That there are localities in which this rock appears to be either above, or below, its usual position is a fact which cannot be disputed. Harwood, in Upper Teesdale, is one of them, and Greenhurth is another. There is, however, a strong probability that the appearance is deceptive, and is the effect of some one, or more, of these causes: (1) The absence from the mountain limestone series of the strata which are usually associated with the whin sill. (2) The presence of other strata which do not extend throughout the series, but occur only in patches. (3) The throw of a strong vein or dyke. A closer examination of the strata in those localities would probably show that the whin sill is really in, or near, its right placè.

Such a phenomenon as the metamorphosis of the rocks resting upon the whin could not very well have escaped the notice of the miners. In Alston Moor many hundreds of fathoms of level have been driven in the Tyne-bottom limestone and shale, yet no signs of such metamorphosis have been noticed. A somewhat similar condition of things exists at Teesside. The miners know that the strata which form the cheeks of whin dykes have been changed both in structure and appearance by contact with the basalt, but they are not aware that the strata which rest upon the whin sill are at all affected. If the strata are changed in both cases, how are such knowledge on the one hand, and such ignorance on the other, to be accounted for?

The mere fact that sedimentary rocks are occasionally interstratified with the whin sill is as consistent with the one view as the other, for the sediment might have been deposited during the intermissions of the flow of lava. The value of this fact as a proof depends upon the condition of the imbedded shale; and the intrusionists have not yet shown that it has been metamorphosed by the action of heat. Much valuable information on the igneous rocks and their relations to the sedimentary formations is contained in the late Dr. Page's "Advanced Text Book of Geology," chapter vii.—ED.]

It is a very hard rock, of a brown or reddish-brown colour, emits fire with steel, and, except in one instance, which will be afterwards mentioned, has not (1821) been productive of metallic ores.*

According to modern geologists the great whin sill is basaltic green-stone, similar in structure and composition to that which occurs at Salisbury Crags, near Edinburgh, Catham Hill, in the vicinity of Glasgow, and at the celebrated Giant's Causeway, in the county of Antrim, in Ireland. †

Underneath the whin sill, we find four plate beds and three hazles, and then come to a limestone, which is commonly called the Jew limestone. This is the next stratum of limestone under the Tyne-bottom limestone. It has been sunk into at Rodderup Fell, in Alston Moor. It crops out on the west side of Cross Fell, and at Dufton Fell. At Hilton lead mine, this limestone lies close to the bottom of the whin sill, and is about eighteen fathoms in thickness.

Below the Jew limestone we have two plate beds and a hazle, and then come to another blue and hard limestone, No. 204, commonly called the Little lime by the miners at Dufton; below which there is a plate bed of about three fathoms in thickness. Underneath the latter we find a hazle sill, No. 206, and again another plate bed, overlying a limestone, which is called the Smiddy limestone.

Below the smiddy limestone there is a hazle, about three fathoms in thickness, and then another limestone, under which we find two thin plate beds and a hazle. We next come to a limestone, which is commonly called Robinson's lime; underneath it there is a thin hazle and some grey beds, resting upon the top of a very thick limestone, called

The Great Rundle Beck, or Melmerby Scar Limestone.—This

* [The rich mines of Settlingstones and Stone Croft are in the whin, and in Providence Shaft, at the head of Teesdale, a large quantity of lead ore was raised from the whin sill.—ED.]

† Mr. Winch says the great whin sill of the lead mine district does not consist of the whin of the colliery sinkers, but is really basalt, coarse-grained in texture, and composed of white feldspar and black horn-blende, the latter mineral predominating, and giving to the rock a dark greenish grey colour.—*See Geological Transactions*, Vol. IV., page 73.—[The great whin sill divides the mountain limestone series into an upper and a lower series.—ED.]

stratum of limestone is blue and hard; it is the thickest that we find throughout the section, and may be seen bursting out at Melmerby Scar, in the county of Cumberland, from which place it has derived its name. It may also be traced along the bearing of the strata to the south, above Dufton, and other places in Westmorland, still keeping pretty regular in thickness.

Below it there is a plate bed, about three fathoms in thickness, which overlies the freestone, No. 219. Underneath the latter there is another plate bed, and again another limestone, below which we find a thick freestone, and several thin plate beds. We then arrive at a thick plate bed, No. 232, with a coal seam in it, about seven inches in thickness. This coal seam is of considerable thickness on Renwick Fell, five miles east of Kirkoswald, in the county of Cumberland.

Below the plate bed, No. 234, we find a freestone about six fathoms in thickness, and then a girdle bed; below which there is another limestone, No. 237—the lowest calcareous stratum in the section. Below this stratum of limestone there is a very white freestone, of a somewhat sandy nature, and more porous and open than several of the other freestones; it is of a siliceous nature, striking fire with steel, but not freely.

Upper Old Red Sandstone.—In the last edition of this work, the great red sandstone which occurs in the vicinity of Penrith, and covers so large a portion of the county of Cumberland, was represented as regularly underlying the series of strata already described. Since the publication of that edition, this part of our island has received considerable attention from modern geologists, and the opinion stated above has been combated by some, and supported by others.* This controversy the author will not presume to decide, but after a recent examination of the district, he is disposed to think that his former statement was incorrect. It may be taken for granted, that on a subject which has excited such difference of opinion, nothing decisive can be advanced, but the reasons that

* [This controversy was set at rest many years ago. The sandstone referred to is the New Red Sandstone. It rests upon the coal measures, whereas the sandstone which bassets at the base of Cross Fell is the upper portion of the Old Red. This latter is the lowest stratum in the General Section. *Vide* Section.—ED.]

have induced the author to modify his opinion are, that in no instance can the red sandstone be traced below the regularly stratified beds, but that it is everywhere broken off and lost, in a very abrupt manner, as it approaches the edges of the strata, at the bases of Cross Fell and Dun Fell.*

It may be remarked, that in the neighbourhood of Kirby-Thore, in Westmorland, the red sandstone contains a bed of gypsum,† or alabaster, about five feet in thickness.

* [In a report which Forster made on some mining property in Cheshire in July, 1825, the following remarks on the great red sandstone occur :—" I consider the red sandstone to be an unconformable rock, overlying the coal measures. It is often denominated by geologists the New Red. When one colliery has been fairly opened, it will be the means of discovering a large coal-field, extending a very considerable distance into the county of Cheshire. Had this sandstone been the Old Red, which occurs at the bottom of the lead measures, there would be no probability of discovering coal under it." Thirty collieries are now (1883) opened out in Cheshire.—ED.]

† Gypsum is usually called alabaster, or plaster of Paris. Its uses, for chimney-pieces, monuments, floors, &c., are well known. It has very different modifications in the earth, being found in large nodulous masses, and stratified. The latter is fibrous, and its fibres run nearly at right angles from its upper or lower surface. It is of an opaque white, and uniform in its colour. The former is neither fibrous nor laminated, but composed of granules, as sugar, and breaks alike in all directions. Some of these masses are of a fine opaque white, like statuary marble ; others are variegated with different colours, as red, green, and bluish. These colours are sometimes so blended with gypsum matter, as to produce the appearance of Italian marble clouded with blackish veins. Gypsum takes a good polish, and though not so hard as marble, is extensively used for ornamental purposes in architecture, &c., but it will not endure the weather.

Selenite, though a gypseous body, is generally found imbedded in clay which is not calcareous. It is laminated, transparent, and, in the crystallized state, assumes a variety of forms.

It may be observed that gypsum is imbedded in marl, in the same way as flint is imbedded in chalk, or chert in limestone. The stratum of marl which contains gypsum is very thick. Pits have been sunk in it from eighty to a hundred yards deep, without cutting through it.

Marl is sometimes much indurated, and even concreted to a perfect limestone. On rare occasions it is burnt for lime.

The six sections which follow, are taken from the lead measures in Teesdale, Arkendale, Wensleydale, Eden Valley, and Derwent. They partially correspond with the upper portion of the series just described.

SECTION OF THE STRATA AT THE GREENHURTH MINE, IN UPPER TEESDALE.*

	Fms.	Ft.	In.
Plate	—	—	—
Single post limestone	I	3	o
Hazle	o	5	6
Plate	4	I	o
Hard post	o	2	o
Plate	6	2	o
TYNE-BOTTOM LIMESTONE	5	o	o
Plate and grey beds	3	o	o
Hazle	2	o	o
Coal	—	—	—
Hazle	5	3	o
Plate	I	o	o
Limestone	4	3	o
Hazle	o	4	o
Plate	o	2	6
Limestone	o	2	o
Hazle	o	3	6
Plate	o	3	o
Hazle	I	5	o
Plate and limestone	—	—	—

* [This section is not given here as a typical section of the strata in Upper Teesdale, where Greenhurth is situated; but as an illustration of the irregularities which occur in the mountain limestone series. Assuming that the strata which are named have been properly correlated with the strata elsewhere, the aptness of the illustration is at once apparent.—ED.]

SECTION OF THE STRATA IN ARKENDALE.

[*I am indebted to Mr. William Peacock, manager for the Arkendale Mining Company, for this Section.*—ED.]

	Fms.	Ft.	In.
Millstone grit	14	0	0
Coal	0	1	0
Plate, or shale	5	0	0
Lime	0	2	0
Plate	3	0	0
Lime	0	3	0
Plate	1	0	0
Lime	0	3	0
Plate	4	0	0
Flinty chert	2	4	0
Plate	1	0	0
First crow chert	1	0	0
Plate	1	0	0
Second crow chert	2	3	0
Crow lime	2	0	0
Grits	1	3	8
Coal	0	0	9
Grit	1	4	6
Plate	0	2	0
Grit	1	4	0
Plate	0	3	0
Grits	3	4	0
Shivery grits	3	4	0
Plate	2	4	0
Iron beds	2	0	0
Plate	1	0	0
Red beds, lime	6	0	0
Plate	1	3	0
Black beds	2	3	0
Plate	0	2	0
Lime bed	1	0	0
Plate	0	4	0
Main chert	3	0	0
Shale	0	1	6
MAIN LIME	12	0	0
Grit	1	0	0
Shivery grit	1	4	2
Plate	2	5	0

					Fms.	Ft.	In.
Middle grit	...	...	...	...	...	0	1	6
Plate	...	...	...	...	...	3	0	4
Undersett chert	...	...	...	...	...	4	0	0
Plate	...	...	...	...	...	0	1	0
Undersett lime	...	...	...	...	...	3	0	0
Grits	...	...	...	...	...	12	0	0
Coal	...	...	...	...	...	0	1	0
Grits	...	...	...	...	...	10	0	0
Plate	...	...	...	...	...	5	0	0
Third lime	...	...	...	...	...	2	0	0
	Total	...	...	...	130	0	5

A SECTION OF THE STRATA AT KELD HEADS LEAD MINE, WHICH IS A TYPICAL ACCOUNT OF THE STRATA IN WENSLEYDALE.

[*I am indebted to Mr. A. Rodwell for this Section.*—ED.]

					Fms.	Ft.	In.
Gravel, varying	...	...	...	...	...	—	—	—
Grit	...	...	...	...	...	6	0	0
Plate	...	...	...	...	...	1	3	0
Millstone and hazle grits	...	...	...	...	7	0	0
Plate and girdles	...	...	...	...	...	4	0	0
Stone plate	...	...	...	...	...	1	0	0
Coal, varying from 6 inches to	...	...	...	0	3	6
Grit, plate, and intermediate girdles	...	...	11	0	0
Crow chert	...	...	...	...	...	3	0	0
Crow lime	...	...	...	...	...	3	0	0
Grit	...	...	...	...	...	1	4	0
Plate	...	...	...	...	...	3	3	0
Black chert	...	...	...	...	...	2	3	0
Main chert	...	...	...	...	...	8	3	0
Plate	...	...	...	...	...	0	3	0
MAIN LIME	...	...	...	...	...	10	3	0
Grit	...	...	...	...	...	5	0	0
Plate	...	...	...	...	...	4	0	0
Grit	...	...	...	...	...	2	4	6
Plate	...	...	...	...	...	3	4	6
Undersett lime and chert	...	...	...	...	3	3	0

					Fms.	Ft.	In.
Plate	...	...	...	...	...	0	2	0
Grit	...	...	...	...	...	4	0	0
Plate	...	...	...	...	...	4	3	0
Thin lime	...	...	...	...	...	1	3	0
Preston grit	...	...	...	...	...	6	0	0
Shales	...	...	...	...	...	1	0	0
Fossil lime	...	...	...	...	...	9	4	0
Grit and shales	...	...	...	...	...	10	0	0
KELD HEADS LIME	...	...	...	...	10	4	0
Grit (flag)	...	...	...	...	...	3	0	0
Plate	...	...	...	...	...	1	0	0
Grit and shales	...	...	...	...	...	8	5	0
Grit and lime	...	...	...	...	...	2	1	0
Plate, &c.	...	...	...	...	...	4	0	0
Ash Bank lime	...	...	...	...	...	7	3	0
Alternate beds	...	...	...	...	...	11	0	0
SIX-FATHOMS LIME	...	...	...	...	10	1	0
Shales and lime	...	...	...	...	...	5	0	0
WEST BURTON, OR TEN-FATHOM LIME*	...	...	—	—	—

SECTION TAKEN IN ROLLINSON BECK, NEAR KIRKBY STEPHEN, WESTMORLAND.

[*I am indebted to Mr. John Cain for this and the following Section.*—E.D.]

					Fms.	Ft.	In.
Coal	...	...	...	...	...	0	2	8
Hazle	...	...	...	...	...	5	0	0
FELL TOP LIMESTONE	...	...	...	...	0	3	0
Plate	...	...	...	...	...	1	4	0
Iron nodules	...	...	...	...	...	0	2	0
Ironstone band	...	...	...	...	...	0	2	0
Plate (thickness not correctly ascertained)	..	...	—	—	—
Girdle beds (?) do. do.	...	...	—	—	—
Slate sill	...	...	...	...	...	3	0	0
Plate	...	...	...	...	...	3	0	0
Slate sill	...	...	...	...	...	4	0	0
Plate	...	...	...	...	...	7	0	0
Hazle	...	...	...	...	...	0	4	0
Plate and ironstone	...	...	...	...	3	0	0

* At a neighbouring mine this stratum is 10 fathoms.

Continuation of the Section as seen in the Ray Gill, Kirkby Stephen.

	Fms.	Ft.	In.
LITTLE LIMESTONE	1	1	6
Hazle	1	1	6
High Coal sill	4	0	0
Plate	1	0	0
Low Coal sill	4	0	0
Plate	1	0	0
TWELVE-FATHOM LIMESTONE, GREAT LIME ...	12	0	0
Tuft	0	5	0
Quarry hazle	5	0	0
Plate	0	4	0
FOUR-FATHOM LIMESTONE	3	3	0
Plate	0	4	0
Nattrass Gill hazle	4	0	0
Plate	0	4	0
Plate and grey beds	3	0	0
THREE-POST LIMESTONE...	2	4	0
Hazle	0	3	0
Plate and hazle	5	0	0
LIMESTONE	4	0	0
Hazle	0	2	0
Plate	2	0	0
Hazle	1	2	0
Plate and Hazle	2	3	0
Hazle	6	0	0
Plate	0	3	0
Hazle	0	3	0
Plate	2	0	0
Hard hazle	1	3	0
Slate and hazle	10	0	0
Plate	5	0	0
LIMESTONE	3	0	0
Plate	0	2	0
Hazle	1	2	0
Plate and coal	1	0	0
Plate and hazle	1	4	0
Hazle	3	3	0
Hard hazle	2	0	0
Plate	1	0	0
Plate and hazle	1	4	0
Hazle	3	0	0

					Fms.	Ft.	In.
Plate and hazle ...	...	...	...	...	2	2	0
Hazle ...	...	...	...	...	3	0	0
Hazle and grey beds	...	...	...	...	0	4	0
LIMESTONE ...	...	...	...	...	2	3	0
Hazle ...	...	...	...	...	0	4	0
Plate ...	...	...	...	...	1	2	0

TABLE OF THE STRATA AT SHILDON, ONE MILE WEST OF BLANCHLAND, IN THE COUNTY OF DURHAM.

					Fms.	Ft.	In.
Hipple ...	...	...	...	...	7	0	0
Plate ...	...	...	...	...	7	0	0
High grit ...	...	...	...	...	8	3	6
Plate and coal ...	...	...	...	...	0	3	3
Plate and white sill	...	...	...	...	1	1	9
Plate, coal and plate	...	...	...	...	3	0	6
Low grit ...	...	...	...	...	11	0	6
Plate ...	...	...	...	...	1	4	9
Pebbles ...	...	...	...	...	1	0	0
Plate, lime, post, and hazle	...	...	...	1	4	0
Crag sill ...	...	...	...	...	4	2	0
Plate ...	...	...	...	...	4	3	6
Pattinson's sill ...	...	...	...	...	6	4	6
White sill ...	...	...	...	...	2	0	0
Hazle ...	...	...	...	...	4	5	0
Plate ...	...	...	...	...	4	0	0
Hazle ...	...	...	...	...	0	3	0
Plate ...	...	...	...	...	2	1	0
Hazle ...	...	...	...	...	0	4	0
Plate ...	...	...	...	...	5	2	0
LITTLE LIMESTONE ...	...	...	...	2	1	0
Plate and coal ...	...	...	...	...	0	5	0
Coal sill ...	...	...	...	...	1	1	3
Plate ...	...	...	...	...	2	0	0
Coal, &c. ...	...	...	...	...	0	3	0
Low coal sill ...	...	...	...	...	1	2	0
White sill ...	...	...	...	...	3	4	0
Grey beds ...	...	...	...	...	0	0	8
Plate ...	...	...	...	...	1	0	0
GREAT LIMESTONE ...	...	...	...	—	—	—
Total ...	...	...		91	0	2

SECTION OF THE STRATA AT JEFFRY'S SHAFT, IN THE
DERWENT MINING DISTRICT, IN THE COUNTY OF
DURHAM.

[*I am indebted to Mr. J. Morpeth, manager for the Derwent Lead Mining and
Smelting Company, for this Section.*—ED.]

	Fms.	Ft.	In.
Moss and clay	2	0	0
Slate sill	5	0	0
Plate and metal posts	2	0	0
Cockle beds	2	3	0
Plate	4	3	0
FELL TOP LIMESTONE and coal	1	0	0
Girdle beds	1	0	0
Plate	2	3	0
Hipple sill	6	0	0
Plate	6	3	0
High grit sill	14	0	0
Plate	0	3	0
Low grit sill	24	0	0
Lime and plate	0	4	0
Crag sill	8	0	0
Plate and lime	1	4	0
Pattinson's sill	5	0	0
Plate	5	5	0
Hazle	1	3	0
Plate	2	0	0
Hazle	1	0	0
Plate	2	0	0
LITTLE LIMESTONE	1	5	0
Coal sill	7	0	0
Low coal sill	4	4	0
Plate	1	3	0
Coal	0	3	0
GREAT LIMESTONE	12	3	0
Tuft	1	1	0
Total	128	2	0

The main lime of the second and third, and the great lime of the fourth, fifth, and sixth of these Sections are supposed to be identical with the great limestone, No. 153, in the engraved section. By comparing the beds above this stratum with those in the Tables it will be seen that there is a considerable want of agreement, a circumstance which might be expected when the distance between the different places is considered.

We shall now insert Mr. Farey's accQunt of the metalliferous strata in Derbyshire; but before doing so we shall present our readers with the following Table which supplies, in some measure, the place of Mr. Farey's illustrative coloured engraving.

TABLE OF THE METALLIFEROUS STRATA* IN DERBYSHIRE.

	Fms.	Ft.	In.	
Grit rock	60	o	o	Siliceous
Limestone shale	80	o	o	Argillaceous
First limestone rock	25	o	o	Calcareous
First toadstone	10	o	o	Basaltic
Second limestone rock	25	o	o	Calcareous
Second toadstone	15	o	o	Basaltic
Third limestone rock	30	o	o	Calcareous
Third toadstone	15	o	o	Basaltic
Fourth limestone rock	65	o	o	Calcareous
Total	325	o	o	

The thickness of each stratum, in the above table, is deduced from Mr. Farey's engraving, before alluded to.

In extracting the following description of the above strata from Mr. Farey's treatise, we have been obliged considerably to abridge his observations, but those who wish for fuller information on this subject are referred to the Derbyshire Report, Vol. I., page 220:—

* Metalliferous strata, or in other words, of the strata which compose the mountain limestone.

"*Grit Rock.*—The uppermost of the strata in the Table is the millstone grit rock, which, by its thickness and its hardness and truly indestructible properties gives rise to the greater part of the siliceous rock scenery in Derbyshire and the adjacent parts of Staffordshire, Cheshire, and Yorkshire. In several places this rock has been proved to be 120 yards thick, composed for the greater part of a very coarse-grained white, yellowish, or reddish freestone, which is easily worked, considering the extreme hardness of its particles and its great durability, which appears to me superior to that of any freestone which I have seen used in England. What are known all over England by the name of peak millstones are from this stratum, and, though formerly these were dug and prepared from various parts of the stratum, yet now few, if any, millstones are made but at Old Booth Edge, and other places near Nether Padley, in Hathersage, in a very inaccessible part of the county, principally, as it seems to me, because here, by long working, a superior part of the stratum has been reached to what is generally met with on the surface; for the fact is, that fine blocks of this rock, of every size that can be wanted, are so plentifully met with, loose and above ground, that anything like a quarry in it is almost unknown, except in Hathersage.

"Some of the beds of this grit rock, which have usually spherical stains in them of a light red colour, are perfectly infusible, and form the best fire-stone which is known for lining the hearths of iron furnaces and others where an intense heat is kept up. The upper beds of the grit rock are often thin, and capable of further division, so as to make excellent paving stones or flags, and even slate for covering buildings.

"In a geological point of view, this lowest regular grit rock is very important, on account of the great length that its basset-edge can be traced, with scarcely any interruption, in the form almost of a lengthened horse-shoe, terminating at its two ends against the great east and west or Derbyshire fault, and including within and beneath it the great or limestone shale, and the limestones and toadstones, whose descriptions are to follow, and having coal measures upon and without it.

" *Great, or Limestone Shale.*—This stratum is a black argillaceous shale, whose thickness, as proven by the shafts of the lead
mines in the first limestone rock underneath it, seems generally
from one hundred and fifty to one hundred and seventy yards.
It sometimes consists entirely of black and brown shale, in very
thin lamina, but subject to great and curious anomalies, the
first and most general of which are, accidental beds of fine-grained
siliceous freestone, very full of mica in minute plates, and stained
with various concentric rings of different shapes and shades of
yellow and red. In some places there are accidental beds of this
shalestone of a canky hardness, and very fit for road making. But
the most extraordinary anomaly attending this great shale is the
great masses and accidental beds of dark blue or black limestone
which it produces, some of the beds of which make a lime which
sets in water, and is little inferior for water works to the famous
Barrow lime; perhaps these beds contain manganese. Ironstone is
found in considerable beds in the limestone shale. Several ochrey
and chalybeate springs issue from this great or limestone shale, and
sulphur in small quantities is also contained in its cavities.

" *Mineral Limestone and Toadstone Strata.*—The strata to be
described under this denomination are seven in number, viz., four
limestone rocks and three basaltic beds or strata, here called toadstones, the position and average thickness of which are explained in
the Table. It must here be observed that the toadstone strata are
liable to vary in their thickness, and the limestones also perhaps, as
the late Mr. Williams showed of the mountain limestones of Scotland. (See his "Mineral Kingdom," Second Edition, Vol. I., pages
55, 56, 124, and 404).

" The first limestone, the uppermost of the series, bassets regularly from under the great shale, which was last described, all the
way from Ranter mine, N.N.E. of Wirksworth Town, south, to near
Quarters House, N.N.W. of Great Hucklow, north, in an irregular
line. The remainder of the boundary of these strata, from Quarters
House, near Great Hucklow, northward, to Castleton town, is
principally limited by a vast fault; from Wirksworth Town, south-
westward, to Hopton, a part of the same great fault separates the
third limestone rock from the great shale, &c., south of it.

" The western boundary of the strata I am describing, is marked by the basset-edge of the third, or lowest toadstone, and the appearance of the fourth lime rock from under it: such boundary, commencing at the great limestone fault, in Hopton, and proceeding first north-west, then west, and then north-east, so as to include Harboro rocks, then near to Griffe House, and to the famous Hopton Wood quarries, till it joins the fault above mentioned, one-third of a mile north-west of Middleton, by Wirksworth. From the south side of Slaley, the boundary is again to be traced from this fault, near to Ible, west, and to Grange Mill, thence to Pike Hall, Dalehead mine, three-quarters of a mile north-east of Newhaven House, nearly half a mile south-west of Benty Grange, west of Cronkstone, west of Hurdlow, east of Great Low Hill, east of Chelmerton Town, and west of the Low, by Flatt House, Topleyhead, and one-quarter of a mile north-west of Blackwell; it crosses the Wye river above Millersdale, thence by the side of Flagdale, to Great-rocks, thence to near Smalldale, to Dalehead, three-eighths of a mile north-west of Wheston, to Copt, Knowl, Portaway mine, and thence across the Cave Dale to Cawler Hills, and along the same to the great limestone fault, above mentioned, in Castleton Town.

" Within the limits described above, each of the three limestone rocks has its regular, but crooked, range, and basset-edge, from south to north, viz.:—The first rock, from Wirksworth to Great Hucklow and to Quarters House, a little north of it, abutting at each end against the great limestone fault, as above mentioned; the second lime, from the great limestone fault in Middleton Wood on the north of Middleton, by Wirksworth, to the same fault again on the south side of the Windmill Houses, near Great Hucklow; and the third lime, from the same fault, between Wirksworth and Hopton, south, to the same fault, against which it abuts, from a point south of Windmill Houses (and passing Hazlebadge, Bradwell, Edingtree, and Pindale) to Castleton Town.

" In like manner the three toadstone strata, each abut against the same fault, at the south and north ends of their respective ranges."

In order still further to illustrate the position and nature of the Derbyshire strata, we subjoin the following extract, from "Phillips's Geology of England and Wales." Speaking of the strata, whose computed thickness is stated in the Table, page 73, Mr. Phillips proceeds :—

" We have to notice the nature of the strata of limestone, toadstone, shale, and gritstone; and shall afterwards say a few words on the veins passing through them.

" *The lowest stratum of Limestone*, being that on the out-going or out-crop of which are situated the Peak Forest, Buxton, and many towns on the south of it, passes across Dovedale and Wettondale: the Weaver hills consist of it. In it are many caverns, as the immense one called Elden Hole, north of Peak Forest Town; the Devil's Hall, connected, by a tunnel, with Speedwell mine; Pool's Hole, near Buxton, and several of less note. Its stratification, and that of all the superior strata, is, in many places, greatly affected by what is termed a great limestone fault, but of which I have not been able to discover any account, except of its direction; it is very long and circuitous. The thickness of this lower limestone stratum is not known; we are consequently ignorant of the rock on which it rests. It is regularly stratified, consisting of very many beds, several of which are of considerable thickness; some thin ones are described as being a freestone (sandstone): its colour varies from white to a yellowish stone colour, it rarely includes dark coloured beds. Small entrochi, numerous anomia, and other shells and organic remains, occur throughout the whole of this stratum: in some mines, a thin bed of clay has been found in it. The lime yielded by this stratum is preferred to that of the strata above it. A bed of toadstone lies on it, but I propose to notice together the three beds of this substance, and therefore proceed to the

" *Second stratum of Limestone.*—This is about 210 feet in thickness, and consists also of many beds; the superior ones are often of a dark colour, and contain nodules of black chert, shells of the genus anomia, madrepores, &c.; some of the beds are quite black. It contains layers of clay, and towards the lower part of it, some dark beds of limestone contain white madrepores. Imbedded

J

masses of toadstone occur in it.   On this lies another bed of toadstone, to which succeeds a

"*Third stratum of Limestone.*—This, like the two preceding
strata, consists of many beds whose aggregate thickness is about 150
feet: and it is worthy of note, that several of them are of Magnesian
Limestone.   In some places the upper beds partake so greatly of the
nature of chert, as to be unfit for the purposes of the lime-burner;
these cherty masses are usually called in Derbyshire, dunstone, or
bastard limestone.   Here and there are masses of white chert or
china stone.   Some few beds contain entrochi; and towards the
lower part, are beds of a very black limestone, which, as it takes a
very brilliant polish, is termed black marble.   It contains thin beds
of clay.   On this stratum lies the third bed of toadstone, on which
reposes the

"*Upper Limestone.*—This, like the preceding, is about 150 feet
in thickness.   In it, as in the three lower strata, some thin beds of
clay are found, and it contains imbedded masses of toadstone, though
rarely.   The upper beds are of that variety of limestone called swine-
stone, and are often dark-coloured or black: near the top are found
layers of nodules of black chert, similar in their arrangement to the
flint nodules in chalk; in the upper beds also the shells called
anomia, and others are common.   The middle beds contain vast
assemblages of entrochi, and are occasionally quarried as marbles;
and it is remarkable, that in some places, where these middle beds
basset out on the surface, masses are ploughed up from beneath the
alluvial soil, exhibiting the casts of the inside of entrochi in chert;
these are commonly called screw-stones.   Blocks of these were
heretofore used in the forming of millstones, which were employed
instead of the French buhr-stone.   This stratum contains beds of
what is termed white chert or china-stone, of which considerable
quantities are used in the Staffordshire potteries.*

"We come now to the consideration of the three beds of *Toadstone interstratified with the four beds of Limestone.* These are
said to be true and regular, and are so calculated upon by intelligent
miners; yet in several places they have proved of great thickness,

---

* It is in a mountain composed of limestone, that the beautiful masses of various
coloured fluor spar, termed blue John, are found.

and in others very thin; in no place are they entirely wanting.
The average thickness of the two undermost beds is about 75 feet,
the upper bed is about 60 feet thick. But it is requisite to say that
each of the limestone strata encloses masses of toadstone, which are
not connected with the regular strata of that substance; to which
is attributed the suspicion entertained by some that it is not stratified
at all.

"All the strata of limestone and toadstone are said to basset out
in certain places in the district before mentioned, but their perfect
regularity and continuity in this respect appears to have been greatly
affected by the fault already mentioned.

"The toadstone is described as a compact, hard, ferruginous
stone, somewhat of the colour of the back of a toad, whence its
familiar name. It frequently effervesces strongly with acids, and
contains globules of whitish calcareous spar from the size of a pin's
head to that of a hazle nut, or larger, having the appearance of
rounded pebbles ; these nodules, when exposed at the surface, fall
out, leaving the imbedded substance with a cavernous or porous
aspect. Occasionally it is schistose; in other places it appears as a
clay, both in deep mines and on the surface, and is of a bluish grey
colour. In these clays it is said that masses of basalt, and others of
the hardest class of these stones, occur, and occasionally in the same
shapes as the pentagonal basaltic columns. It is not uncommon to
find in the upper bed of toadstone, chalcedony, hornblende, jasper,
zeolite, and green earth.

"In the cave at Castleton, which is a deep ravine at the back of
the castle, the toadstone is seen in the form of an irregular column,
is as hard as ordinary basalt, compact, and contains hornblende and
some patches or streaks of red jasper ; a similar variety is also found
near Buxton, containing zeolite and chalcedony. The toadstone has
no internal appearance of stratification, no impression of vegetables,
nor of marine exuviæ, which occur plentifully in the limestone in
which it is interstratified.

" *The Great Shale, or Limestone Shale*, resting on the uppermost
of the four beds of limestone, occupies a large tract on the surface.
Its thickness is averaged at about 450 feet. Its general colour is
black ; it disintegrates on the surface, forming a strong loam or clay,

which, when it is not too wet, is a very productive soil; but in some places the shale itself is durable, remaining for ages in the soil, of the size of a half-crown or penny-piece, from which it is persumed to have taken the name of *penny shale.* From the decomposed shale of this stratum bricks and tiles are made in several places. It contains occasional beds of a fine-grained siliceous freestone, full of mica in minute plates, and is stained with concentric rings of several shades of yellow and red. It is considered to be the most perfect freestone of the district, and is quarried in several places, having been used in the construction of some of the finest buildings in Derbyshire. This stratum also contains great masses and occasional beds of a dark blue or black limestone, which, at Ashford, is quarried as a black marble. The stratification of this shale is by no means regular, being, in different places, horizontal, inclined, and even contorted. The rottenstone of Derbyshire is considered to arise from the occasional decomposition of these limestone beds near or upon the surface. They sometimes contain ironstone. This stratum contains vegetable impressions; and some beds of coal of small extent, varying from a quarter of an inch to two inches in thickness. Sulphur, in small quantities, is found in its cavities, and geodes of limestone, filled with liquid bitumen, in several of the mines. The hot springs of Buxton issue from this stratum.

"We have now arrived at the consideration of the *stratum of gritstone* overlying the stratum of shale, the four limestones, and three interposed beds of toadstone. It is requisite here to remark that this gritstone is the stratum on which the great Derbyshire and Yorkshire coal measures lie; so that its situation might render it, in some degree, uncertain whether it ought not to be considered as a member of that important series rather than as belonging to the limestone formation; but the question seems decided in favour of the latter, by its containing metallic veins in common with the limestone. It is interposed between the shale and the coal, and the places at which it crops out on the surface from beneath the latter are known with great precision along a great length of country.

"The out-going of the strata just described forms the great lead district of Derbyshire; very numerous veins have been worked in it, principally for lead, but the ores of zinc, manganese, copper, and iron, also occur in them; but they are more plentiful and productive when in the limestone than when in the other strata. It has been supposed that lead ore has not been found in the toadstone; but nineteen instances of its discovery in that situation, in strings and short branches, are mentioned.

" *The east and west veins, in descending, are always cut off by the strata of toadstone,** which, therefore, pass through and divide them ;* and, it is worthy of note, that when the vein is again found in the stratum of limestone, beneath the toadstone, it is not immediately on a line with the upper part, nor exactly of the same nature; in this case a vein is said to have squinted. The toadstone is said sometimes to assume the consistence of clay. It has been before noticed, that the limestone strata contain thin beds of clay, termed, by the miner, way-boards; these sometimes pass through and divide the veins of ore in the same manner as the toadstone does: and so complete is the separation of the veins of ore by the clay and the toadstone, that not even the water in the upper part of the vein penetrates through them into the part beneath."

* In the North of England the east and west veins traverse the whin sill.

THE BRITISH CARBONIFEROUS SERIES IN DESCENDING ORDER, WITH LOCALITIES.

(See the President's Address in the "Quarterly Journal of the Geological Society,"
Vol. XXXVII., pages 201 and 202.)

	Names of Formations.	*Localities.*
Essentially Fresh Water and Estuarine Beds.	Stage G.—*Upper Coal-measures.* Thin coal-seams and limestones.	Manchester, Stoke-on-Trent, Newcastle - under - Lyme, south part of Dudley coal-field; banks of the Dee, near Ruabon; Hamilton and Ayrshire, Scotland.
	Stage F.—*Middle Coal-measures.* Thick coals.	Central portions of all the coal-fields of England and Wales; Upper Coal-measures of Scotland.
Essentially Marine.	Stage E.—*Gannister Beds or Lower Coal-measures.* Thin coals, with hard siliceous floors; flagstones and shales.	South Lancashire, North Staffordshire, and North and South Wales.
	Stage D.—*Millstone-grit Series.* Coarse grits, flagstones, and shales; a few thin coal-seams.	Uplands of Yorkshire, Lancashire and Derbyshire, North Staffordshire, and North and South Wales.
	Stage C.—*Yoredale Series.* Shales and grits, passing down into dark shales and earthy limestones.	Uplands and valleys of Lancashire, Yorkshire, Derbyshire, North Staffordshire, and Wales.
Essentially Marine (excepting Stage A. in Scotland).	Stage B.—*Carboniferous Limestone.* Massive limestone in many beds, with intervening shales and grits (thick in south, thin in north).	North and South Wales, Derbyshire, Yorkshire, Cumberland; in Scotland, the Lower or Main Limestone.
	Stage A.—*Lower Limestone Shale and Calciferous Sandstone.* Dark shales in some places; grits, conglomerates, and red sandstones; and shales in northern districts.	South Wales, Gloucestershire and Somersetshire, Northumberland and Durham; in Scotland, Calciferous Sandstone Series.
	Basis.—*Upper Old Red Sandstone.* Yellow sandstones and conglomerates.	South Wales, Northumberland, Scotland (Dura Den), Ireland (Kiltoran).

AN IDEAL SECTION OF THE ROCKS COMPOSING THE CRUST
OF THE EARTH, WHICH SHEWS THE RELATION OF THE
CARBONIFEROUS SYSTEM TO THE OTHER SYSTEMS.

(See D. Page's "Advanced Text-book of Geology," pages 273 and 274.)

Groups.	Systems.	Periods.	
Deposits in progress, Recent,	POST-TERTIARY.	CAINOZOIC.	NEOZOIC CYCLE.
Pleistocene, Pliocene, Miocene, Eocene,	TERTIARY.		
Chalk, Greensand,	CRETACEOUS.	MESOZOIC.	
Wealden, Oolite, Lias,	OOLITIC.		
Saliferous marls, Muschelkalk, Upper new red sandstone,	TRIASSIC.		
Magnesian limestone, Lower new red sandstone,	PERMIAN.		
Coal-measures, Millstone grit, Mountain limestone, Lower Coal-measures,	CARBONIFEROUS.	PALÆOZOIC.	PALÆOZOIC CYCLE.
Yellow sandstones, Red sandstones, and Conglomerates, Devonian limestones and Schists, Fissile flags and tile-stones,	DEVONIAN.		
Upper silurian, Lower silurian, Cambrian (?),	SILURIAN.		
Clay slate, Mica schist, Gneiss and granitoid schists,	METAMORPHIC.	HYPOZOIC.	

PART I.—COAL MEASURES.

Local Names.	No.		Fms.	Ft.	In.	Nature of each Stratum.
lluvial cover	1		5	0	0	Argillaceous
rown post, or grindstone bed...	2		12	0	0	Siliceous
OAL	3		0	0	6	Bituminous
lue metal stone	4		2	5	0	Argillaceous
'hite girdles	5		2	1	0	Siliceous
OAL	6		0	0	8	Bituminous
'hite and grey post	7		6	0	0	Siliceous
ft blue metal stone	8		5	0	0	Argillaceous
OAL	9		0	0	6	Bituminous
hite post girdles	10		3	0	0	Siliceous
hin	11		2	0	0	Siliceous
rong white post	12		2	5	6	Siliceous
OAL	13		0	1	0	Bituminous
ft blue thill	14		1	5	0	Argillaceous
ft girdles, mixed with whin...	15		3	5	0	Siliceous, &c.
OAL	16		0	0	6	Bituminous
ue and black stone	17		3	4	0	Argillaceous
OAL	18		0	0	8	Bituminous
rong white post	19		1	3	0	Siliceous
ey metal stone	20		1	4	0	Argillaceous
OAL	21		0	0	8	Bituminous
ey post, mixed with whin ...	22		4	1	0	Siliceous
ey girdles	23		3	1	0	Siliceous
ue and black stone	24		2	2	0	Argillaceous
OAL	25		0	1	0	Bituminous

Local Names.				No.		Fms.	Ft.	Ins.		Nature of each Stratum
a—Post girdles	...	...	...	31	...	0	2	0	...	Siliceous
b—Blue metal	...	...	...	32	...	0	4	0	...	Argillaceous
c—Girdles	...	...	...	34	...	0	1	2	...	Siliceous
d—Slate clay	...	...	...	37	...	0	1	6	...	Argillaceous
e—Post	...	...	...	38	...	0	1	0	...	Siliceous
f—White post	...	...	...	46	...	0	4	0	...	Siliceous
g—Strong white post	...	...	49	...	1	2	0	...	Siliceous
h—Whin	...	...	...	50	...	0	0	7	...	Siliceous
i—Blue metal stone, with whin girdles	53	...	1	4	3	...	Argill. and silic.
j—Blue grey metal	...	...	...	55	...	0	3	8	...	Argillaceous
k—Dark blue metal	...	...	...	59	...	0	2	2	...	Argillaceous
l—White post, mixed with whin	...	63	...	1	1	6	...	Siliceous
m—Dark grey metal stone	...	...	65	...	1	0	0	...	Argillaceous
n—Grey metal and girdles	...	...	67	...	1	3	0	...	Argillaceous
o—White post	...	...	...	68	...	0	3	0	...	Siliceous
p—Blue and grey metal	...	...	70	...	0	4	0	...	Argillaceous

Local Names.	No.		Fms.	Ft.	In.	Nature of each Stratum.
Grey metal stone	26		2	0	0	Argillaceous
Strong white post	27		6	0	0	Siliceous
Black metal stone	28		3	0	0	Argillaceous
High Main COAL on Tyne; Three-quarter Seam on Wear; Shield Row Seam of Tanfield District	29		1	0	0	Bituminous
Grey metal	30		4	3	0	Argillaceous, *a, b*
COAL, called metal coal	33		0	1	7	Bituminous, *c*
Blue metal stone	35		5	0	0	Argillaceous
The stone COAL on the Tyne; Five-quarter on the Wear; the Grey Seam of Northumberland	36		0	1	2	Bituminous, *d, e*
Blue metal stone	39		3	0	0	Argillaceous
Blue metal stone and whin	40		0	1	6	Argillaceous
Strong white post	41		3	3	0	Siliceous
Brown post, with water	42		0	0	7	Siliceous
Blue metal, with grey girdles	43		2	2	0	Argill. and silic.
Yard COAL on Tyne; Main Seam on Wear; brass thill of the Tanfield District	44		0	3	0	Bituminous
Blue metal	45		3	0	3	Argillaceous, *f*
COAL	47		0	0	6	Bituminous
Grey metal, with post girdles	48		2	0	6	Argill. and silic., *g, h*
Blue metal stone	51		1	2	0	Argillaceous
Grey metal stone, with post girdles	52		2	4	5	Argill. and silic., *i*
Maudlin Seam Wear COAL, and Bensham Tyne COAL	54		0	3	3	Bituminous, *j*
White post	56		2	0	7	Siliceous
White post, mixed with whin	57		2	0	0	Siliceous
White post	58		1	2	0	Siliceous, *k*
Grey metal stone and girdles	60		2	2	0	Argill. and silic.
White post, mixed with whin	61		3	0	0	Siliceous
Whin	62		0	0	7	Siliceous, *l*
Six-quarter COAL of Sheriff Hill; part of Low Main on Wear	64		0	3	6	Bituminous, *m*
Grey metal and whin girdles	66		1	4	10	Argill. and silic., *n, o*
Five-quarter COAL, part of Low Main, Wear	69		0	3	2	Bituminous, *p*

** The Italics refer to the different strata on the opposite page, which correspond with the strata next below those on which the letters are placed.

Local Names.	No.		Fms.	Ft.	In.	Nature of each Stratum.
...AL	71		o	o	9	Bituminous
...e and grey metal	72		2	o	o	Argillaceous
...ite post, mixed with whin...	73		o	4	6	Siliceous
...ey metal stone	74		1	o	6	Argillaceous
...to and girdles	75		1	o	9	Argill. and silic.
...w Main **COAL** on Tyne, Hutton Seam on Wear ...	76		1	o	6	Bituminous
...ey post, with blue stone ...	7 /		13	3	o	Silic. and argill.
...AL	78		o	1	6	Bituminous
...ie metal stone	79		7	3	o	Argillaceous
...AL	80		o	o	6	Bituminous
...ey metal, with post	81		3	o	o	Argill. and silic.
...o-Quarter **COAL** of Sheriff Hill	82		o	o	2	Bituminous
...ey metal and white post ...	83		5	o	o	Argill. and silic.
...AL	84		o	o	6	Bituminous
...ey metal stone	85		2	o	o	Argillaceous
...AL	86		o	o	6	Bituminous
...ie metal	87		6	o	o	Argillaceous
...aumont Seam on Tyne; Whickham Stone **COAL** of Sheriff Hill; divided into Harvey and Townley Seams on the Wear	88		1	o	o	Bituminous
...ey metal and metal stone ...	89		5	o	o	Argillaceous
...ockwell Seam;* Splint Seam at Walbottle; Horsleywood Seam at Wylam ...	90		o	3	2	Bituminous

*[The top and bottom Busty Seams of Sheriff Hill, which form one seam at Marley Hill, occur between the Beaumont and the Brockwell Seams. The Three-Quarter Seam called, in the Auckland district, the Top Coal of the Brockwell.—ED.]

MILLSTONE GRIT SERIES.

Local Names.	No.		Fms.	Ft.	In	Nature of each Stratum.
ate sill	91		2	3	0	Silic. and argill.
ate, clay, or plate	92		4	0	0	Argillaceous
ifferent girdle beds	93		2	0	0	Argill. and silic.
ate	94		2	0	0	Argillaceous
reestone	95		7	0	0	Siliceous
oarse hazle	96		1	4	0	Siliceous
late	97		1	0	0	Argillaceous, *a*
late and grey beds	99		1	3	0	Argillaceous
ard stone ditto	100		0	4	0	Siliceous
late and grey beds	101		1	3	0	Argill. and silic.
rey beds	102		0	3	0	Argill. and silic.
late and ditto	103		1	0	0	Argillaceous
illstone grit, or grey millstone	104		4	3	0	Siliceous
late	105		4	3	0	Argillaceous
ard hazle	106		1	3	0	Siliceous
rey beds	107		1	3	0	Argill and silic.
reestone	108		7	3	0	Siliceous
late	109		1	0	0	Argillaceous
azle, or slate	110		2	0	0	Argill. and silic.
late, or famp	111		1	1	6	Argillaceous
azle and plate...	112		0	3	0	Argill. and silic.
late	113		2	1	0	Argillaceous
azle, or slate	114		1	4	6	Siliceous
late and grey beds	115		3	0	0	Silic. and argill.

Local Names.		No.	Fms.	Ft.	Ins.		Nature of Stratum.
a—Blue stone		98	...	0	2	0	... Calcareous

PART II.—LEAD MEASURES.

Local Names.	No.		Fms.	Ft.	In.	Nature of each Stratum.	
ernating thin strata of grey eds	116		14	4	0	Argillaceous and siliceous	The representatives of the Yoredale Series.
D							
indstone sill	117		4	0	0	Siliceous	
ate	118		5	3	0	Argillaceous	
zle	119		1	3	0	Siliceous	
ate	120		1	4	0	Argillaceous	
RST, OR FELL-TOP LIMESTN.	121		0	4	6	Calcareous	
al	122		0	0	8	Sulphureous	
zle, or upper coal sill ...	123		2	0	0	Siliceous	
ate	124		5	0	0	Argillaceous	
zle, or whetstone sill ...	125		1	3	0	Argill. and siliceous	
ate	126		2	0	0	Argillaceous	
zle	127		2	0	0	Siliceous	
ate	128		1	1	0	Argillaceous	
per slate sill	129		4	0	0	Siliceous	
ate	130		1	1	6	Argillaceous	
wer slate sill	131		3	3	0	Siliceous	
ate	132		5	3	0	Argillaceous	
zle, or hard dry slate ...	133		1	3	0	Argillaceous & silic.	

Local Names.	No.		Fms.	Ft.	In.	Nature of each Stratum.
ate	134		3	3	0	Argillaceous
nstone and Coal	135 136		0	4	6	Sulph, and siliceous
restone	137		5	3	0	Siliceous
ate	138		4	0	0	Argillaceous
hite tuft	139		1	5	0	Siliceous
ate	140		2	1	0	Argillaceous
rdle bed	141		1	0	0	Siliceous
ate	142		2	1	0	Argillaceous
ttinson's sill, or hazle ...	143		2	0	0	Siliceous
ate	144		3	0	0	Argillaceous
COND, OR LITTLE LIMESTONE	145		1	3	0	Calcareous
ate	146		3	0	0	Argillaceous
al	147		0	1	6	Sulphureous
igh coal sill	148		2	0	0	Siliceous
ate	149		1	1	6	Argillaceous
al	150		0	1	0	Sulphureous
w coal sill	151		1	4	0	Siliceous
ate	152		3	0	0	Argillaceous
umbler beds, black bed, and THIRD, or GREAT LIMESTONE	153		10	3	0	Cal. and argillaceous
uft, or water sill	154		1	3	0	Siliceous
ate	155		3	3	0	Argillaceous

Local Names.			No.		Fms.	Ft.	In.		Nat. of each Stratum
a—Hazle	...	...	171	...	o	3	o	...	Siliceous
b—Hazle	...	...	176	...	o	2	o	...	Siliceous
c—Plate	...	...	179	...	o	2	o	...	Argillaceous
d—Hazle	...	...	180	...	o	1	o	...	Siliceous
e—Hazle	...	...	182	...	o	2	6	...	Siliceous
f—Hazle	...	...	184	...	1	3	o	...	Siliceous

Local Names.	No.		Fms.	Ft.	In.	Nature of each Stratum.
...ALL Limestone	156		0	1	6	Calcareous
...uarry hazle	157		5	0	0	Siliceous
...ate	158		5	3	0	Argillaceous
...ll bed	159		1	1	6	Argillaceous & silic.
...OURTH, OR 4 Fathom Lime-stone	160		4	0	0	Calcareous
...attrass Gill hazle	161		3	0	0	Siliceous
...ate	162		5	3	0	Argillaceous
...FTH, OR 3 Yards Limestone	163		1	3	0	Calcareous
...x Fathoms Hazle, called Arthur's Pit Hazle	164		6	0	0	Siliceous
...ate	165		1	4	6	Argillaceous
...XTH, OR 5 Yards Limestone	166		1	1	6	Calcareous
...aty hazle	167		2	0	0	Siliceous
...ate	168		3	0	0	Argillaceous
...EVENTH, OR Scar Limestone	169		5	0	0	Calcareous*
...ate	170		0	3	0	Argillaceous, *a*
...oal	172		0	0	6	Sulphureous
...ate	173		1	1	6	Argillaceous
...azle	174		2	0	0	Siliceous
...ate	175		0	3	0	Argillaceous, *b*
...ate	177		1	3	0	Argillaceous
...azle	178		0	2	0	Siliceous, *c, d*
...H, OR Cockle-shell Limest.	181		0	2	0	Calcareous, *e*
...ate	183		0	1	0	Argillaceous, *f*
...ate	185		0	5	0	Argillaceous

* The satin-stone occurs about two fathoms below this stratum, on the east side of the River Tyne, about a mile and a half south of Alston.

₊ The Italics refer to the different strata on the opposite page, which correspond with the strata next below those on which the letters are placed.

Local Names.	No.		Fms.	Ft.	In.	Nature of each Stratum.
NTH, OR SINGLE POST LIME-TONE	186		1	0	0	Calcareous
te	187		0	3	0	Argillaceous
y stone	188		0	3	0	Siliceous
ne-bottom plates, alternating late and grey beds	189		9	0	0	Argil. and Siliceous
NTH, OR TYNE-BOTTOM LIMESTONE	190		4	0	0	Calcareous
etstone bed	191		0	3	0	Argillaceous
in sill	192		20	0	0	Basaltic green stone
te	193		1	3	0	Argillaceous
zle	194		1	4	0	Siliceous
te	195		1	5	0	Argillaceous
zle	196		1	5	6	Siliceous
te	197		0	3	0	Argillaceous
zle	198		3	0	0	Siliceous
te	199		1	3	0	Argillaceous
EVENTH, OR JEW LIMESTONE	200		4	0	0	Calcareous
te	201		1	1	0	Argillaceous
te	202		2	3	0	Siliceous
te	203		0	4	6	Argillaceous
ELFTH, OR LITTLE LIME-TONE...	204		3	0	0	Calcareous

The Scar Limestone Series begins here.

SCAR LIMESTONE SERIES.

LOWER LIMESTONE SERIES OF SCOTLAND.

Local Names.	No.	Fms.	Ft.	In.	Nature of each Stratum.
Plate and grey beds	205	2	3	0	Argil. and siliceous
Hazle	206	8	3	0	Siliceous
Plate	207	4	0	0	Argillaceous
SMIDDY LIMESTONE	208	5	1	6	Calcareous
Hazle	209	2	0	0	Siliceous
LIMESTONE	210	4	1	6	Calcareous
Plate	211	0	4	6	Argillaceous
Hazle	212	2	0	0	Siliceous
Plate	213	0	5	0	Argillaceous
ROBINSON'S LIME	214	3	3	0	Calcareous
Hazle	215	1	3	0	Siliceous
Plate	216	0	3	0	Argillaceous
GREAT LIMESTONE, RUNDLE, OR MELMERBY SCAR LIMESTONE	217	22	0	0	Calcareous
Plate	218	2	0	0	Argillaceous
Freestone	219	1	0	0	Siliceous
Plate and small Coal ...	220	1	0	0	Argil. & sulphureous
LIMESTONE	221	2	0	0	Calcareous

TUEDIAN SERIES.
CALCIFEROUS SANDSTONE SERIES OF SCOTLAND.

Local Names.	*No.*		*Fms.*	*Ft.*	*In.*	*Nature of each Stratum.*
FREESTONE (Sandstone) ...	222		17	3	0	Siliceous
Plate	223		1	3	0	Argillaceous
FREESTONE	224		1	1	6	Siliceous
Plate	225		1	3	0	Argillaceous
FREESTONE	226		1	1	6	Siliceous
Plate	227		1	3	0	Argillaceous
FREESTONE	228		1	3	0	Siliceous
Plate	229		1	3	0	Argillaceous
Limestone	230		1	1	6	Calcareous
HARD FREESTONE	231		2	0	0	Siliceous
Plate	232		7	0	0	Argillaceous
Coal	233		0	0	7	Sulp. & inflammable
Plate	234		21	3	0	Argillaceous

Local Names.	No.		Fms.	Ft.	In.	Nature of each Stratum.
EESTONE	235		5	0	0	Siliceous
rdle bed	236		1	1	6	Siliceous
nestone	237		3	0	0	Calcareous
EESTONE	238		29	0	0	Siliceous
ate, upper part black, the lower reddish	239		10	0	0	Argillaceous
			634	3	10	
PPER OLD RED SANDSTONE	240					

PART II.

A SHORT SUMMARY OF CONTENTS.

I.—THE ORIGIN AND CLASSIFICATION OF MINERAL VEINS.

They were originally fissures in the rocks.

Veins are divided, according to their form, into:—

(1) Rake veins.
(2) Pipe veins. } (See Sections I., III., and IV.)

According to their positions they are divided into:—

(1) Slip veins, which hade or incline from the perpendicular, and are accompanied by a throw, or displacement of the strata.

(2) Gash, or chasm veins, which have no throw. (Section I.)

They are divided according to their bearing, *i.e.* the direction in which they run, into:—

(1) East and west, or right running, veins.
(2) North and south, or cross, veins.
(3) Quarter joint veins, *i.e.* those whose bearing is between the bearings of 1 and 2. (Section I.)

II.—CONTENTS OF VEINS.

These consist of:—

(1) Vein-stone, or rider.
(2) Mineral spar, crystallised and amorphous.
(3) Mineral soil.
(4) Metallic ores. (Section II.)

III.—RAKE VEINS.

These are subdivided into:—

(*a*) The regular rake vein.
(*b*) The irregular rake vein.
(*c*) The flat, or dilated vein. (Section III.)

IV.—PIPE VEINS.

These are subdivided into:—

(*a*) The simple pipe vein.
(*b*) The accumulated pipe vein. (Section IV.)

Characteristics of Mineral Veins.

(1) The slip vein is very irregular in respect of width, sometimes opening out to many fathoms, at other times closing in to a few inches.

(2) The gash vein is widest at the surface, gradually decreasing in capacity as it descends into the earth.

(3) The slip vein also loses in strength and capacity when it penetrates the deep strata.*

(4) Veins are most productive in the limestones (especially in the Great Limestone) when these strata lie near the surface; they are also productive in the sandstones and whin sill when these form the surface rocks. They are least productive in the shales.

(5) The east and west veins are more productive than the north and south veins.

(6) The most productive veins are those which dislocate the strata to the extent of six to eighteen feet.

(7) When veins cross each other deposits of ore are frequently found at the points of intersection.

(8) When several veins converge towards a point there is frequently a deposit of ore at that point.

(9) When several veins occur close together and run parallel with each other, the circumstances are favourable for a deposit of ore.

(10) When a vein "flys to pieces," or, in other words, becomes divided into strings, it ceases, for the time being, to be productive; but if the strings come together again, and the vein be thus reformed, it may again become productive. When productive, veins are said to be *quick;* when non-productive, they are said to *dead*.

(11) The north and south veins *traverse* the east and west veins; hence the reason why the former are called *cross* veins; and hence, also, the reason why they are supposed to have been *posterior* in origin to the east and west veins.

(12) When a north and south vein crosses an east and west vein, at a considerable angle, the former frequently removes the latter from its line of bearing; that is, carries it a short distance either to the north, or to the south; but the vein which is thus removed returns to its proper course at some distance beyond the point of intersection.

---

* By "deep strata" are meant those which lie at a considerable depth—forty fathoms and upwards—below the surface of the earth, and not necessarily those which are low in the section. The Fell Top Limestone may be a deep stratum; the Tyne-bottom Limestone may be a surface stratum.

ON MINERAL VEINS.

I.—THE ORIGIN AND CLASSIFICATION OF VEINS.

VEINS were originally fissures,* or gashes, in the rocks. They were subsequently filled up with mineral and earthy substances. Miners believe that the slips and faults of the coal measures are identical with the veins of the lead measures.

Mineral veins are of two kinds:—

    1.—The Rake Vein.

    2.—The Pipe Vein.

The rake vein is much more common than the pipe vein. It is well known to practical miners as a longitudinal gash in the strata, usually cutting them quite through to a great depth and for a considerable distance.†

Sometimes the rake vein stands nearly perpendicular, but it usually overhangs with more or less slope, which slope is called by miners the *hading*, or the *hade* of the vein. The rock on each side of the gash is called the side or cheek of the vein, and the two sides are called the *hanging* side, and the *ledger* or laying side, or the *up cheek* and the *down cheek* respectively. Some miners call them the hanging side and the hading side; and the longitudinal line, which the vein follows horizontally, the *bearing* of the vein.

* [These fissures were caused by the elevation, or subsidence, of the rocks subsequently to their consolidation; the movement proceeding at unequal rates over different portions of the area which was subject to it. The fissures probably followed certain previously existing lines of fracture, which were caused by the contraction of the rocks during the process of consolidation. They were filled up partially by the closing in of the sides, partially by the deposition of matter which was held in a state of solution, or suspension, by the water which circulated through them.—ED.]

† Some metallic veins, in the mining districts of Alston Moor, Allendale, and Weardale, may be traced for eight or ten miles on the line of bearing; as, for instance, High Coalcleugh Vein, which is a continuation of Rampgill Vein. It proceeds to the westward, and passes through Breagill Burn, near Nenthead, where it takes the name of Browngill; from thence, crossing the South Tyne river, near Garrigill, in Alston Moor, it may be traced to Dry Burn, and Rodderup Fell, about three miles and a half south-west of Alston.

Mr. Bakewell, in his introduction to "Geology," second edition, page 283, states that "Molina, in his interesting history of Chili, mentions a vein of silver, at Uspalata, in the Andes, which is nine feet in thickness throughout its whole extent, and has been traced ninety miles. Smaller veins branch off from each side of it and penetrate the neighbouring mountains to the distance of thirty miles.

L

Of rake veins there are two species, namely the *gash*, with the accompanying *slip*, and the gash without the slip. In the latter the sides of the gash are separated and opened asunder; but the edges of the strata, on both sides of the fracture, continue opposite to one another, so that there is no slip (see Fig. 1). An instance of one of these may be seen at about a quarter of a mile above the smelting house, near south Tynehead, in the county of Cumberland. This vein is about six fathoms wide, the cavity being entirely filled with basalt, whilst the Tyne-bottom limestone is opposite, or upon a level on both sides of it. It is known as the *Whin Dyke*,* and can be traced westward over Tynehead Fell to Kesh Burn.

It is necessary to point out some characteristics of each of these two species of veins in order to enable the miner to distinguish the one from the other when he meets with them. The slip vein is more subject to *checks*, or *twitches*, than the gash vein; that is to say, the two sides come more frequently together, and leave no space between them for any material quantity of ore.

There is a great number of twitches in every rake vein, which continue for many feet, or for many fathoms; and the cavities or openings between the twitches vary greatly in size. The sides of many of the veins of this description are often very close together near the surface, but open out to very different degrees of width below. The open places are called the *bellies*, or cavities, of the vein. Many of the veins, however, are found to be regular and uniform, and carry a good rib of ore for a considerable length upon the line of bearing. Others carry some ore, and good mineral soil, in small quantities, yet never open out to any great width.

* [*The Whin Dyke* and the adjacent Sulphur vein are both lost sight of on Tynehead Fell. No traces of either can be found on the east side of Yad Moss. In connection with the former a fact should be mentioned here, which is not only interesting in itself, but which has a direct bearing upon the controversy respecting the origin of the great whin sill. The dyke cuts asunder the mineral veins which cross its path. This fact proves that the veins are older than the dyke. But the whin sill is proven to be older than the veins by the fact that it is traversed by them. Wherefore, the whin sill must be much older than the whin dyke, and cannot, therefore, be an expansion from it. The dyke must necessarily traverse the sill. See note on the whin sill, page 61.—ED.]

The gash, or chasm vein, as it is sometimes called, is always wide
above (as at A in figure below) and grows narrower as it descends
into the earth.   It often closes altogether in the deep strata (as at B).

Though not so subject to twitches in the line of bearing as the
slip, the gash vein is yet crossed by other dykes and veins, which
generally move it a little to one side of the line of bearing.

THE GASH, OR CHASM VEIN.

A

Fig. 1.

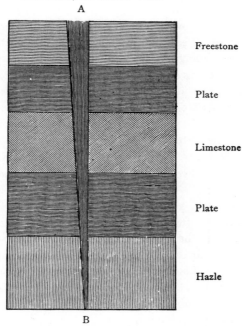

Freestone

Plate

Limestone

Plate

Hazle

B

According to Williams, a famous vein of this species was worked
at Llangunog, in Wales, in the Duke of Powis's time, whose property it was.   Llangunog was, perhaps, the richest vein of lead ore,
for the time being, ever yet discovered in this island.   The miners had
at one time a solid rib of ore, five yards wide, in the middle of the
vein, which continued for some distance.   The ore was so pure that it
was poured out of the kebbles at the shaft head into the waggons, and
carried directly to the smelting house.   They had also several feet
of ore upon the sides of the vein, which was mixed with spar and
other stony matter, and went through the hands of the washers.

This rich and noble vein was cut out below by a bed of black schistus, or plate, and so entirely that not the least fissure, or vestige of the vein, remained; nor could any trace of it ever be found afterwards, though diligent search was made for several years by the most skilful miners.*

In the great mining fields the very strong veins are accompanied by a number of small ones, all being very near to each other. There are, also, veins crossing one another. And, again, sometimes two veins run down into the ground in such a manner that they meet in the direction of their depth; in which case the same observations apply to them which are applicable to those that meet in a horizontal direction. See Plate IV., Fig. 3.

Most of the veins in Weardale, Allendale, and Alston Moor, extend from East to West, or, to speak more accurately, one end of the vein points west and by south, while the other points east by north. Hence the reason why they are called East and West Veins. There are other veins running nearly North and South, which are called *cross* veins; and it should be remarked that North and South, or cross veins are not so productive of metallic ores as the others; though, when the East and West, or *right running veins* and the *cross* veins intersect, the latter generally carry ore for some distance from the point of intersection, but rarely in any other stratum than limestone, and especially the great limestone.

The great limestone (see No. 153 in the engraved section) is the predominant stratum for producing lead ore throughout all the extensive mines in Alston Moor, in Cumberland, the two Allendales, in Northumberland, and Weardale and Teesdale, in the county of Durham.

It is not, perhaps, too much to assert that, if a correct estimate of the produce of all the above-mentioned mines was presented to

* Mr. Farey supposes that the Llangunog not being found to penetrate the strata beneath it, behaved as do the veins in Derbyshire when they reach the shale above or the toadstone below. He conjectures that, at the formation of the vein, the toadstone and shale were not disposed to contract in the same manner as the limestone rock which they enclose; and that the fissures, at that time, produced in the limestone have been subsequently filled up by means which, at present, we cannot explain.

public view, it would be found that the great limestone alone has produced as much lead ore as all the other strata throughout the whole section, annexed hereto, and described in Part I.*

The writer of these pages has frequently observed that most of the east and west veins, in Weardale, throw the north cheek up, and that their inclination, or hade downwards, is therefore to the south, according to the remark on page 124. He has observed also that most of the veins, in Allendale and Alston Moor, throw the south cheek up, and that their hade is to the north.

As a rule, the most regular *bearing* veins in all the mining districts are those which have six, or eight, feet of throw; for the same stratum is then, ordinarily, found on both cheeks; veins which have a greater throw dislocate the strata to such an extent that strata of a different kind are placed on the same level, and a plate bed is, perhaps, found opposite a bed of limestone.

Although the plate beds are not, as a rule, productive of metallic ores, yet, when strong veins carry a rider in them, they are sometimes productive.

When right running veins are intersected by strong cross veins at considerable angles, they are sometimes moved a very little way, either to the north or south, as in figure on next page.

Supposing ff to be a strong cross vein, and ee an East and West vein, intersected by ff at right angles; in such a case, the latter vein may be carried a little to the north, or south. If the East and West vein be intersected on the east in an oblique manner, as at d, it may be carried to the south, perhaps for a distance of ten, or twenty fathoms. If, on the other hand, the East and West, or right running vein come in the direction of a, on the east side of the cross vein, it may be carried as far to the north; and so on, according to the angle that the veins make with each other. Instances of right running veins being thrown out of their courses may be seen at Nentwater, in Alston Moor, where Old Carr's cross vein intersects the other veins. The right vein, which is called Goodamgill, on the

* [Since this was written some very rich deposits of ore have been discovered in other strata than the great limestone. At Langley Barony the ore is found principally in the four fathom limestone; at Stonecroft in the whin; at Greenhurth in a limestone which is supposed to be the Tyne-bottom limestone.—ED.]

east side of the cross vein, is thrown out of its course, and on the west side is called Greengill vein; Brownley Hill vein on the east

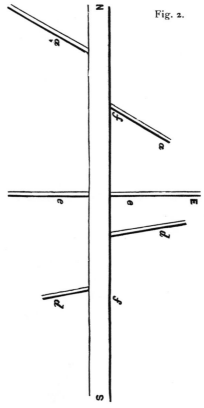

Fig. 2.

side is known as Grassfield vein on the west side; these veins being each thrown about fifteen, or twenty, fathoms to a side by the cross vein.

Plate IV., Figs. 1 and 2, show two remarkable instances of the influence which veins seem to have upon each other at the points of intersection. Fig. 1 is a ground plan of Rampgill vein, which has been remarkably productive in several of the strata. It is here intersected by the vein called Patterdale vein, and is removed 150 feet out of its course, and is also ramified into three parts on the western side of the intersection.

Fig. 2 shows several veins, which are crossed by Smallcleugh vein, in Handsome Mea lead mine, near Nenthead. The position of these veins, with respect to each other, is very different on the two sides of the intersecting vein, but the most singular change occurs in the second sun vein, which, on the south-east side, tilts nine feet down to the north, and on the north-west side tilts the same distance down to the south. The arrows, in the plate, are intended to show the dip of the strata under the influence of the veins. The Figs. 1—3, denote that the strata, at that place, dip one yard in three, in the direction of the arrow's point. The arrows, with the Figs. 1—9, show the true dip of the strata, at a distance from the vein.

Veins, however, which have been carried out of their course, return, in a short distance, to their former bearing. Plate III. represents a phenomenon of this kind, which occurs at Scale Burn Moss lead mine, near Nenthead. Here, it seems, that Scale Burn vein intersects Scale Burn cross vein, which last is found at a considerable distance to the east, and by an abrupt bend (at X), rapidly regains its line of bearing.

According to Werner, "By the crossing and intersecting of veins, the antiquity, *or relative age*, of each can be easily assigned. The distinguishing characteristics, for the relative age of veins and their substances, are the following:—Every vein, which intersects another, is *newer* than the one traversed, and is of *later* formation than all those which it traverses; of course, the oldest vein is traversed by all those that are of a posterior formation, and the newer veins always cross those that are older. When two veins cross; one of them, without suffering any derangement, or interruption, traverses the other and cuts it across, through its whole thickness. The vein which crosses another is of newer, whilst this last is of older, formation. This crossing of veins is of great importance, and deserves to be kept in remembrance by all who wish to become acquainted with the study of veins; yet, till very lately, it has escaped the observation of mineralogists."

It is a curious fact that in Alston Moor cross veins generally traverse the right running veins. If the Wernerian doctrines are correct, we may, therefore, infer that cross veins are of a more recent formation. Plate IV., Fig. 3, shows the crossing of two veins having different hades but pursuing, longitudinally, the same direction; the letters *g g* show the traversing vein, *x x* the vein traversed, and *a b c d e* represent the strata, with the throw and influence of the veins.

The curious phenomena which are presented by veins at the points of intersection cannot be explained in the present state of our knowledge.

Allowing that the traversing veins are of posterior formation, we cannot conceive in what manner they could influence the points of the veins previously in existence. In the instances of Scale Burn and Rampgill veins, represented in Plate III. and Plate IV., Fig. 1, we might suppose a force acting longitudinally, in both cases, in the direction of the throw, and removing the veins from their former positions; the bend in Scale Burn cross vein, Plate III., affording grounds for such a supposition : but when it is considered that previous to the formation of these veins the strata must have been consolidated, and that the veins could not have been removed without the removal also of the whole mass of strata in which they are found, it is difficult to conceive how any force could produce such effects. If we allow a force acting longitudinally in the above instances, we are compelled to deny it in the cases of Plate IV., Fig. 2, where the veins, traversed, seem to be moved in different directions. The same reasoning will apply to almost every instance of the intersection of veins, and would lead us to imagine that some other cause, than either a longitudinal force, or a difference in the periods of rock formation, must have produced these appearances. The author does not presume himself to offer a theory, but he cannot help stating the observations that occurred to him upon the subject.*

A rake vein is sometimes thrown off its course to one side, either by a *close joint*, or by an *open cross vein*. When this happens it is generally found that the vein is cut off by a smooth joint, which meets the miners full in the face, in place of the vein they have been

* [No satisfactory explanation of the phenomena here referred to has yet been found. Why cross veins should affect right running veins in the manner described by our author is a question which still continues to puzzle the miner.—ED.]

Plate 3

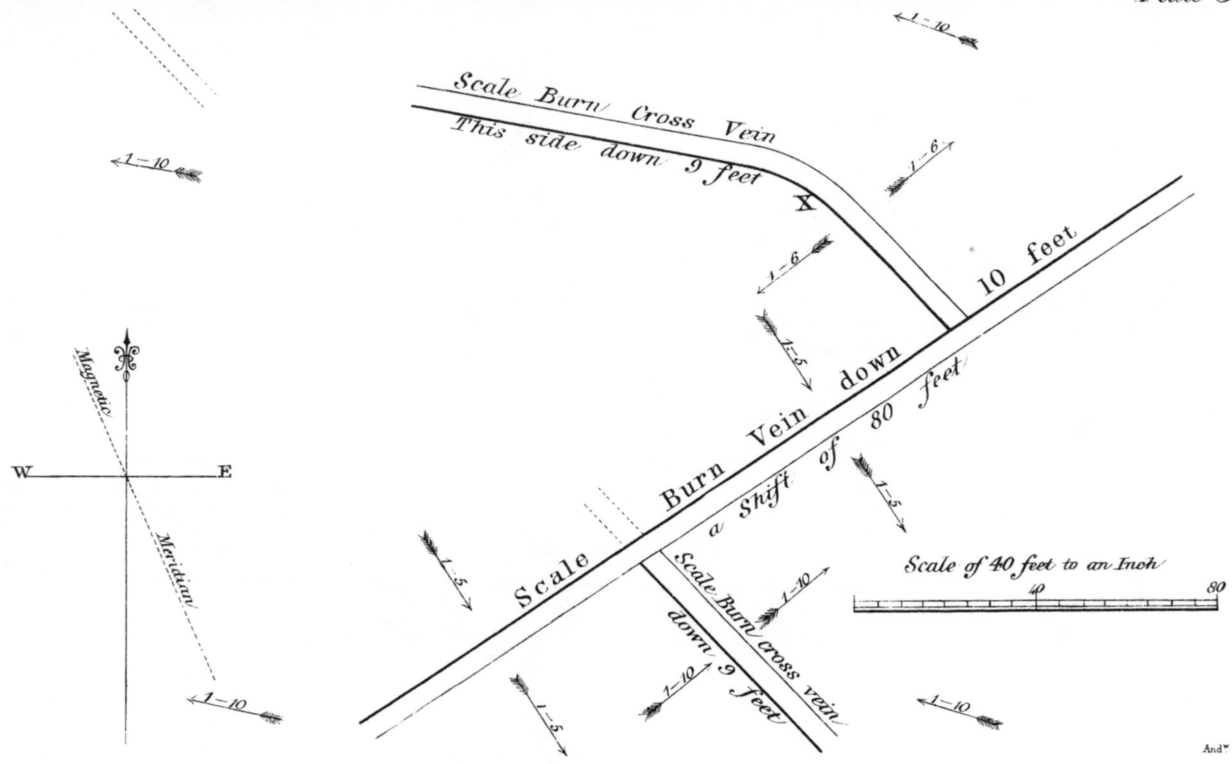

Scale Burn Cross Vein

This side down 9 feet

10 feet

Scale Burn Vein down 80 feet

a Shaft

Scale Burn cross vein

down 9 feet

Scale

1-10
1-6
1-5
1-6
1-5
1-5
1-10
1-10
1-5
1-5

Scale of 40 feet to an Inch

80   40

Meridian

E

W

Magnetic

1-10

And.ᵈ Reid. Newcastle.

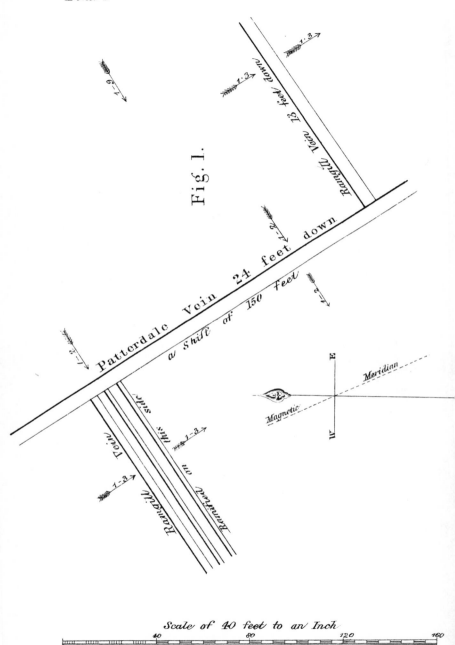

Plate 4

Fig. 1.

Patterdale Vein 24 feet down

a shift of 150 feet

Randtill Vein 13 feet down

Randtill Vein

Randtill on this side

E

W

Meridian

Magnetic

Scale of 40 feet to an Inch

40   80   120   160

Andᵂ Reid, Newcastl.

Fig. 2

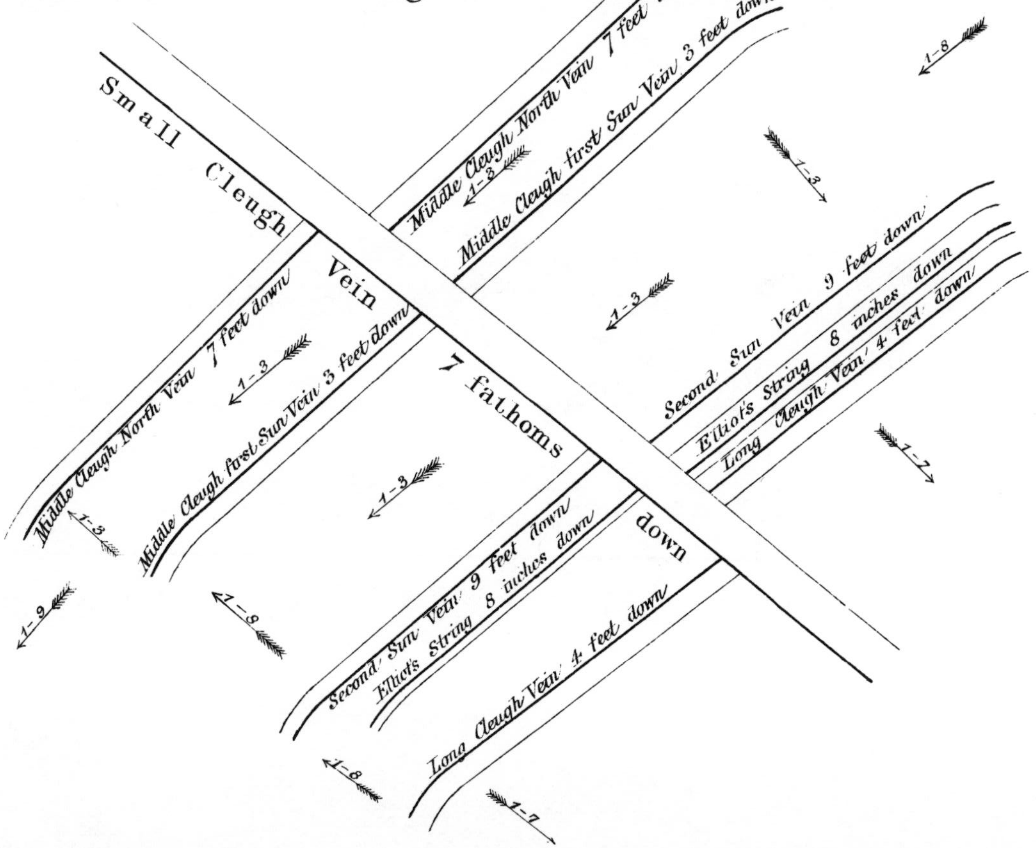
Small Cleugh Vein 7 fathoms down
Middle Cleugh North Vein 7 feet down
Middle Cleugh first Sun Vein 3 feet down
Second Sun Vein 9 feet down
Elliot's String 8 inches down
Long Cleugh Vein 4 feet down
Middle Cleugh North Vein 7 feet down
Middle Cleugh first Sun Vein 3 feet down
Second Sun Vein 9 feet down
Elliot's String 8 inches down
Long Cleugh Vein 4 feet down
1-8
1-3
1-3
1-3
1-7
1-3
1-3
1-3
1-9
1-9
1-8
1-7

Fig. 3.

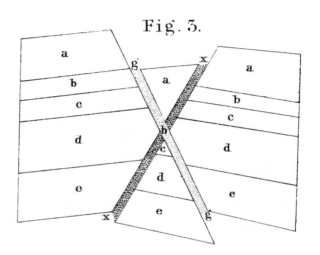

following; behind this joint, straight forward in the line of bearing, there is usually not the least trace of the vein.

There is one circumstance relating to this back joint which deserves to be particularly remarked. If the vein is started to the right hand side the smooth joint which cuts it off will meet the miner first on the left hand, and, on the contrary, if the vein is thrown to the left hand, the joint usually meets the miner first on the right hand, and so passes on, in a slanting, or diagonal direction, across the forehead of the mine.

The majority of the veins in the mining district of Alston Moor, Allendale, and Weardale, are generally more compressed in the hazles, than in the limestone strata; and it is not unusual to see a vein, so squeezed, in a hard hazle that it is not above six inches wide, whereas it is three, or four, feet wide in the limestone strata.

The mineral vein is bounded by two sides of stone, which are sometimes parallel with each other. Many veins are very variable in their breadth, being narrow in the upper strata, and wide underneath, and *vice versa.* A vein may be many fathoms wide in one place, yet, a little further to the east or west, it may not be more than one inch wide. This great variation happens, generally, in very compact strata; where the vein is squeezed, as it were, between the hard rocks. A true vein, however, is never entirely obliterated, but always shews a string of ore, or veiny substance, which serves as a guide to the miners, until it leads them to the wider portions of the vein.

In general, the strata most productive of the metallic ores, in Alston Moor, Allendale, and Weardale, lie between the grindstone sill and the four-fathom limestone.*

The parts of the rock in Cornwall which are richest in copper (according to Mr. Price), are from forty to eighty fathoms deep; for tin, from twenty to sixty; and though a great quantity of either may be raised at eighty or a hundred fathoms, yet it is often poor in quality.†

* [The unfavourable opinion of the Four-Fathom limestone as an ore-bearing stratum which was formerly prevalent among miners, and which led Forster to exclude it from the series of productive strata, has recently been shewn to be erroneous by the discovery, at Langley, near Haydon Bridge, of a valuable deposit of ore in that stratum.—ED.]

† [Tin of good quality is now being obtained at great depths in the Cornish mines.—ED.]

Before proceeding to give a detailed description of the rake and pipe veins I shall give an account of their contents.

II.—THE CONTENTS OF VEINS.

Veins contain between their sides a great variety of vein stuff. The most common, and the most promising of the minerals, as concomitants of ore, are the spars and vein stones.

In many veins there is found a stony concretion, which is called by miners *rider*. This mineral is usually hard, compact, and heavy, though sometimes it is cracked and cavernous. It stands out from the sides of the vein in irregular and misshapen masses. The rider frequently contains a variety of substances differing from each other in kind, as well as in colour, such as calcareous spar, quartz, fragments of the rocks near the vein, and occasionally, sulphur in grains and flowers. It also sometimes contains the ores of lead, copper, &c. All these minerals are cemented strongly together by a whitish, or a brownish-white, substance somewhat resembling quartz and agate, which seems to have enveloped the several ingredients in the composition whilst the whole was in a fluid state. This is properly called vein-stone, or vein-stuff—a term which is well understood both by naturalists and miners, the rider being always present either in veins, or on the cheeks of veins.* The vein stone does not, however, always contain all these minerals in its composition. It is occasionally pretty white, and then appears like a quartzy concretion of a cavernous structure. The insides of the caverns, though small, frequently contain a brownish ferruginous soft soil, of a snuffy appearance. But all the vein-stones are not white, nor whitish. In some places they are of a brown, a reddish brown, and several other

---

* This change of the strata, which constitutes the sides or cheeks of the vein, into rider, appears to have been effected by the action of acids, that existed in the solution which filled the vein at the time of its formation. These acids insinuated themselves into the neighbouring rocks, which they have changed in a greater or less degree.—*See Werner on Veins.* ["By the term rider is to be understood a part of the rock forming the sides of veins, the nature and appearance of which have been changed in consequence of its oxidation and impregnation with some metallic oxide, or salt, or other substance, whereby both its colour and induration are rendered more or less different from that of the rock in its native state."—John Leithart "On Mineral Veins," page 33.—ED.]

colours. Strong wide veins often contain a rib of this vein-stone between the sides, varying in thickness from a few feet to a few inches in width. Very strong veins indeed sometimes show a body of rider above the surface of the ground in the form of a ridge, as, for instance, the great sulphur vein, called the back-bone, which is found in Alston Moor.

The next most common mineral found in veins is spar, of which there are several species. Spar of various colours is met with in veins which contain copper and iron.

The mineral spars may be divided into the calcareous and vitrescible; or, to speak as a miner, into *calcareous, fluor, cauk* or *barytic*, and *quartzy spars.*

Both the homogeneous and the mixed varieties of *calcareous spar* are generally, though not always, of a white or whitish colour. They are occasionally tarnished by the soft soils in which they are often found, or by the mineral water, especially the chalybeate water, which most of the plate beds contain.

Fluor spar occurs in veins in a great many different colours, viz., white, green, violet, yellow, red, and brown. Its most general form, when crystallized, is a cube, but it is frequently met with in the form of an octohedron and cubo octohedron; it also occurs in amorphous masses.

The occurrence of *calcareous* and *fluor spars* in a vein is generally regarded as an indication of the presence of lead ore. All the extensive mines in Weardale, Allenheads, and Coalcleugh, have calcareous and fluor spars for the matrix; and it was from a mine in Weardale that the beautiful green fluor was formerly obtained in such quantities.

Cauk, or *barytic spar*, is not generally of so pure a white as the calcareous spars. The writer has seen cauk spar of a dead white, but usually it is of a yellowish, a brownish, or a reddish white, or else of a flesh colour. It is sometimes crystallized and transparent, as at Dufton Fell, in the county of Westmorland. Cauk spar is peculiar in having its crystals laminated and radiating from a centre, but the radiation seldom amounts to a whole circle. It is a dull, ill-looking spar, frequently rising in globes and irregular masses, and so exceedingly heavy that some miners have imagined that it contained metal. This mineral undoubtedly contains vitriolic acid.   Its ponderosity renders the separation of it from the metallic ores a very difficult operation.*

Quartz spar is generally of as pure a white colour as the calcareous, is frequently more beautiful, and, sometimes, not unlike it in shape; but it is of quite a different quality since it will neither effervesce with aquafortis nor burn into lime like calcareous spar; on the contrary, instead of calcining it, vitrifies in the fire.

Some kinds of cauk spar are of a cubical structure and resemble the common blue potter's ore of lead. Others are fine, smooth, and uniform throughout, without any visible grain or texture, and shot into prismatical crystals, which are usually found so pure and pellucid as almost to vie with the diamond in lustre. The crystals are frequently hard enough to cut glass.

Most of the mineral spars are found shot into prismatic, cubic, or hexagonal crystals. These geometrical crystals are generally transparent and very beautiful. The large cavities in which the spars are found are very interesting. They are frequently met with in hard mineral veins, and are called, by miners, *shakes*, *lochs*, or *loch-holes*.

The miners know nothing of these cavernous vacuities until they strike into them whilst working. They find them to be of various sizes, some not larger than the inside of a nut, others large enough to hold three or four men.

Their size generally bears some proportion to the size of the veins in which they are found. Their insides frequently exhibit all the variety, beauty, and splendour, of the most curious grotto work.

There is usually a rider adhering to the inside of the cavity, out of which, as out of a root, an innumerable multitude of short prismatical crystals are shot, which sparkle like a thousand

* There was a vein in Welhope, in the county of Northumberland, belonging to Colonel Beaumont, which contained the common cauk spar, or sulphate of barytes, in the upper beds, but changed its matrix in the great limestone, and then contained the ærated or carbonated barytes.   The spar lies mostly in the cavities, or shakes, of the vein, in round balls; when broken, it is striated, as if radiated from the centre.

diamonds, under the light of the candle, or when brought up to the sun. Between these clusters of mock diamonds, and sticking to them promiscuously, there are often lead ore, black jack, pyrites, or sulphur, and spar, shot also into prismatic, cubic, or other figures; and, besides these clusters of grotesque figures which grow out of one another, and are, as it were, piled upon one another, the insides of these caverns are sometimes magnificently adorned with the most wildly grotesque figures, which grow upon, and branch out of, one another in a manner which cannot be described, and shine in all the gay and splendid colours of polished gold, and of the rainbow.

It should be remarked that those caverns are never so magnificent as when there is some yellow copper ore, or pyrites, or black jack, in them; these minerals producing, in hard veins, very beautiful colours. Many well-known instances, in proof of this assertion, can be seen in the lead mines at Allenheads, Coalcleugh, and Nenthead.

These mineral loughs, shakes, or caverns, are the great source of materials for grotto work; and the specimens, collected from them are generally the most showy and dazzling articles in the grotto.

Neither the calcareous, fluor, nor cauk spars will strike fire with steel, unless there is a mixture of pyrites in them; but the quartzy spar gives fire plentifully. Pure quartz is often found in those mines where the quartzy spar prevails; quartz is also found mixed with ore.

What is properly called pure quartz, is a white, semi-transparent, hard, and heavy mineral, of a fine and uniform texture, of considerable brightness, and without any visible grain. Its crystals are frequently hexagonal in form, terminating in points. They break like glass.

Quartz does not rise in blocks, or large regular masses, either in the mine or elsewhere; it is so full of cracks and flaws, that it breaks into small irregular masses, with various sharp angles; and it is so hard that it wastes the tools of the miners more than any other stone. Where quartz and quartzy spar prevail, the veins are usually very hard and difficult to work.

The following is a list of such mineral soils as are most generally known :—

The *soft mineral soils* are as various, in quality and appearance, as the hard.

White, or whitish soils and clays abound in veins near the surface. They are usually fine, tenacious, and smooth; but not unfrequently they are friable, and like slaked lime when it is mixed with small sand. The presence of these species of mineral soil is generally regarded as a sign of lead ore.

The presence in veins of a *red fatty clay*, which stains the hands and clothes, is an indication of iron ore. The better sorts of iron ore are always accompanied by a soft red staining matter, by which they are easily distinguished; but it should be observed, that some lead and copper veins contain a considerable quantity of iron, and, consequently, a red or a brownish-red soft soil.

There are also *bluish and greenish mineral soils*, some of which are light and friable, others heavy and tenacious. These will be treated of when we come to treat of the signs and appearances of mineral veins.

The *yellowish, ash-coloured, and marbled soft soils and clays* cannot easily be distinguished from the surface clays of the same colours by any one but the skilled miner.

There are also *black, and blackish-brown soft soils*, which are usually light and friable, though there are some of them weighty and tough. The latter are called douk or donk by the Alston Moor miners.

But the most remarkable and promising of all the soft mineral soils is that which is of a *brown colour*, and of a lax and friable texture. It often resembles rappee and other snuff in colour and appearance. The brown is of various shades, sometimes deepening into a blackish colour. This soil is frequently met with in the large shakes, or cavities, which occur in flat veins.

III.—THE RAKE VEIN.

The Regular Rake Vein.—The kind of vein esteemed the most regular is one which runs in a straight line to a considerable distance upon the bearing. It sets downwards, near the perpendicular, with an equal hade, and has room enough between the sides for a drift of three or four feet in width. A good regular vein of this kind continues open between the cheeks, or hanger and ledger sides, for a considerable distance upon the line of bearing and for a great depth, excepting when shiver, or plate is met with.

Whatever may be the extent of the hade in strata of stone, it is generally greater in strata of plate.* (Fig. 4.)

It may be observed here, as a general remark, that the rake veins seldom carry any of the metallic ores in the plate beds, but are often filled with a soft clayey substance, called, by miners, the *douk* or *donk* of the vein.†

Some of these veins are said to be *quick*, and others *dead*. A quick vein, or, in other words, a bearing vein, is one which carries ore; a dead vein contains no ore, but is filled with mineral and earthy matters.

Some of these regular veins bear a solid rib of ore, of one, two, or three feet in width, for a considerable distance, forwards and downwards; and others bear two, three, or more, thin ribs of ore, of various dimensions, from half an inch, to five or six inches in thickness, with spar, or other mineral matter, interposed between them.

Before we proceed any further, it will be proper to point out some general rules relating to the inclination, or hade, of regular rake veins. If a vein bears, or runs, nearly east and west, and

---

* Mr. Farey explains this fact by assuming that the fissures in the stone were opened to a certain extent by shrinkage before any fissure existed in the adjacent shale, but that the further opening of fissures in the stony strata, when they happened not to be perpendicularly under each other, tore the shale asunder, and then opened a continuous vein downwards through the argillaceous stratum.

† Although the author of this work has, in some instances, seen the Wernerian theory, of the formation of veins, remarkably confirmed, yet, he cannot help observing that the fact here stated seems, in some measure, to militate against it. It was, it seems, the opinion of Werner, that all veins were originally open fissures, which have been gradually filled up by depositions from the surface. Had this been the case, we should have been led to infer that the contents of the vein ought to have been pretty uniform from top to bottom, and that the substances it contains in the siliceous and calcareous beds, would not so invariably and so widely have differed from its contents in the argillaceous parts of the strata. An observation, something similar to this, the author recollects to have seen, made by Mr. Bakewell, in the " Philosophical Magazine," and it would be well if the subject were considered by some able supporter of the theory in question.

throws up the south cheek, or, as the Alston Moor miners term it, the sun cheek, it will generally hade downwards to the north : on the other hand, if the north cheek be up, the inclination, or hade, will be generally downwards to the south; and so of any other vein, whatever cheek be up, the hade will generally be in the opposite direction.

There are some veins which are quite irregular in their hade, being of a zig-zag form—as in the annexed figure :—

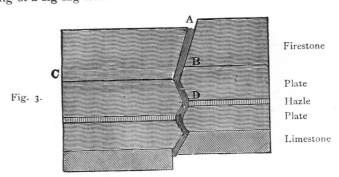

Fig. 3.

Firestone

Plate

Hazle
Plate

Limestone

Supposing a vein to take the superficies of the strata at A, it will hade down through the stratum of firestone pretty regularly, until it comes to the bottom of the upper cheek, B; then, having the low cheek, C, of firestone on one side, and plate on the other, it will hade back towards D; and so on, where it has nothing but plate on one side, and a harder stratum on the other, until it comes to a thicker stratum, where its hade will be more regular, having both the cheeks of the same substance.

There are other veins, of a weaker kind, which have not so much throw, and yet are irregular in their hade, sometimes lying quite flat in a stratum of coal, plate, or shiver. See figure below.

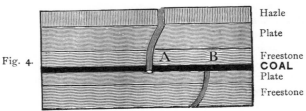

Fig. 4.

Hazle

Plate

Freestone
COAL
Plate

Freestone

The vein hades pretty regularly, until it comes to a soft stratum; for instance, coal, as at A; from thence it slips away to B, perhaps a distance of three or four fathoms, and then takes its regular hade again. When this is the case, we must look on the contrary side; that is, on the opposite side of the down cheek, for the vein.

There are other species of rake veins, which are pretty regular in their hade. Whatever may be the angle which they make with the horizon at the surface, they make nearly the same angle down below. These veins are usually very strong, and have forty, or even a hundred, fathoms of throw; as for instance, Old Carrs, at Nenthead, in the county of Cumberland; and the Burtreeford Dyke, at Allenheads, in the county of Northumberland.

Veins which occur in the Greywaucke have, generally, a regular hade which continues perfectly uniform to the greatest depth, as in the figure below, where the letters A and B show the vein.

A

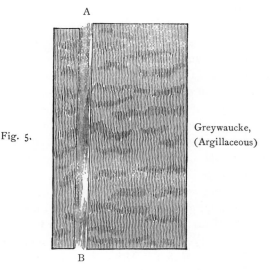

Fig. 5.

Greywaucke,
(Argillaceous)

B

There are a great many regular veins, which carry no ore at all. There are others which carry a small rib, or ribs, and are yet unprofitable. Others, again, contain small detached fragments, here and there, which are too insignificant to make them worth working.

M

It is a very usual thing to see dead veins, that is, such as bear no ore at all, continue very promising, in respect of minerals, and very regular, for a great way, both in driving and sinking. More than fifty fathoms have been driven in some of these regular veins, under great cover, perhaps twenty or more fathoms down from the surface, where the minerals were promising; yet no ore was found, or only so much as to induce the miners to proceed. Some of these dead veins are perfectly regular, and keep their sides about four or five feet asunder for long distances.

There are, again, many regular veins which are not so wide and roomy between the sides as those described; yet in these have been found several rich mines which have yielded ore for two or three miles in length, on the line of bearing, and to the depth of a hundred fathoms or upwards, and in every stratum, excepting the plate beds; as, for instance, Rampgill, at Nenthead, which belongs to the Commissioners and Governors of Greenwich Hospital; and the adjacent mine of Coalcleugh, which belongs to Mr. Beaumont. The deposit of ore in the Rampgill vein was sometimes twelve feet wide, in the great limestone. At Coalcleugh a single length (that is fifteen fathoms in the great limestone only) has been known to yield, in the course of twelve years, ten thousand bings* of lead ore.

The writer has, in the course of his travels, seen great numbers of perfectly regular veins, less than two feet in width, which were uniform for a considerable length. Some of these regular, thin, and close veins contain ore at the superficies of the strata. Whether, or not, they would carry ore further down cannot be known without proper trials.

When two veins, in the neighbourhood of each other, run in an oblique direction, and, therefore, meet together, they usually produce a body of ore at the place where they intersect. If both are rich, the quantity will be considerable; but if one be poor and the other rich, then both are either enriched, or impoverished, by the meeting. After some time they separate again, and each continues in its former direction. Sometimes, though rarely, they continue united.

When two veins have the same bearing, and are consequently parallel to each other, and are, moreover, near each other, they

---

* A bing of lead ore is eight hundredweight.

generally have the same hade. If they throw the contrary cheeks up, that is, if one throw a fathom up to the south and the other a yard up to the north, they will, notwithstanding, both hade downwards to the north.

Fig. 6.

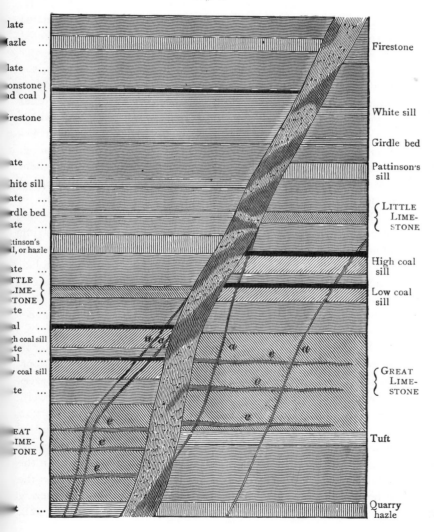

When a vein separates into strings, the circumstance is regarded as a sign of approaching poverty; but, on the contrary, when several strings are found running into the vein as the work proceeds, the circumstance is accounted a favourable sign.

Sometimes there are branches, or strings, *outside* the cheeks of the vein, in the adjacent strata, which come either obliquely, or transversely into it. If these branches are found impregnated with ore, or if they appear to underlie, or hade faster (as represented in Fig. 6, *a, a, a*) than the true vein, that is, if they dip deeper into the strata, they are then said to overtake, or come into, the vein, and to enrich it; if they do not, then they are said to go off from it, and to impoverish it. But neither these nor any other signs are to be entirely depended upon; for many veins which have a very bad appearance at first, nevertheless turn out extremely well afterwards; whilst others which, in the beginning, were very rich turn gradually worse and worse. Generally, where a vein has a bad appearance at first it would be imprudent to spend money on trials in it.

Mineral veins, as has been already observed, are frequently not more than an inch in width; nevertheless, if they contain a string of good ore it may be worth while to pursue them. They occasionally turn out well when they have come into soft ground. In like manner it is an encouragement to go on if the strings, or leaders of ore, enlarge, either in width or depth, as they are worked. If they stand upright and maintain an uniform thickness, the circumstances are regarded as unfavourable.

It is a very usual circumstance to find a large body of rider in a strong, hard vein, like the great sulphur vein in Alston Moor, standing in a rib in the middle of the vein, like a wall, with spaces between it and the sides of the vein. Sometimes, though rarely, there are two, or three ribs of rider. (Page 118.) The ribs vary in width from five or six inches to five or six feet. In strong veins, it is not an unusual circumstance to find a body of vein-stone several feet in thickness. The rider is not, however, always found in the middle of the vein, but is occasionally nearer to one side than the other; and it is not unusual to find a similar vein-stone, adhering strongly to the side, and also mixed with ore. When a rib, or wall, of rider is thus situated in the middle of a wide vein, good ore is occasionally found upon both sides of it; though, usually, the ore is found upon one side only. Some veins do not carry any rider at all in one stratum, but a great deal in another. When the ore is found in ribs between the rider and the sides of the vein, these ribs vary in thickness from two, or three inches, to two, or three, feet. In strong, wide veins ribs of good ore have been found upon each side of the rider, one, two, or even three feet in thickness; though usually a thick rib is found upon one side of the rider and a thin rib upon the other.* These continued regular ribs of ore, which run parallel to the rib of rider, and between it and the cheeks of the vein, are not always solid and pure, but are very often mixed with mineral substances.

Again, the ore found between the rider and the cheeks of a vein does not always occur in regular continued ribs. It is sometimes found in a discontinuous rib, that is to say, in a succession of large, flat slabs or masses, which present the appearance of ribs for two or three feet. These slabs, or flat masses, of ore are of various sizes; some are very large, others very small, and the distances between them are as various as the dimensions of the masses themselves. In different veins, and in different parts of the same vein, the masses are sometimes so near to one another that they almost touch; and at other times there is a distance of from a foot to five or six feet, or even more, between them. These discontinuous ribs of ore generally occur *in soft mineral soils.* They are not uniform in thickness throughout, but become thinner and thinner towards their edges. It has already been said that ribs of ore vary in thickness from one inch, or less, up to two or three feet or more. Instances of ribs more than three feet in thickness are rare.

In some very wide, loose veins, irregular masses of rider are found in one side of the vein and irregular masses of ore in the other; and both the masses of rider and the masses of ore are found lying without any definite order among soft, loose mineral soil. The masses of rider are frequently very hard, even when they occur in soft mineral soil. They are of various colours; the white, yellow,

---

* Mr. Farey says, "the two sides of a large rider, or near and parallel veins, are seldom, if ever, rich together.—*See Derbyshire Report, page* 246.

red, brown, black, green, and ash-coloured being most common. They are sometimes richly flowered, spotted, and veined, with ore; but it frequently happens that when ore is present it is found in such small specks and threads, and in stone so hard, that it will not repay the cost of extraction. When the masses are poor they are said to be *riders mixed with ore:* when they are very rich they are said to be *masses of ore mixed with rider.* It is not an unusual circumstance to find several kinds of ore in the same mass of rider, as for instance, the ores of lead, copper, iron, pyrites, &c. A mixture of this kind is generally useless, inasmuch as the riders are often so hard and so heavy that it is not possible either to separate the ores from them, or to separate the ores from each other.

Wide, soft, loose veins sometimes, though very rarely, contain masses of ore of various sizes without the accompanying riders. The ore in these cases is often coated over with other minerals. Some of these masses of ore are so large that they cannot be removed from the place where they are found, but must be wrought out piecemeal; in some very wide, soft, veins they are occasionally so large that one of them will yield a great many tons of lead. They are very seldom pure, being generally mixed with vein-stone. Sometimes the ores of lead, copper, and iron are found blended together.

All the substances found in the inside of soft, loose veins have a corroded and wasted appearance; the masses, large and small, being of no determined shape. The phenomena of the inside of these veins are so various that it would be tedious to give a minute account of them. It must not be assumed that all bold, wide, veins are soft. Many of them are very hard. Some of these bold veins have produced large bodies of lead ore, both in the rock and change of beds;* as at Wanlockhead and Lead Hills, in Scotland, where, it is said, that the miners have frequently had veins from six to fourteen feet wide of solid lead ore in the rock. In Allendale and Alston Moor veins have been found from six to twelve feet wide of solid lead ore.

* [Forster applies the term rock to the Greywaucke. By "the change of beds" he means the sedimentary strata.—ED.]

About six years ago* a very rich mine was opened in Alston Moor by John Wilson, Esq., and Company—known by the name of Hudgill Burn—which is now raising considerable quantities of lead ore. The mine contains two principal veins, denominated the sun vein and north vein, with other collateral strings or veins between them. The east forehead of the north vein contains a rib of pure galena, which is three feet in width, in the tuft, or water sill No. 154 in the section), and four ribs of galena, from two to four feet each, in the great limestone (No. 153 in the section). The sun vein is about twelve feet wide, and is blended with galena. The mine has yielded upwards of 12,000 bings of ore in one year. This is the largest yield that has been known in Alston Moor, or perhaps in the world. The number of miners employed is eighty.

The inside of a *hard vein* is almost as difficult to describe as that of a soft one; its riders, spars, and ores, usually occurring in such a variety of conditions and mixtures. The ore in this kind of vein is generally blended with a strong body of refractory rider, and therefore it is that it must be present in considerable quantities in order to defray the cost of extraction and dressing. Sometimes it is so blended with cauk spar, or black jack, as to be rendered useless; and some good veins of ore are spoiled by the presence in them of a great quantity of pyrites and mundic, or sulphur-stone. Occasionally a rib of three, or four, feet, or more, of pyrites, is found in a wide vein, with a considerable quantity of fine lead ore blended with it. If the ore happens to lie in a rib of moderate thickness, on one side of the vein, it will generally repay the cost of extraction and yield a profit.

Hard bold veins which contain no metal at the outcrop, are very discouraging to miners. The ground is so difficult to cut that trials soon become expensive: though sometimes this difficulty is partly obviated by the presence of a thin seam of clay, which the miners call a *steeking*, between the rider and the side of the vein. This seam helps them forward very much, since they can cut out the clay for the length of a pick helve, and thus free the *hards*, and render them more workable.

* [This was written in 1820. The Hudgill Burn mine is now closed.—ED.]

Wide sparry veins, sometimes carry two or three, or more, thin ribs of ore, separated from one another by as many ribs of spar. It often happens that when ore is in this, or any other way, divided, it is rendered valueless. Much, however, depends upon its quality. If the ribs consist of pure ore, and each of them be some inches in thickness, they can be worked with profit.

The Irregular Rake Vein.—We shall now proceed to give some account of such rake veins as are called irregular. These are, first, such as open suddenly into very wide bellies, then as suddenly close again; second, *waving* veins, or such as open and close alternately at very short distances.

It is not unusual to see a pretty wide and rich belly of good, solid, ore gradually, or suddenly, checked or twitched out by the coming together of the sides of the vein. Thus the ore fails at the end of a few fathoms. The twitch is either total, or partial. Occasionally it carries a thin rib of solid ore quite through until the vein opens out into another belly : usually, there is a rib of rider mixed with ore going quite through the twitch; but in many of these twitches there is neither ore, nor rider, the sides of the vein being as closely squeezed together as the joint between two hewn stones; and especially is this the case in the Greywaucke.

Sometimes there is a thin streak, or seam, of clay, running through the twitch. Where this is present there is no difficulty in the case, excepting as regards the labour and expense; because even an inexperienced miner will easily find his way through the twitch; but where the sides come into close contact, and are cemented together, which is often the case, the care and attention of an experienced miner are required to follow the vein through the twitch.

The twitches are of various lengths. No miner can possibly foretell how far any one of them will continue, or, in other words, how many fathoms he may have to drive before the vein opens out again, unless he has cut through the same twitch at a higher or lower random.* This uncertainty in the length of twitches is one of the chief difficulties met with in the practice of mining. They

---

* [That is, in a higher or lower stratum. In mining phraseology the term random is synonymous with stratum.—ED.]

may continue for ten, twenty, thirty, or forty fathoms, or sometimes even sixty, eighty, or a hundred; so that the miners are frequently left in a state of extreme doubt, after they have driven ten or fifteen fathoms in an unknown twitch, whether they should push forward, or stop short. When the miners have cut through a twitch they find the vein opening out again, and the sides, or cheeks, parting asunder. If a thin rib of ore has been present, serving to lead them through the twitch, it begins to grow thicker: if there has been no ore, the miners now, perhaps, find a rib of an inch, or two inches, in thickness. As they go forward the rib gradually increases in thickness and grows better and better until they come to the best and widest part of the belly. In respect of form, the rib resembles a fish, which gradually increases in thickness from the tail forwards.

The lengths of these bellies of ore are, of course, determined by the lengths of the twitches. Their depths and breadths are various. Some continue at their full width, where the ore is best, for several fathoms; others begin to dwindle almost as soon as the miners arrive at the best and thickest part of the belly. It sometimes happens that the miners meet with a false appearance whilst driving through a twitch; that is to say, they find a small deposit of ore which does not continue either horizontally, or vertically: such a circumstance causes them great disappointment, inasmuch as they naturally expect that when they have got through a twitch they have reached one edge of a belly of ore.

When one belly of ore in a vein proves pure and solid, it generally happens that all the bellies in the same vein prove so, and especially is this the case in contiguous parts of the same mining field. The contents of a vein often change greatly in any considerable distance.

There have been remarkably rich bellies of lead ore found in the mining field at Allenheads, where the the rake veins have *flatted*, that is, have formed flat veins. Eight hundred bings of ore have been raised by six miners, in one of these bellies, in the space of nine weeks.

Thus far, mention has only been made of masses of pure ore. The bellies are not, however, generally filled with pure ore, but often contain a mixture of ore, spar, and rider, like that in the ribs. Not unfrequently is it discovered that the bellies contain only spar, or rider, without any ore, or so little ore that it is not worth extracting. The open cavities, or drusses, which are lined with perfectly formed crystals, are most frequently met with in the irregular vein. Dead veins of this kind behave in the same way as the bearing veins.

The irregular vein is as frequently soft as hard. The soft soils found in it are like the soils which have been already described. The ore occurs in it in much the same way as it occurs in the regular vein, excepting that there are no regular ribs. In the wide and spacious cavities of soft, irregular, veins, the ore is generally found in globes or irregular masses, of very various dimensions, which are usually buried in soft soils.

It is not an unusual thing to find the bellies in this sort of vein swelling out to an enormous width, and sometimes the sides, when discovered, are shaken and loose. Working these soft wide veins is one of the most difficult things in mining.

No progress can be made in them without the aid of square timbers, which are advanced as far as the drifts go, in the form of a trance, or passage into a house, each pair of timbers consisting of two door cheeks, or side posts, and of a lintel and sole tree. The miners stand within this square timber, where they work, and still set more timber before them, as they can make room for it. This method of working is not only expensive and troublesome, but dangerous also, especially if the miners are not skilled in setting timber ; for the soil is generally quite soft and loose, and being usually mixed with masses of ore and stone, the whole frequently rushes down with violence in front of the timber. A skilful miner does all he can to prevent an accident of this kind by driving in polins, or sharp pointed stakes. He enters these above the lintel, or head tree, and *without* the sideposts of his foremost pair, and with his mallet drives them forward, past the square timbers, into the softness. If a mass of ore, or any hard substance, retards the point of one of his polins, he draws the impediment out of the way with his pick; and when the end of his polin is freed, he pushes it forward again until it is driven up. When the polins

have been driven up as far as seems necessary, the miner proceeds to work out room for another pair within the last, &c.
Whether the miners advance horizontally, sink down, or rise
upwards in these soft places, they must do all with square timbers.
It frequently happens that the ore is so plentiful and good in these
veins as abundantly to compensate the miners for all their trouble
and expense.

The second sort of irregular rake vein is called the *waving vein*.
This is a rake vein, which opens and closes at very short distances.
It is very near akin to the one last described, inasmuch as it contains bellies and twitches; but the twitches are so numerous and so
near to one another, that there is not room enough between them
for large expansions of the bellies. This vein is, therefore, never so
rich as the last mentioned, since the smaller cavities do not contain
such large quantities of ore. It is called the waving vein because
the small bellies resemble the hollows between the waves on a pool
of water.

The writer has dwelt the longer upon the history of the rake vein,
or perpendicular mineral fissure, because it is the most common.

He will now give a brief account of some of the strings, and
other partial veins, which branch out from the principal veins, since
they properly belong to the rake vein.

A *string* is a weak vein which flies out in a right line, but with
an acute angle, from the principal vein; and which, when it has
run in that line to an indeterminate, though no great distance,
ends in a point, not leaving a mark in the strata. If there be
another vein, at no great distance, running parallel with the
principal vein, then the string will continue its bearing until it
comes into it. The *true* string joins the principal vein at an acute
angle, but does not cross it; for if it should cross the vein, and
appear upon the other side, it is not a string, but an oblique, or
diagonal vein.

Strings fly out from the veins in various directions, though
always diagonally; they are sometimes as rich, and on rare occasions,
even richer, than the vein itself.

A *skew* is an irregular, discontinuous, mineral fissure, striking out
from the principal vein in an uncertain direction, and lying in a

very slanting, irregular position. This imperfect mineral fissure seldom extends to any considerable distance from the principal vein.

A *back*, or *sweep*, is a mineral fissure which often resembles the segment of a circle. It breaks off from the hanging, or upper cheek, of the vein ; strikes out to a greater or less distance, fetches a sweep, and then comes back into the same vein again at a short distance from the point where it first set out.

All these inferior branches produce good ore in favourable situations.

The Flat, or Dilated Vein.—The kind of vein which comes next under our consideration is the *streek*, or *flat*, or *dilated vein*, which is the third in the order of those called principal veins. Neither this nor the pipe vein should, perhaps, come under the denomination of mineral fissures, since they are scarcely fissures at all. The flat, or dilated vein, is a space or opening between two strata of stone ; one of which lies above, and the other below, this vein, in the same manner as the roof and pavement of a stratum of coal are above and below that coal. When the strata, between which this kind of vein is found, lie nearly parallel to the horizon, the vein likewise occurs in the same horizontal position; and when the strata vary from the horizontal position, the dilated vein varies likewise. This must always be the case, since the vein does not burst the strata, but always continues between the same two beds of stone.

These flat veins lie between the strata in much the same as seams of coal, and may, so far as regards their position, be investigated upon the same principles as seams of coal; and there is also this further resemblance, that these veins are liable to be interrupted, broken, and thrown up and down by dykes, slips, or faults, in the same manner as seams of coal. (See Figure.)

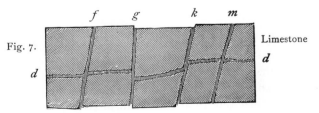

Fig. 7.

Suppose the flat vein to traverse a stratum of limestone, as at *d;* it will continue its course until it comes to the mineral fissure, vein, or string, *f;* and from thence to *g*, *k*, and *m*, being thrown up and down by those slips, veins, or fissures, in the same manner as seams of coal; with this difference only, that in the coal these interruptions are generally real troubles, and the cause of much loss of money and time; whereas, on the contrary, when they are met with in a flat vein, they often prove to be a great advantage, since they are, in reality, only mineral veins of a different kind from the one which traverses them; so that, when these interruptions are met with in a flat vein, they bring additions of vein material, and increase the chances of meeting with more treasure. In other respects, the cases of the flat vein and the seam of coal are widely different: the seam of coal preserves an equal thickness between roof and pavement, and, in fact, is a stratum fully as regular as any of the strata above and below it; whereas, on the contrary, the flat, or dilated vein, is only a space between the strata, of very unequal width and depth, which is filled with mineral matter.

Sometimes these flat, or strata veins, as they might be called, are of great width between the roof and floor, or lid and sole, and contain a variety of mineral matter, mixed with ore. Not unfrequently the whole space is filled with good solid ore. In some rich mining fields the flat veins produce nearly as much lead ore as the rake veins; as, for instance, at Coalcleugh and Nenthead. In these two mining fields the flat veins have produced a prodigious quantity of lead ore, in the great limestone. It is, however, necessary to observe here that flat veins are generally mineralized by the rake veins. They seldom carry ore to a great distance from the rake veins, excepting where there are smaller strings or cross veins, by which they are enriched. Flat veins are frequently discovered by sinking, or working, downwards in the rake veins; and, when this happens, it is reckoned a lucky accident, as the miners can then turn off, and work away horizontally, with the same shaft, &c., as in Fig. 8, on following page.

D is a shaft sunk down upon the limestone, and then cut horizontally through the vein at F. The three flat veins, *a a a*, may thus be reached from the same shaft. The flats seldom carry ore close up to the sides or cheeks of a strong rake vein; for there is generally a rider, five or six feet in width, on the sides of the vein which prevents the flat veins from coming close up to it.

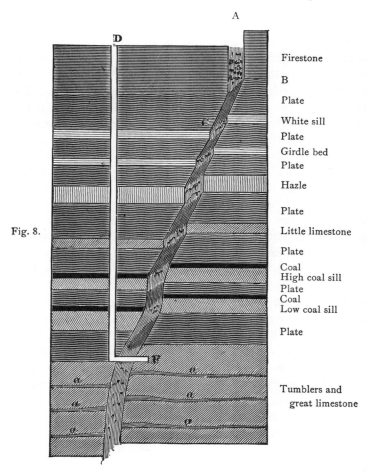

Fig. 8.

The flat veins are discovered in different strata, but they are most frequently found in the limestones. In argillaceous strata, or plate, the vein itself is frequently nothing more than a soft argillaceous stratum, containing nodules, or masses of pyrites, spar, quartz, and other stones. The flat vein opens and closes in the same way as the rake vein. Sometimes the stratum, which forms the roof, or lid, comes down closely upon that below it, so closely indeed that there is no spar left between them, and little or no vestige of a vein. Sometimes the flat veins continue of a moderate and pretty regular height between the roof and sole for a consider- able distance; at other times, the roof and sole come together, and open again, at short distances.

When the space between the roof and sole is very low, the workmen find it necessary to take down a portion of the roof, in order to make room for a further advance. Sometimes the concavity opens out so wide and high as to furnish sufficient space for a good body of ore; at other times it opens up to an enormous height and forms a belly.

In some mining fields there are three flats working at the same time, as in Fig. 6, page 127, at *e e e*, or in Fig. 8, page 138, at *a a a*, usually called the high, low, and middle flats.

It was observed before, that the species of pipe which approaches, in form, to the streek, or flat vein, lies mostly between the strata, and has, therefore, the same declivity as the streek, or flat vein, so that there is a close similarity between them. When twitches run parallel with each other in one of these streeks, and the roof rises up into a considerable cavity between them, the name pipe is then given to the vein by the miners.

The richest flats occur in the large mining fields in connection with rake veins, as at Nenthead, in Alston Moor, Allenheads, and Coalcleugh. Soft, sparry, rake veins are not so often accompanied by flat veins as the hard ridery rake veins. Veins which have black jack, or sulphuret of zinc, blended in them* have flats attached to them.

* Considerable quantities of blend, or black jack, and calamine are now raised in Alston Moor. One of the largest spelter, or zinc, works in England has been lately established, by Mr. Thomas Shaw and Company. It is worthy of remark, that for many years previous to this establishment, the black jack was commonly thrown away as waste when dressing and washing the lead ore. [The Nenthead and Tyne- dale Lead and Zinc Company have recently become the owners of these spelter works.—ED.]

IV.—PIPE VEINS.

Pipe veins resemble, in many respects, huge irregular caverns, pushing forward as these do into the body of the earth in a slanting or sloping direction, but with very different degrees of slope; some of them having but a few degrees of slope from the horizon, others declining precipitately, so that they are nearer to the perpendicular position than to the angle of forty-five. Pipe veins, in short, stand in all positions between the perpendicular and the horizontal.

The simple pipe does not generally cut the strata like the rake vein, but is simply an opening between them, so that if the lie or position of the strata is nearly horizontal, such is also the bearing of the pipe; but if the declivity of the strata is precipitous the pipe shoots down headlong, almost like a shaft. Some pipes are very wide and high, others are very low and narrow; sometimes they are not so large as an ordinary adit.

Pipe veins are hard or soft like rake veins. The hard ones contain all the variety of mineral matter which is usually found in hard rake veins. Some of them are quite full of solid ore; others are full of ore mixed with spar, rider, &c.; and others, again, are full of spar, or rider, without any ore at all. When large pipe veins are filled with solid ore, they are exceedingly productive.

The soft pipe veins are as frequently met with as the hard. They also are found in various positions: some set down with a rapid, and others with an easy, slope. These veins do not always approach the tubular form. Many of them are very wide but not high. These flat pipes frequently become very low between the roof and sole, or upper and lower stratum, towards the skirts, or extremities, of the pipe upon either hand.

The bearing of those pipes, which continue between the strata, corresponds with the declivity of the strata; that is to say, their bearing is parallel with a line drawn across the strata from crop to dip. Pipes have, generally, no longitudinal bearing.

All pipe veins do not continue between two distinct beds of stone. Sometimes they burst their way upwards through the strata, and then they have a much greater slope than the ordinary declivity of the strata. These can scarcely be said to have any bearing at all, since the one end dips down towards the centre, and the other end points up towards the surface; and such of them as do not stand so near to the perpendicular, seldom or never run in a straight line, but wind downwards in a sloping and oblique direction.

The fourth and last capital vein is the *accumulated pipe.*

The accumulated, concentrated, or conical vein cannot easily be described. It sometimes approaches to the form of a vast irregular cone, and at other times resembles an inverted frustum of a cone; but whatever may be the form of this vein, it frequently contains a great deal of wealth, in a small space of ground.

In some of the large pipes, a great, and in others a less, number of nearly perpendicular fissures or rake veins meet, and join in one common centre, as in the annexed figure; where *b* is the pipe or accumulated vein, and *e e e*, &c., so many different fissures or rake veins, which spread out, like radii, to different distances from the main body of the shaft or cone. These branches frequently contain rich deposits of ore, which, when worked out, leave a vast perpendicular concavity.

The main pipe, or shaft, of the accumulated vein somewhat resembles the inside of a glass-house, its vast capacity being often stored with a rich body of metallic ore, imbedded in mineral soil. The veins and branches which unite together in this pipe, usually resemble the rake veins. In fact, the accumulated vein is formed by the intersection of a number of rake veins, the pipe being the point of intersection, as represented in the above figure. A number of pipe veins have been worked at Pike Law, in the county of Durham, where many rake veins meet and intersect each other.

N

When the ore is worked out of a large pipe, a horrid and frightful gulf is formed, which is sometimes fifty or sixty feet wide, and of great depth.

Some of the pipes are very irregular in their bearing, standing nearly erect in one place, and sloping very much in another. The ores of iron, lead, and copper have been found in them.

Having now given a description of mineral veins, I shall next give the reader a few particulars concerning the mines in the different mining fields of Derwent, Weardale, Teesdale, Allendale, and Alston Moor. At the end of this part there are lists of these mines. I shall commence by enumerating the different cross veins, or those which pursue a direction nearly north and south, beginning at the eastern boundary of the mining district, and concluding with the most western of the cross veins.

The first vein worthy of notice, is Whiteheaps, in Derwent, which is a wide sparry vein, having a south-east and north-west bearing, but unaccompanied by any great throw. It was formerly worked by the London Lead Company and yielded a considerable quantity of lead ore, but was never rich. There is another cross vein at a little distance to the west, which runs nearly due north and south, but is considerably weaker than Whiteheaps; it is called Linnbank vein.

The next remarkable cross vein, is the Great Burtreeford dyke, which is the strongest of all the veins in the mining districts before-mentioned. It crosses at the west end of the mining field of Allenheads, and at Burtreeford (from which it has taken its name), in Weardale, and may be traced for several miles southward, into Yorkshire; first at Cronckly Scar, on the river Tees; and again in Lunedale, in the manor of the Earl of Strathmore. Its course has been ascertained to the north of Allenheads, at Bridge Eals, where it crosses the East Allen river, about two miles below Cattan, in Northumberland. It throws more than eighty fathoms*

---

* Whatever may be the extent of the throw of dykes and veins, it never happens, as might have been expected, that a precipitous face of rock is left standing on the elevated side ; the surface of the ground having been rendered level by the absolute

up to the west, and its bearing is nearly north and south. It probably forms an intersection with the Stublick Dyke.

About two miles to the west of the last cross vein, is another called Whetstone Mea, whick runs rather in a south-east and north-west direction; and divides into two branches southward of West Allendale Burn. The branches come together again at Barney Crags, one mile north of Coalcleugh. The eastern branch throws down to the west about twenty-four fathoms, and the western throws down to the east about eighteen fathoms. They cross the mining field of Coalcleugh, to the eastward; from thence they pass a little to the west of Kilhope Law Boundary Currock,* into the county of Durham, intersecting the mining field of Kilhope, to the eastward; they probably effect a junction with the Great Burtreeford dyke, not far from Wearshead, in Weardale; they probably also cross the path of the Stublick dyke, between Cupola Bridge, over the Allen, and Eals Bridge, over the South Tyne, near Alston.

removal of strata, on that side. The same phenomena have been observed in other parts of the kingdom, and are evidently the work of a most powerful agent, which tore up the surface, and dispersed the fragments of the ruin. [The phenomena of which the author here speaks, were produced, not by one agent only, but by several. The strata were in the first instance, broken up and stripped off by breaker action during the slow process of their upheaval: when lifted above the action of the waves, they came under the influence of such sub-aerial agents as solar heat, rains, winds, and circulating waters. A faint idea of the extent of the denudation which has taken place over the lead mining districts, may be formed from a consideration of the following facts :—At the close of the Carboniferous period, these districts were covered by the coal-measures and millstone grit, that is, by the whole of the series given in Forster's section of the strata, the total thickness of which is nearly 4,000 feet. Before the commencement of the New Red period, a considerable proportion of these strata had been swept away. The rocks then sank again beneath the waves and the deposition of the New Red commenced. In process of time— geological time—the lower New Red, the magnesian limestone, the Upper New Red, and probably some other formations, were spread out upon the carboniferous floor. Then began another process of upheaval, during which the whole of these comparatively new rocks, and probably another portion of the carboniferous series, were broken up and washed away. Since this last upheaval, sub-aerial agents have been unceasingly at work, and have given to the mining districts the configuration which they now possess.—ED.]

* A cairn of stones.

A strong vein, known by the name of Fallowfield, crosses the North Tyne, about four and a half miles south-west of Hexham, bearing in a south-east and north-west direction. It formerly yielded great quantities of lead ore. It throws down to the north.

To the west of the veins which have been mentioned, and running parallel with them, there are three or four weak veins, which have been cut through at Coalcleugh; some of these throwing up, and others, down, towards the east. The Bounder End cross vein, which throws about one yard up to the west, runs nearly north and south, a little to the west of Coalcleugh. It has been productive, in some tolerably rich flats connected with it, in the great limestone, both at Coalcleugh and Rampgill.

About four hundred yards to the west of the Bounder End cross vein, there is another vein, called Moss cross vein, which throws about six fathoms up to the east, and down to the west: its bearing is nearly north and south. The next to it is Handsome Mea vein, which runs in a south-east and north-west direction, and throws the east, or rather the north-east, cheek up about twelve or fourteen fathoms. This vein has yielded a considerable quantity of lead ore, both in the vein and the flats, in the great limestone.

At a little distance to the west of the last-mentioned vein, we have Old Carr's cross vein, running nearly north and south, which is the strongest vein in Alston Moor, its throw being in some places nearly forty fathoms up to the west. Very good flats have been worked along the side of this vein at a little distance, and some remarkable rich cavities of lead ore, &c., have been discovered in or near it.

About four hundred fathoms further west we have the Black Ashgill vein, which runs nearly north and south. It throws about six fathoms up to the east, and has been tolerably rich, in the great limestone, both at Black Ashgill Head (from which it takes its name), and likewise at the Dowgang and Nenthead fields. Three miles further to the west we have Sir John's vein, running nearly parallel to Black Ashgill vein, which has a throw up to the west.

The next principal cross vein is the Great Backbone, or Sulphur vein, which runs south-east and north-west, and throws the south-west cheek up about twenty fathoms. This great vein contains quantities of pyrites, or sulphur-stone, blended with yellow copper ore, in Crossgill Burn, Alston Moor; but the produce of copper was so inconsiderable, when it was formerly worked, that it would not defray the expense of extraction. The workings were never prosecuted to any great extent on account of the quantity of water which inundated them; but the Commissioners and Governors of Greenwich Hospital have lately (1821) thought proper to re-open the workings at their own expense, and there is some probability that the vein will prove productive. The operations are conducted in a manner likely to make an effectual trial, as the miners are now driving a water level under the scar limestone, which will drain the former workings, and greatly facilitate their future operations.* It is exceedingly probable that this, as well as some other strong veins which traverse the mining district, may contain metallic ores in the lower parts of the strata, and, if the present trial should confirm this supposition, it will open a new field for mining adventurers.

The Backbone may be traced for a considerable distance on its line of bearing. To the northward it may be seen at a waterfall, or cascade, known by the name of Kesh Burn Force, which falls over the great whin sill about five miles south-west of Alston: it appears again upon the summit of Hartside. To the southward, it may be seen crossing the South Tyne river at Tynehead: from thence it passes into Tynehead Fell.

Since the Commissioners and Governors of Greenwich Hospital commenced operations in Crossgill, under the scar limestone, No. 168 in the section, the miners (under the direction of the late Mr. John Dickinson, of Lowbyer, the moor master) have cut through a collateral string, or vein, on the north side of the principal vein, which has produced some very fine specimens of copper pyrites, or yellow copper ore, blended with malachite, which is a strong indication of the presence of ore in the lower series of the strata.

The veins on the east side of the Great Burtreeford dyke are generally softer than the veins on the west side. Thus the mines

---

* [Mining operations in this powerful vein have, for some time, been suspended, but now that improved methods of assaying pyrites, and of extracting from them the metals which they contain, have been discovered, there is some probability that operations in the Backbone will soon be resumed.—ED.]

in Allendale, Weardale and Derwent, are softer than the mines at
Coalcleugh, Kilhope, Alston, and Teesdale, the latter containing
more blende and rider than the former.*

On the west side of the dyke the veins contain a great deal of
cauk, or barytes, especially in Teesdale and West Allendale;
whereas, on the east side the veins contain a great deal of calcareous
and fluor spar.†

I shall now give a brief account of each of the principal mining
fields.

The first lead mine which we find, after leaving the coal
measures, is that of Healy Field, which has been worked for a
great number of years, and still continues to produce lead ore,
although in smaller quantities than formerly. (See List of Mines.)

The next, which is about six miles to the west of Healey
Field, is that of Shildon, in Derwent, which was formerly in
the possession of the London Lead Company, and at that time
yielded a considerable quantity of lead ore, in the higher parts of
the strata. The works were, however, abandoned for a number of
years, until they were re-opened, some time ago, by Easterby, Hall,
and Company, who drained the mines, by means of powerful steam
engines, and sunk into the great limestone, which, on account of
the declivity of the strata, lies buried at a great depth in this part
of the mining district. (See the section of the mines at Shildon,
page 71.) Their endeavours, unfortunately, did not prove successful.

---

* [I am informed by Mr. J. C. Cain, manager of the W. B. mines, that the
above statements have been fully borne out by recent discoveries.—ED.]

† [A great variety of fluors, compact and foliated, amorphous, and crystallized are
found at Allenheads, and in the lead mines in Weardale and Alston Moor. The
crystals are cubical, with the edges sometimes bevelled, octohedrical, polygonal,
and irregular. The colours are very numerous, viz.: red, green, blue, yellow,
purple, violet, and different shades of them, from very pale to almost black.
The surface is often drusy, covered with minute crystals, and is not unfrequently
frosted over with marcasites. Sometimes, though rarely, the spar is studded with
brilliant quartz, crystals, and crystallized galena.

Jeffrey's Rake,* another vein, about two miles south-west of Shildon, is being worked (1821), in the great limestone, by the same mining company, and at present produces ore in small quantities.

The mining fields, which lie contiguous to those of Derwent, are Allenheads, in Northumberland, and Rookhope, in Durham; the former have been very productive for several years. Although we have no certain information when these mines were first discovered, yet it is probable that they were worked nearly two hundred years ago, as they have belonged to the Blackett family for upwards of a hundred and twenty years. The main water level, called the Haugh level, was begun by Sir William Blackett, in the year 1684, as appears from the inscription upon a stone found at Shieldridge level mouth, the main water level at Coalcleugh. It is supposed that these two levels were begun about the same time.

There is a complication of veins, at Allenheads, which are very productive, both in the rake veins and in the flats. Many large and remarkably rich cavities of lead ore have been found in the great limestone, some of which have produced upwards of one thousand bings: most of the ore was found in a loose state, lying upon the soles of the cavities, as if it had fallen from the roof at some remote period of time.

The strata, towards the west end of the mining field of Allenheads, has a great acclivity or rise, which is supposed to be occasioned by the Great Burtreeford dyke, before described, the rise amounting to about a yard in two before it reaches the dyke. It should be observed here that the veins at Allenheads have not yet been proven,† through the dyke. Most of them present the same appearances as those in Kilhope Head.

The third mining field is Wolfcleugh, in Rookhope, in the county of Durham, which has yielded considerable quantities of lead ore, though the mines have of late been very poor. There are several veins in Rookhope, besides those at Wolfcleugh, which have been worked at different times.

The next mining field is Middlehope, in Weardale. The principal bearing veins of this field run south-east to north-west. Most

* [Now occupied by the Derwent Mining Company.—ED.]
† [The veins at Allenheads have not yet, 1882, been proven through the Great Burtreeford dyke.—ED.]

of the veins in Rookhope intersect the principal veins in Middle-hope, and are supposed to enrich them.   The Lodgefield veins are probably among these intersecting veins.*

Most of the mines in Weardale are soft, and are, therefore, easily worked.   The veins usually carry much soft fluor spar.   The miners open out a great deal of ground, and raise immense quantities of bouse,† before they obtain any considerable quantity of ore.   The mine-masters raise large quantities of lead ore by employing a large number of workmen, who slit out much ground in a short time.

The best lead mine, which was working in Weardale, in 1809, was that of Breckon-syke.‡   This famous mine has, it is said, yielded nearly ten thousand bings of lead ore in one year.   It is intersected to the westward by the Burtreeford dyke.

The next principal mining field is Coalcleugh, in which, some time ago, three leading veins were being worked, viz., High Coal-cleugh vein, Whitewood vein, and Low Coalcleugh vein.   This lead mine was at one time very rich.

Contiguous to Coalcleugh, are the extensive mines of Alston Moor, which, with a few exceptions, belong to the Commissioners and Governors of Greenwich Hospital, and which are now (1821) probably more numerous and productive, in proportion to the extent of the mining field, than any others yet discovered in the world.‖   These mines are chiefly worked by private mining adven-turers.   Those at Nenthead have been in the possession of the London Company for many years.   (See List of Mines.)   The manor of Alston Moor affords many facilities for working mines and making discoveries, since the bearing strata basset out on the sides of the vales of the Nent and the Tyne; levels can, therefore, be driven in the plate beds, to the different veins, at a comparatively trifling expense.

* The Governor and Company have opened a very valuable mine, in Middle-hope, which raises considerable quantities of lead ore.

† *Bouse*, undressed ore, in the state that it is drawn out of the mine.

‡ [This mine is now closed.—ED.]

‖ The produce of the lead mines, in Alston Moor, as appears from the Moor Master's Book, for the three following years, was :—

							£	s.
In the year 1766—18,600 bings, worth, on an average, £2 15s. per bing							61,950	0
1767—24,500 ...	...	...	...	...	...	...	77,162	10
1768—18,730 ...	...	...	...	...	...	...	62,213	10

The next valuable lead mine is that at Cross Fell.* This noble vein, which was discovered only a few years ago, carried lead ore close up to the moss, in the coal sills. It was first discovered to be rich near the surface. The throw of the vein is about a fathom up to the north; the matrix is chiefly amorphous fluor spar.† It is worthy of remark, that the same veins, which are here generally filled with fluor spar and galena, are, on the west side of Cross Fell, filled with sulphate of barytes and galena.‡

* For a short time Cross Fell mine yielded nearly 5,000 bings of lead ore per annum, the average price, per bing, being £5 10s.

† There are other veins in this neighbourhood which have raised considerable quantities of lead ore. They were opened by John Little, Esq., and Company, of Raise House, near Alston, prior to 1821.

‡ [To the mining fields here mentioned by the author, should be added Tyneside, in which are situated the mines of Langley Barony and Stonecroft, Upper Teesdale, where Greenhurth is situated; Nidderdale, Swaledale, Wensleydale, and Wharfedale, in the North Riding, and Keswick, in Cumberland.

The following table shows the "yield" of the above mining fields for 1881. (See "Hunt's Mineral Statistics") :—

The Bing = 8 cwts.   The Ton = 20 cwts.

	Ore.	
	Bings.	Tons.
Alston Moor and Cross Fell mines ...	5,322½ equal to	2,129
Tyneside	17,755 ,,	7,102
Weardale	10,265 ,,	4,106
Allendale	1,120 ,,	448
Derwent	1,265 .,	506
Teesdale	12,755 ,,	5,102
Westmorland	3,090 ,,	1,236
Yorkshire—		
Airedale ... ..., ...	31¾ ,,	$12\frac{7}{10}$
Nidderdale	1,780 ,,	712
Swaledale	7,472½ ,,	2,989
Wensleydale	937½ ,,	375
Wharfedale	77¼ ,,	31
Keswick	567½ ,,	227
Total	62,439¼ ,,	$24,975\frac{7}{10}$

This ore yielded 18,754 tons of lead, and 83,891 ounces of silver, which were worth £240,000.—ED.]

A LIST OF LEAD MINES IN THE MANOR OF ALSTON,

IN THE COUNTY OF CUMBERLAND,

Belonging to the Lords Commissioners of the Admiralty, including the mines at Cross Fell and Tynehead, together with an account of the metallic substances found in them.

MINES OCCUPIED BY THE NENTHEAD AND TYNEDALE LEAD AND ZINC COMPANY, LIMITED,

WITH THEIR SITUATIONS WITH RESPECT TO ALSTON.

1. *Guddamgill*, S.S.E.—Lead, in strata, from slate sills to the bottom of tuft; zinc, in great limestone, downwards.
2. *Rampgill*, S.S.E.—Lead, in strata, from slate sills to the four-fathom limestone; zinc, from firestone, downwards.
3. *Scaleburn*, S.S.E.—Lead, in strata, from little limestone to bottom of quarry hazle; zinc, from great limestone, downwards.
4. *Hangingshaw*, S.S.E.—Lead, in strata, from little limestone to great limestone inclusive.
5. *Middlecleugh*, S.S.E.—Lead, in strata, from slate sills to great limestone; zinc, in great limestone, downwards.
6. *Longcleugh*, S.S.E.—Lead, in strata, from firestone sill to quarry hazle; zinc in great limestone only.
7. *Caplecolugh*, S.S.E.—Lead, in strata, from slate sills to coal sills; zinc in great limestone.
8. *Carrs*, S.S.E.—Lead in strata—great limestone.
9. *Smallcleugh*, S.S.E.—Lead in strata—great limestone.
10. *Browngill*, S.—Lead, in strata, from grindstone sill to bottom of slaty hazle.
11. *Tyne-bottom*, S.—Lead, in strata—Tyne-bottom limestone.
12. *Slaggyburn*, S.W.—Trial for lead, in Sir John's vein, in scar limestone.
13. *Baylehill*, S.—Calamine, in great limestone.
14. *Farnberry*, S. by E.—Carbonate of zinc, principally in great limestone.
15. *Priorsdale*, S.—Lead, in strata, from Pattinson's sill to bottom of scar limestone.*

---

* Priorsdale mine is in the Company's own freehold, and, therefore, on their own royalty.

MINES OCCUPIED BY OTHER COMPANIES.

16. *Ayle Burn*, N.—Lead, in great limestone; occupied by the Ayle Burn Mining Company.

17. *Benty Field*, S.—Lead, principally in great limestone; occupied by the Alston Moor Mining Company.

18. *Bleagate*, S.W.—Lead, from great limestone to scar limestone; occupied by the Alston United Mining Association, Limited.

19. *Grassfield*, S.E.—Lead and calamine, principally in great limestone; occupied by the Alston Moor Mining Company.

20. *Nentsbury*, S.E.—Lead and zinc, principally in great limestone; occupied by the Alston Moor Mining Company.

21. *Blagill*, S.E.—Lead and carbonate of barytes, from slate sills to four-fathom limestone; occupied by T. Wilson, J. Dickinson, and Company.

22. *Calvert*, S.—Lead, from quarry hazle to the scar limestone; occupied by the Calvert Mining Company.

23. *Cash Well*, S.W.—Lead, from four-fathom limestone to copper hazle; occupied by the Cash Well Mining Company.

24. *Crag Green*, S.—Lead and sulphate of bartyes, from great limestone to scar limestone; occupied by the Crag Green Mining Company.

25. *Crookburn*, S.—Lead, principally in Tyne-bottom limestone; occupied by the Crookburn Mining Company.

26. *Cross Fell*, S.S.W.—Lead, from firestone to four-fathom limestone; occupied by C. W. Bell and Company.

27. *North Cross Fell*, S.W.—Lead, from coal sills to great limestone; occupied by C. W. Bell and Company.

28. *East Cross Fell*, S.W.—Lead, in great limestone; occupied by C. W. Bell and Company.

29. *Dowgang*, S.S.E.—Lead, principally in great limestone; occupied by the Dowgang Mining Company.

30. *Dowpot Syke and Guttergill*, S.E.—Lead, from little limestone to great limestone; occupied by John Carruthers and Company.

31. *Crossgill and Lee House*, S.—Lead, principally in six-fathom hazle; occupied by John Millican and Company.

32. *Gallygill Syke*, S.E.—Lead, principally in great limestone; occupied by T. Dickinson, Jos. Greenwell, and others.

33. *Holy Field*, S.S.E.—Lead and crystallized arragonite, principally in great limestone; occupied by the Holy Field Mining Company.
34. *Horse Edge*, W.—Lead, in great limestone; occupied by the Alston United Mining Association.
35. *Park*, W.—Lead and sulphate of barytes, from coal sills to copper hazle; occupied by the Park Mining Company.
36. *Patter Syke and Clargill Head*, S.—Silver lead, from scar limestone to single-post limestone; occupied by the Pattersyke Mining Company.
37. *Rodderup Fell*, S.W.—Lead, in six-fathom hazle to the whin sill; occupied by the Rodderup Fell Mining Company.
38. *Thorngill*, E.—Lead, from firestone to the four-fathom limestone; occupied by the Blagill Mining Company.
39. *Windy Brow*, S.—Lead, in great limestone and scar limestone; occupied by John Hodgson.

LIST OF LEAD MINES IN THE TYNESIDE DISTRICT.

1. *Burnhope*, Benfieldside.—Lead, in slate sills; occupied by S. Leybourne and others.
2. *Fallowfield*, Hexham.—Lead and barytes, from slate sills to great limestone; occupied by Walton and Cowper.
3. *Haydon*, Haydon Bridge.—Lead, from coal sills to four-fathom limestone; occupied by John P. Walton and Company.
4. *Langley Barony*, Haydon Bridge.—Lead, in four-fathom limestone and in strata immediately above and below; occupied by Bewick and Partners.
5. *Lepper Moor*, Fourstones.—Lead; occupied by the Lepper Moor Mining Company.
6. *Settlingstones*, Fourstones.—Carbonate of Barytes, in the whin sill; occupied by the Executors of the late F. W. Hall.
7. *Stonecroft and Greyside*, Fourstones.—Lead, principally in the great whin sill; occupied by the Stonecroft and Greyside Mining Company.
8. *Waterhouse*, Haydon Bridge.—Lead, in great limestone; occupied by the Waterhouse Lead Mining Company.

LIST OF LEAD MINES IN WEARDALE.

The property of the Ecclesiastical Commissioners.

MINES OCCUPIED BY W. B. BEAUMONT, ESQ., M.P.

1. *Killhope*, N.W. of St. John's Chapel.—Lead and blende, from slate sill to the four-fathom limestone.
2. *Burtree Pasture*, N.W. of St. John's Chapel.—Lead, from fell-top limestone to the whin sill.
3. *Craig's Level*, W. of St. John's Chapel.—Lead, from the top sills to great limestone.
4. *Black Dean*, N.W. of St. John's Chapel.—Lead, from firestone to four-fathom limestone.
5. *Greenlaws*, S. of St. John's Chapel.—Lead, from coal sills to scar limestone.
6. *Slitt and Middlehope*, N.E. of St. John's Chapel.—Lead, from coal sills to the whin sill.
7. *Height and Northgate*, N.E. of St. John's Chapel.—Lead, principally in the great limestone.
8. *Swinhope*, S. of St. John's Chapel.—Lead, in great limestone.
9. *Western Hope*, S.E. of St. John's Chapel.—Lead, in great limestone.
10. *Rookhope*, N.E. of St. John's Chapel.—Lead, from slate sills to the great limestone.
11. *Stanhope Burn*, E. of St. John's Chapel and N. of Stanhope.—Lead, in great limestone and four-fathom limestone.
12. *Wolsingham*, E. of St. John's Chapel and E. of Stanhope.—Lead, in top sills.

MINES OCCUPIED BY THE LONDON LEAD COMPANY IN WEARDALE.
STANHOPE PARISH.

Bollihope Tract Mines, in the Township of Newlandside, as follows:—

13. *Whitfield Brow.*—Lead, in strata, from high slate sill to low coal sill and great limestone.

14. *Wager Burn.*—Lead, in strata, from little limestone to low coal sill.

15. *Bollihope Burn.*—Lead, in strata, from low coal sill to quarry hazle.

16. *Cornish Hush.*—Lead, in strata, from the slate sills to the great limestone.

WOLSINGHAM PARISH.

17. *South Green.*—Trial for lead in the hazle above fell-top limestone.

LIST OF LEAD MINES IN THE TWO ALLENDALES.

The property of W. B. Beaumont, Esq., M.P.

1. *Allenheads*, S. of Allendale Town: the principal veins in this district are Poverty vein, Sun vein, Diana vein, Blackett vein, Style vein, &c., which yield lead in strata, from grindstone sill to the four-fathom limestone.

2. *Coalcleugh*, E.S.E. of Alston, where there are also several veins which yield lead and blende in same strata as above.

3. *Hearty Cleugh*, E. of Alston.—Lead, in great limestone.

4. *Kearsley Well*, E. of Alston.—Lead, in great limestone.

5. *Welhope Head*, S.E. of Alston.—Lead, with sulphate and carbonate of barytes, from the high slate sill to the bottom of great limestone.

LIST OF LEAD MINES IN TEESDALE.

The property of the Duke of Cleveland.

MINES OCCUPIED BY THE LONDON LEAD COMPANY.

1. *Ashgillhead*, N.W. of Middleton.—Lead, in strata, from the low slate sill to the bottom of four-fathom limestone.

2. *Bleagill*, N.W. of Middleton.—Trial for lead, in strata, from coal sills to bottom of great limestone.

3. *Coldberry*, N. of Middleton.—Lead, in strata, from high slate sill to bottom of firestone.

4. *Coldberry Skears*, N. of Middleton.—Lead, in strata, from firestone to bottom of great limestone.

5. *Redgroves*, N.W. of Middleton.—Lead, in strata, from low slate sill to bottom of high coal sill.

6. *Highdyke*, N. of Middleton.—Lead, in little limestone and great limestone.

7. *East Rake*, N.E. of Middleton.—Trial level of East Rake vein and Manor Gill North vein, in high slate sill.

8. *Wiregill*, N.E. of Middleton.—Lead, in strata, from high slate sill to bottom of little limestone.

9. *Little Eggleshope*, N.E. of Middleton.—Lead, in strata, from grindstone sill to top of firestone.

10. *Flakebrigg*, N.E. of Middleton.—Lead, in strata, from millstone grit to fell-top limestone.

MINES OCCUPIED BY OTHER COMPANIES.

11. *Grass Hill*, N.W. of Middleton.—Lead, from firestone to Nattrass Gill hazle; occupied by J. Byers and Company.

12. *Greenhurth*, N.W. of Middleton.—Lead, supposed to be in Tyne-bottom limestone; occupied by the Greenhurth Mining Company.

13. *East Cowgreen*, W. of Middleton.—Lead, with sulphate of barytes, from scar limestone to Tyne-bottom limestone; occupied by the Teesdale Mining Company.

14. *Metal Band*, N.W. of Middleton.—Lead, in stratum called the Tyne-bottom limestone; occupied by the Metal Band Company.

15. *Pike Law, East and West*, W. of Middleton.—Lead, from coal sills to great limestone; occupied by T. Wilson and Company.

16. *Willy Hole*, N. of Middleton.—Lead, in scar limestone; occupied by John P. Walton and Company.

17. *Crookburn*, 12 miles W. of Middleton and 10 miles S. of Alston.—A trial in Tyne-bottom limestone, by the Crookburn Mining Company.

18. *North Greenhurth*, 12 miles W. of Middleton and 10 miles S.S.E. of Alston.—A trial in Tyne-bottom limestone, by the North Greenhurth Mining Company.

A LIST OF LEAD MINES IN WESTMORLAND.

The property of Lord Hothfield.

1. *Augill*, Brough.—Lead; occupied by Bell and Company.
2. *Dufton Fell*, N.N.E. of Appleby.—Lead and sulphate of barytes, principally in Tyne-bottom limestone. A few workmen have permission from the proprietor to explore the mine.
3. *Hardshins*, N.E. of Appleby.—Lead in the whetstone bed and hazles; occupied by W. H. Robinson.
4. *Silverband*, N.E. of Appleby.—Lead, crystallized sulphate of barytes, from the firestone to bottom of great limestone.
5. *Middlefell Mines*, W. of Kirkby Stephen.—Crystallized sulphate of barytes, in four-fathom limestone; occupied by John Slack and Company.
6. *Hartley Ford*, *West*, Kirkby Stephen.—Lead and sulphate of barytes; the property of Sir Richard Musgrave; occupied by John Slack and Company.

———

LIST OF MINES IN YORKSHIRE.

1. *Lunehead*, Lunedale.—Lead, in the twelve fathom (great) limestone; occupied by the London Lead Company.
2. *Whitewell*, Forest of Bowland.—Lead, in carboniferous limestone; occupied by Whitewell Mining Company, Limited.

AIREDALE DISTRICT.

3. *Cononley*, Skipton.—Lead, in the upper grits of the Yoredale series; the property of the Duke of Devonshire.
4. *Gavel*, Starbottom.—Lead, in great limestone; occupied by Lodge and Bowden.

NIDDERDALE DISTRICT.

5. *Appletreewick*, Skipton.—Lead, in carboniferous limestone; occupied by Edwin Dunkin.
6. *Appletreewick Gill Heads*, Otley.—Lead, in carboniferous limestone; occupied by the Appletreewick Gill Heads Mining Company.
7. *Blayshaw Gill*, Pateley Bridge.—Lead, in grits; occupied by the Blayshaw Gill Company.

8. *Craven Moor, East*, Pateley Bridge.—Lead, in carboniferous limestone; occupied by the East Craven Moor Company.

9. *Craven Moor, West*, Skipton.—Lead, in carboniferous limestone; occupied by the Messrs. Sharp.

10. *Hardcastle*, Skipton.—Lead, in carboniferous limestone; occupied by the Sunside Mining Company.

11. *Pateley Bridge*, Pateley Bridge.—Lead, in carboniferous limestone; occupied by the Pateley Bridge Mining Company.

12. *Pateley Bridge, West*, Pateley Bridge.—Lead, in carboniferous limestone; occupied by the West Pateley Bridge Mining Company.

13. *Stoney Groves*, Pateley Bridge.—Lead, in carboniferous limestone; occupied by the Stoney Groves Mining Company.

14. *Middle Hill, Level and Storey's Shaft*, Skipton.—Lead, in carboniferous limestone; occupied by the Appletreewick Gill Head Mining Company.

15. *Nidderdale*, Greenhow Hill, Pateley Bridge.—Lead, in carboniferous limestone; occupied by the Nidderdale Mining Company.

16. *Ramgill*, Greenhow Hill, Pateley Bridge.—Lead, in carboniferous limestone; occupied by the Ramsgill Mining Company.

SWALEDALE.

17. *Arkendale*, 11 miles west of Richmond.—Lead, principally in the great limestone; occupied by the Arkendale Mining Company.

18. *Beldi Hill*, Swaledale.—Lead, principally in great limestone; occupied by the Beldi Hill Mining Company.

19. *Ellerton Moor*, Swaledale.—Lead, in great limestone; occupied by the Ellerton Moor Mining Company.

20. *Fell End*, Swaledale.—Lead, in great limestone; occupied by the Fell End Mining Company.

21. *Grinton Moor P.S.*, Swaledale.—Lead, in great limestone; occupied by the Ellerton Moor Mining Company.

22. *Hurst*, Swaledale.—Lead, principally in great limestone; occupied by the Hurst Mining Company.

23. *Old Gang*, Swaledale.—Lead, principally in great limestone; occupied by the Old Gang Mining Company.

24. *Skelhorn*, Rimmington.—Lead, in carboniferous limestone; occupied by Baynes and Colville.

25. *Surrender*, Healaugh.—Lead, principally in great limestone; occupied by Thomas Raw.

26. *Swinnergill*, *A. D. Sir Francis*, Gunnerside.—Lead, principally in great limestone; occupied by A. D. Lead Mining Company.

WENSLEYDALE DISTRICT.

27. *Apedale*, 9 miles from Leyburn.—Lead, in carboniferous limestone; occupied by the Apedale Mining Company.

28. *Keld Heads*, 2 miles from Leyburn.—Lead, in carboniferous limestone; occupied by Thomas Dymond, Esq.

29. *Longcleugh*, Whitfield.—Lead; occupied by the Longcleugh Mining Company.

30. *Penhill*, West Witton.—Lead; occupied by Messrs. Beetham, Milliner, and Company.

31. *Sargill Side*, Hawes, Bedale.—Lead, in carboniferous limestone; occupied by the executors of Henry Pease.

32. *Walden Head*, 13 miles from Leyburn.—Lead, in carboniferous limestone; occupied by J. A. Rodwell and Company.

33. *Worton*, Bedale.—Lead, in carboniferous limestone; occupied by the Worton Mining Company.

34. *York and Lancaster United*, Rimmington.—Barytes, in carboniferous limestone; occupied by John Borlase.

WHARFEDALE DISTRICT.

35. *Burhill*, 11 miles from Skipton.—Lead, in carboniferous limestone and millstone grit; occupied by the Burhill Mining Company.

36. *Elbolton*, Skipton.—Lead and zinc, in carboniferous limestone; occupied by J. Mason.

37. *Grassington P.S.*, Skipton.—Lead, principally in the gritstone beds; the property of the Duke of Devonshire.

38. *Ray Gill*, Lothersdale.—Barytes, in carboniferous limestone; occupied by P. W. Spencer.

39. *Yorkshire*, 14 miles from Skipton.—Lead, in carboniferous limestone; occupied by the London Lead Company.

LANCASHIRE.

1. *Coniston*, Ulverston.—Copper, in green slate and porphyries; occupied by the Coniston Mining Company.
2. *Great Coniston*, Ulverston.—Copper, in green slate and porphyries; occupied by McGowan and Cooper.
3. *Warton*, Silverdale.—Silver-lead, in carboniferous limestone; occupied by the Warton and Silverdale Mining Company, Limited.

KESWICK DISTRICT.

1. *The Thornthwaite Mines*, Thornthwaite.—Lead and zinc, in Cambrian slate and spathic rocks; occupied by the Keswick United Silver-Lead Mines Company.
2. *Greenside*, Patterdale.—Silver-lead, in green slates and porphyries; occupied by the Greenside Mining Company.
3. *Helvellyn*, Keswick.—Lead, in the Skiddaw slates and porphyritic rocks; occupied by the West Cumberland Company, Limited.
4. *Threlkeld*, Keswick.—Silver-lead and zinc, in the Skiddaw slate and porphyries; occupied by the Threlkeld Mining Company, Limited.
5. *Brandley*, Keswick.—Lead and zinc, in the Cambrian slate and spathic rocks; occupied by the Keswick United Silver-Lead Mining Company, Limited.
6. *Yewthwaite*, Keswick.—Lead, in the Cambrian slate and spathic rocks; occupied by the Keswick United Silver-Lead Mining Company, Limited.
7. *Barrow*, Keswick.—Lead, in the Cambrian slate and spathic rocks; occupied by the Keswick United Silver-Lead Mining Company, Limited.

CALDBECK.

8. *Millom*, Hesket Newmarket.—Pyrites, in carboniferous limestone; occupied by the Millom Mining Company.

PART III.

SUMMARY OF CONTENTS.

I.—THE DISCOVERY OF MINES.

The experience which is gained by those who are engaged in actual mining operations is the best guide in the search for deposits of ore. For the benefit of those who are not so engaged, it may be well to point out some of the signs which indicate the presence of a mineral vein in the rocks beneath the surface of the earth. The most certain of those signs are:—

    1. Pieces of ore, or vein-stone, lying on the surface.
    2. Mineral water.
    3. The discolouration of the leaves of trees, or of the blades of grass.
    4. Warm exhalations.

Where all the above signs are met with, a close search should be made for the hidden vein; where one of them appears, the others should be looked for in the immediate neighbourhood before any expenditure of capital is incurred.

If none of these signs appear, there may yet be others which can be interpreted only by the experienced miner. He notices the configuration of the surface, ascertains the bearings of the veins which are already opened out in other mining fields, and can find out, approximately, their points of junction, and of crossing. When he has reasons for supposing that certain veins bear towards a particular point, he proceeds to drive an adit, as low down in the strata as he may think expedient, across the bearing of the veins, by which means he is sure to cut through them. In driving adits for the purpose of *unwatering* mines, new veins are sometimes found which prove to be richer than those already discovered.

After the vein is *cut*, the next thing to be considered is, whether it can be worked to advantage. In order to determine this point, we ought carefully to consider the nature of the place, its situation with respect to roads and water and other conveniences, and whether the ore is sufficiently abundant to repay the expenses of extraction, washing, and smelting, and leave a margin of profit.

The configuration of the place ought especially to be considered. Mountains and hills offer many advantages for mining operations, since adits may be readily driven into their sides. Veins are sometimes exposed by heavy rains, by streams and rivers, by drains and excavations. Wherever found, they should, if rich enough, be operated upon. After heavy floods pieces of ore are frequently found in the beds of streams. If they are much water-worn, they are called *float ores;* if they are not water-worn, they are called *shoad ores.* Float ore is generally mixed with water-worn bullets and gravel; shoad is never so mixed unless it has been washed off the superficies of the vein, by some rivulet or by heavy rains.

Shoad ore is a pretty sure indication of the presence of a vein near the place where it is found, though at a higher elevation. We must form our opinion of the extent of that elevation by an inspection of the slope. If the side of the hill be very steep, the ore may have slid a great way down: if there is little declivity, the ore will probably have slid a less distance. Shoad ore is found in pieces of all sizes, from very large masses, down to pieces of the size of peas, or even smaller. It is produced by the decomposition of the sides of the vein. A custom once prevailed in the mining districts for the miners to go *a shoading*, that is, to search for shoad. On such an occasion they traversed rivulets, gullies, scars, and other places, where the surface of the ground is broken, and where the superficies of the strata rise up to the grass-roots.

From the above description of float and shoad ores, there is little doubt that an intelligent person, though no miner, might be able to distinguish the one from the other. In case either of the kinds of ore should be found by the reader, it may be proper to point out the methods which should be taken to discover the vein.

Shoad ore is found in rough irregular masses, and has frequently a whitish or bleached appearance. When it happens to be discovered upon a level piece of ground, a cross trench should be cut to the strata, in the place where it is found: but if it is found upon a slope, or immediately at the foot of a slope, then the vein should be looked for at some distance up the slope. When shoad is found upon the slope, or at the foot of it, the first business is to look about on all sides for other signs of the vein; if none be seen, then we must judge, from other circumstances, what methods should be adopted to discover the vein.

If we find that the cover of alluvia upon the superficies of the rock is thin, and that the distance from the place where the shoad was found to the highest part of the slope is but short, we should make a trench to the rock upon the spot where we found the ore, and push it right up the slope, keeping the surface of the rock until we discover the vein. If we fail to discover the vein by cutting upwards in a right line, then we should come down again to the foot of the trench, and there cut a little across, in order that, in case the vein should run in a right line, up and down, parallel to the cut, or in a diagonal direction, and we should have been a little to one side at the first trial, we may by this means intersect it. If the cover upon the superficies of the rock is thick, the cutting of the trench will be troublesome and expensive; and, therefore, the best method in that case is to sink a small shaft down through the cover, until we come to the strata.

Particular notice must be taken of everything we see in making this shaft: if we should find bits of ore, spar, or vein-stone, we may conclude that we are below the vein; but if we discover no mineral soil, nor any other signs of the vein, either in the alluvium or the strata, we may conclude that we are too high, and should proceed to sink another shaft at a lower random, about half-way between the first shaft and the place where the shoad was found. If, on the other hand, we find small pieces of ore, or good mineral soil, in going down with the first shaft, we should sink another, still higher up, in the line of the first; and, if the signs should be clearer in the second shaft than in the first, a third, a fourth, &c., must be sunk, still in the same line.

If the signs of ore should be clearer and more numerous in one side of the shaft than in the other, it is probable that the vein runs up and down the slope, parallel to the line of shafts. In this case, we should go to the shaft which contains most of the best mineral matter, and drive across, upon the face of the firm rock, into the most promising side; and, if the signs increase as we advance, we should push forward the drift until we cut the vein.

With respect to float ore, it would not be prudent to recommend any method of trial for discovering the vein it originally came from, until such vein has been discovered by other means, since it is a very difficult thing to find out how far the ore was carried by the water before it was lodged in its present bed. Diligent search should be made on all sides, especially on the higher grounds, in order to ascertain whether any other signs of the vein can be discovered, before expensive trials are made. Trials may, however, be made upon the float ore itself, in order to discover what quantity there is of it, so that we may be able to judge whether or not it is worth pursuing. A trench should be cut quite down to the surface of the rock, and pushed forward towards the place where the ore is most abundant. Cross-cuts should then be made from the trench in every direction where the ore may lead us, since there may be nests, or parcels, of it lodged on either hand. The flats and hollows deserve the most careful attention.

When the ore is sufficiently abundant to be worth working, we should consider whether we cannot secure it most expeditiously either by throwing off the cover which lies above, so as to lay the whole of the ore bare, or by mining underground. If it lie upon the surface of the rock there is a chance of discovering the vein during the search for it.

When either float, or shoad, ore is found in a small flat spot in the middle, or near the bottom, of a sloping piece of ground, *hushing** is a very good method of securing it. Where circumstances are favourable for it, this is undoubtedly the most effectual, and, at the same time, the most economical method of trial. There should be a slope of considerable declivity, and there should also be a suitable place for making a dam-head, or reservoir, for collecting water; the more elevated the dam the better it will be. If a little dingle, settle, flat, or hollow place can be found for the site of this reservoir, so much the better, as the head can, in that case, be made with the less expense; but when such a convenience cannot be found, the dam should be made upon the slope of the declivity in the form of a half circle. A large dam is always better than a small one. Where the ground which is to be hushed is of any considerable length, the reservoir must contain a considerable quantity of water, otherwise its force will be spent too soon and will prove ineffectual for carrying down to the bottom the soil, earth, &c. If, therefore, the dam has not a level area upon which a large body of water can be collected, the head should be raised as high as possible in order to make up in depth what is wanting in length and breadth. It is necessary to observe that the breast of this reservoir should be strong in proportion to the quantity of water we wish to collect, and that a sluice of the necessary strength should be used.

From this hush-dam a line should be drawn right down the hill, if there be no hillock, or other obstruction, in the way. Should we meet with an obstruction we should carry the line past one side of it. When we have marked out the line of the hush-gutter from

* Mr. Thomas Shaw and Company have raised, and are now raising, considerable quantities of float ore at Greengill mine, in Alston Moor, by hushing. This mine is now, 1821, yielding a large quantity of white lead, or fine white crystals of carbonate of lead.

the top to the bottom of the slope, we should next cut off the sod to the width of two, or three feet, and to the depth of a foot, or a foot and a half, through the whole length of the line, in order to make room for a small stream of water. A small force of water should then be let out of the dam, the workmen, meanwhile, standing by the side of the gutter, at proper distances from each other, with their tools in their hands, ready to loosen the earth as the water rushes down, and to remove such obstructions as may stop the water, or turn it out of the gutter. After a little time the whole force of water should be let out. The steeper the declivity, and the longer the gutter, the greater will be the effects produced by the hush.

The writer has seen stones of several tons weight, and as big as little huts, carried several hundred yards down a large hush-gutter. The torrent and the rush of stones wear out, not only the surface and the soil, but also a considerable depth of the superficies of the rock itself, and thus they discover and wash clean all the veins, the useful and curious stones, &c., which lie in or cross the line of the gutter. Valuable discoveries are often made in this way.

When a hush is worn pretty deep, and especially where there is a thick covering of earth on the rock, great stones or other obstructions frequently turn the water to one side of the gutter. Sometimes both sides are worn and undermined so as to fall in, and thus cause the water to spread so wide that its force is lost. In both cases it is necessary to turn the stones out of the way, so as to give the water a straight course, and thus allow it to scour the bottom effectually. This method deserves the preference over others, because it lays bare the rock.

Mineral veins are frequently discovered upon the rocky shores of the sea and of lakes, in precipices, in the banks and beds of rivers, in dingles and ravines, scars and cliffs, and in other places where the solid superficies of the strata are either laid quite bare, or are so thinly covered with soil that the shoads are exposed.

The presence of mineral veins is sometimes indicated by fractures in the strata. All fractures should, therefore, be examined. Vein fissures are easily distinguishable from such cracks as are caused by rains and frosts, or by the gradual yielding of a precipice.

The sides of recent fissures are generally unequal, and jagged, and the spaces between them are generally open; whereas, the sides of mineral veins are tolerably regular, and run in pretty straight lines, the spaces between them being always filled with minerals and metallic ores.

The strata which are the most productive of metallic ores are the limestones, though ores are also found in the sandstones and indurated argillaceous rocks, of which there are many varieties. Many rich and valuable mines are being worked in the granite, among them being the lead mines of Strontian, in the Highlands of Scotland, and several mines in Cornwall, &c.

II.—THE OPENING AND WORKING OF MINES.

When the fact has been ascertained that the ores of a metal are present in any particular place in sufficient quantities to repay the cost of extraction and leave a fair profit, the mine-master commences operations, either by sinking a shaft, or by driving a level (adit) in the vein which contains the deposit of ore, using for that purpose various machines for raising the water, renewing the air, and facilitating the ingress and egress of the workmen. The level, or adit, is preferred to the shaft, if the situation be suitable for it. If the shaft must be resorted to, it is, in the first instance, made square in shape, and sufficiently capacious to afford room for ladders, pumps, and the machinery which is required for raising to the surface the *deads* (stone) and the *bouse.* If the ore cannot be reached by one shaft, another is put down. A horizontal gallery is opened out at the bottom of the first shaft, at the end of which a second shaft, or sump, is made; and thus the workmen proceed until they reach the ore. It is obvious that in cases where the flow of water is great, a single perpendicular shaft must be put down from the surface to the deepest part of the mine.

When the rock is hard and compact, and thus capable of supporting itself, the shaft, or shafts, will not require to be guarded within; but if the rock be soft and friable, or, from any other cause, threatens to fall, it is then necessary to support it, either with a wooden frame, or a circular stone wall.

A current of fresh air is an absolute necessity in all mines. This is obtained in various ways. Where it is practicable to construct a gallery which shall lead from the bottom of the shaft to the day, or open air, a current can easily be obtained; but if this is not possible, a second shaft is put down, opposite to the first, either from the surface, or at the extremity of the gallery, and a passage being opened between the two, a circulation of air is thus produced. If the second shaft be equal in depth to the first, the circulation will not take place spontaneously, and a furnace must be lighted near the bottom of one of the shafts, to destroy the equilibrium of the confined air.

The destructive gases which are so frequently disengaged from the cavities of mines, and particularly carbonic acid gas, and the different kinds of mixed hydrogen gas, are among the most formidable enemies of the miners. The former of these gases is more generally known by the term *choke damp*, or *foul air*, and the latter by that of *fire damp*. Galleries, fires, ventilators, in those parts of the mines which are thus mephitized, and particularly the various plans for causing a circulation of fresh air, are the only remedies which, until lately, have been applied to these subterraneous evils. Within these few years a lamp has been invented by that distinguished philosopher, Sir Humphrey Davy, the flame of which is covered with wire-gauze, and is by that means prevented from igniting the inflammable gases. The occurrence of choke damp is very common in many of the mines which we have mentioned, but the fire damp has not been met with excepting in the Nent Force level, where it has once or twice exploded.

I shall now give an account of the best method of *working mines* in an extensive district. In the first place, it is necessary to collect and arrange all the knowledge we can acquire respecting the veins which traverse the district, and the relations they severally bear to one another. We should afterwards construct a geognostic plan of the district, and attach to it a geognostic description. This plan and description should be formed according to the same principles, be equally complete, and have such a relation to each other, that the same explanation will apply to both. If these two works are well and properly done they will form a ground-work, from which may be drawn, in the surest manner, all the plans and schemes relative to the future working of the mines in the district from which they are taken.

The geognostic plan should consist of two maps, or principal designs; one, the ground plan, taken at the surface, called the external plan of the district; the other, which is the horizontal plan, and is accompanied by a vertical section, made to represent the strata of the district. It is upon this latter that all remarkable geognostic objects should be traced.

On the *external* plan should be marked the situation of each vein, as on Fig. 1, Plate V., where the vein D makes its appearance at the outburst, or basset, of the high coal sill, and the low level, or principal draining level, commences at A, upon the great limestone, the uppermost level, C, being upon the high coal sill, &c.

The throw of each vein ought to be represented upon the plan thus $\frac{a}{b}$; the upper side, or cheek, with a weak line, as at *a*, and the lower side, or cheek, with a strong line, as at *b*.

On the *internal* plan, or horizontal map, should be represented all the windings and turnings of the different levels driven upon the veins, with all the subterranean shafts, or sumps, made from those levels: each separate level should be distinguished by different colours, as in Plate V., Fig. 2. Those who wish for further information, relative to the surveying of mines, are referred to Mr. Thomas Fenwick's " Treatise on Subterraneous Surveying."

The internal section, Plate VI., Fig. 3, shows the depth of each subterranean shaft, or sump, sunk into the strata upon the vein, and corresponds with the horizontal map, Plate V., Fig. 2. Upon the south vein, at *e e e e e* and *d*, the low level is driven through the East Cross vein, at *g*, the horizontal map showing the points of intersection and traversion. At *r*, Plate VI., Fig. 3, is a shaft

Plate 5

Fig. 1

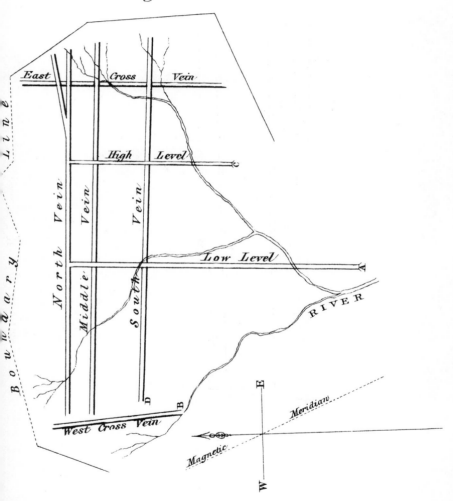

Fig. 2

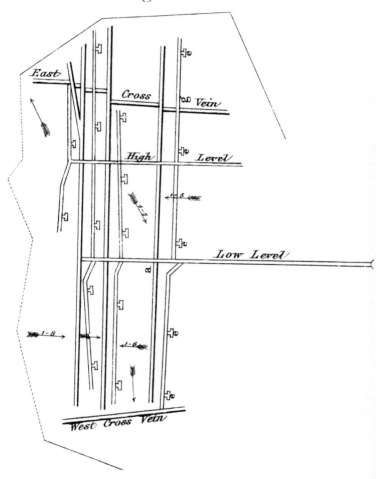

Plate 6

Fig. 3

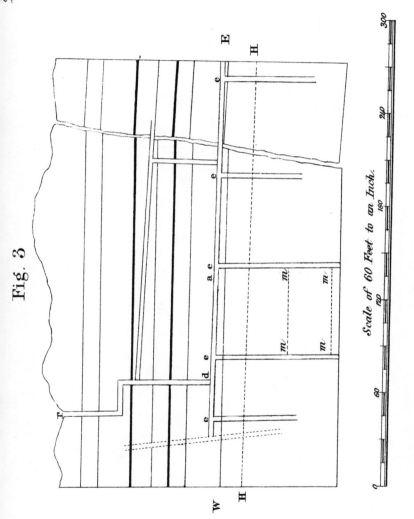

Scale of 60 Feet to an Inch.

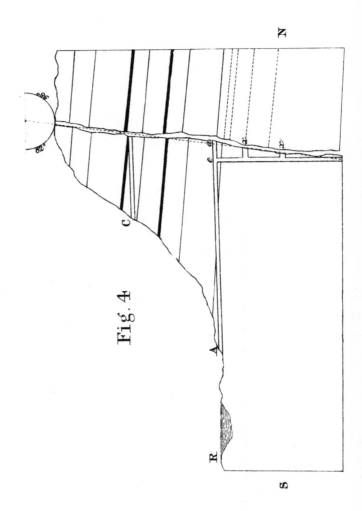

Fig. 4

Fig. 5.

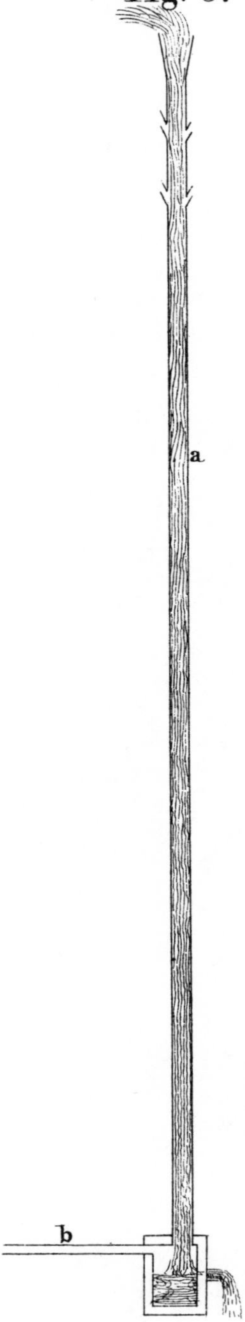

sunk from the surface, in order to cause a current of air to circulate through the different workings made upon the vein: the space *m m m m*, shows the portion which has already been excavated in the search for ores.

There ought, likewise, to be a description of the mining district, and an account of its external surface, its situation, limits, and the strata which it contains: this description ought to contain an exact account of all the veins and remarkable mineral deposits which have been found in the district.

Books of record should also be kept, in which should be specified all the traversions, ramifications, and throws, of the different veins, as far as they can be ascertained, together with the rise and dip of the strata, both within the influence of the different veins and at a distance, where they seem to pursue their natural inclination.

The section of the strata, Plate VI., Fig. 4, is intended to show the inclination, or hade, of the south vein, with its influence upon the strata on both sides; it corresponds both with the external plan, Plate V., Fig. 1, and the internal plan, Fig. 2. The distance, *e a*, shows how far the sump, *e*, ought to be from the vein, at *a*, in order to cut it again near the bottom of the stratum of limestone. S. N. and *x x* are two cross cuts into the vein, supposed to have been driven in the course of sinking: the dotted lines are intended to show the occurrence of the black bed, high, middle, and low flats of the great limestone (see page 57).

Books for recording the bearings of the veins which occur in the district should likewise be kept, the bearings being reduced to the true meridian on account of the variation of the needle.

The expense of working mines varies greatly at different mining fields and in different countries. It is, therefore, impossible to give any estimate which will be universal in its application. I shall, however, endeavour to give an idea of the expenses incurred in the mines at Alston Moor and the places adjacent. Even here, however, the cost depends a great deal upon the situations of the places where the mines occur, with respect to drainage, drawing out the stones and ores, and the ore-bearing strata.

As mines are generally found in hilly and mountainous tracts of country, and are, therefore, drained by means of levels or adits, driven into the sides of the mountains from the bottoms of the valleys, I shall commence by specifying the cost, per fathom, of those levels, 1st, in the plate beds, and 2nd, in the harder strata. Excavations can be made in the plate beds at a comparatively small cost. Levels of the ordinary size, that is, six feet by four, can be driven in the plate beds to the distance of twenty to thirty fathoms, for thirty to forty shillings per fathom, exclusive of the charges for *arching*, *wooding*, and *railing;* but as the level penetrates deeper into the hill, and the superincumbent weight becomes greater, and the plate, therefore, more indurated, the cost of driving increases, until it attains the maximum of eighty to ninety shillings per fathom.

When a plate bed cannot be found in a convenient situation, and it, therefore, becomes necessary to drive in the limestone, or sandstone, the figures are much higher than those just quoted. These rocks cannot be wrought without the aid of gunpowder ; and blasting* is a costly process. Eight to ten pounds per fathom are frequently given for driving in a compact stratum of limestone, or sandstone.

When a level has been driven to the length of fifty to sixty fathoms, the miners generally require a current of fresh air. To obtain this either a bore-hole is put down or a shaft is sunk, and a communication is opened between it and the farthest part of the workings. If there is a small stream near, it may be allowed to fall into a cistern or tub at the bottom of the bore-hole, or shaft ; it will carry down with it a current of air. This contrivance, which is called by the miners a *water-blast*, is represented in Plate IV., Fig. 5, where *a* is the pipe or shaft through which the water

* The method of blasting is performed thus :—The miners bore a long cylindrical hole, like the hollow of a large gun barrel, with an iron instrument, hardened with steel at the end like a chisel, which is called the *jumper*. After the hole is bored as far as they think necessary, it is filled with a proportionate quantity of gunpowder and an instrument, called the *pricker*, is introduced into it ; then the miners ram down the charge, together with some plate, or hardened clay, by means of another instrument called the *driver* or *drivel*. When the pricker is withdrawn, the miners introduce a fuse, to which they set a match. [Gun cotton is now extensively used in blasting operations.—ED.]

descends into the cistern; and *b* the box which conveys the air to the workmen. The manner in which it operates can easily be understood from an inspection of the Plate. By this simple artifice a level may be driven to the length of four to five hundred fathoms.*

The expense of sinking increases according to the depth, and the strata through which it is desired to sink.

The measures used for *whimsey,* or horse engine, shafts, are generally about four feet six inches long, by three feet broad. Such shafts may be sunk to the depth of ten to fifteen fathoms, at from about two pounds ten to four pounds per fathom : beyond that the cost will be from five to eight pounds per fathom, exclusive of the charges for timber, walling, &c.

In Alston Moor, when a mine has been opened and promises to be productive, the miners take a certain piece of ground, commonly called a *length*, in which they propose to raise ore, for a certain time, at so much per bing, according to the richness of the mine. A length of ground is usually either twelve, fifteen, or twenty fathoms. The cost of excavating the strata depends much upon their degree of hardness, the expense of drawing the stone and ore out of the mine, and the probable quantity of metal that can be raised. The miners generally take *bargains*, in *partnerships*, of two, four, six, or eight men, and the prices range from eight to fifteen, twenty, thirty, forty, or fifty shillings per bing; the miners themselves always paying for candles, gunpowder, the expenses of drawing the ore and stone from the mine, and the dressing and preparing of the ore for the process of smelting.†

But it frequently happens that the quantity of ore in a vein is so inconsiderable that it is necessary to give the workmen both so much per bing and per fathom; and, occasionally, when a vein is twitched, and hard riders must be driven through, the price per

---

* [Premising that there is a sufficient supply, it may be predicated of a water-blast that its pressure will be in proportion to the height of the column of water. —ED.]

† [The practice of taking lengths has become obsolete. Bargains, per fathom or per bing, or per fathom and bing, are still taken by the miners.—ED.]

fathom will require to be advanced to eight, ten, twelve pounds, or upwards.*

The expense of drawing the ore and stone out of the mine depends much upon the length of the level and the depth of the shaft, but is always considerable when horses are employed. In Alston Moor it is usually drawn out at so much per shift, a shift containing six or eight waggons. A miner's waggon, calculated for an eight waggon shift, contains thirty *kibbles*, the capacity of each kibble being fourteen quarts, or thereabouts; a waggon, calculated for six waggon shifts, contains forty kibbles : the shifts in both cases being equal. The cost of a shift, in horse levels, varies from 3s. 6d. to 8s., inclusive of the cost for filling, driving, and emptying the waggons, no allowance being made for the difference of weight between the ore and the stone.

In situations where it is necessary to use whimseys, or horse-engines, for the purpose of raising the ore and stone to the surface, the same proportion is followed respecting the shift; which, in these cases, generally consists of sixty horse kibbles, each horse kibble containing four miner's kibbles, making the quantity drawn in a shift two hundred and forty kibbles as before. The expense of raising a shift, including filling, banking, and driving, varies from four to eight shillings.

* Supposing a cubic foot of pure galena weighs, on the average, 7,000 ozs., Avoirdupois, a bing will then be equal to 14,336 ozs. We shall, according to this scale, have as under, viz. :—

ORE.

Inch wide.	Feet high.	Feet long.		Cubic feet.		Bing.	Cwts.	Qrs.	Lbs.	Ozs.
1	6	6	equal	3	equal	1	3	2	24	8
2	6	6	,,	6	,,	2	7	1	21	0
3	6	6	,,	9	,,	4	3	0	17	8
4	6	6	,,	12	,,	5	6	3	14	0
5	6	6	,,	15	,,	7	2	2	10	8
6	6	6	,,	18	,,	8	6	1	7	0
12	6	6	,,	36	,,	17	4	2	14	0
36	6	6	,,	108	,,	52	5	3	14	0

III.—THE DRESSING OF LEAD ORES.

From the account of the contents of mineral veins which has been given in these pages, the reader will have already inferred that the material which is dug out of the veins by the miners, consists of a great variety of substances, such as vein stone, mineral soils, spars, and ores, the latter forming a small proportion of the whole. Among miners this material is known as bouse—a word which is frequently heard in the lead-mining districts. Bouse is rich, or poor, according to the amount and the quality of the ore which it contains. If it contain fifty per cent. of ore—a rare circumstance—it is accounted very rich indeed; if it contain twenty per cent. it is considered rich; if ten per cent., very good; if five per cent., good; if only two per cent., it is not despised. Mine-owners are frequently obliged to be content with less than the least of these proportions. Whatever the proportion of ore to dross may be, a separation must be made between the two before the former can be taken to the market. In olden times the very limited demand for lead, and, therefore, for the ores from which the metal is extracted, was met by the supplies of float and shoad ores. The streams which issue from the Pennine valleys then rolled down their leaden sands, and supplied the hunters of the red deer with as much pure ore as they could smelt in the boles which they had built on the western escarpments of the hills.

At a later period, when the supplies of float and shoad ores were almost exhausted, and men had acquired some knowledge of mineral veins and some skill in surface-mining, a rough separation of the ore from its matrix was effected by the simple process of washing the vein-stuff in the nearest stream and picking out the pieces of ore. Where a natural stream was not available, a supply of water was obtained by artificial means: either a water-course was constructed between the mine and some distant stream which flowed at a higher level; or a hush-dam, such as has been described, was built.

Mining had now become an important industry, by which a considerable number of people gained a livelihood. When the wealth which had lain near the surface, and which, on that account, was

P

within the reach of anyone who cared to pick it up, was almost exhausted, the miners followed the mineral veins into the bowels of the earth. The shallow pit of former times was deepened into the *shaft ;* the short gallery was driven forward until it became a *level.* The material which was brought out of these deep mines was harder, more mixed, and therefore more intractable, than that which was obtained from the surface mines. For the proper dressing of it, better appliances than the water-course and the hush-dam were required.

Towards the end of last century the buddle was invented. It was a very simple contrivance. A number of flat stones with smooth surfaces, such as abound in the mining districts, were placed together so as to form an oblong-shaped, though not a level, floor, one of the longer sides being raised a little in order to obtain a gentle slope. The raised side was called the back, the opposite side the front, of the buddle. The bouse having been placed upon the buddle in convenient quantities by the washer boys, a strong current of water was allowed to flow over it in the direction of the slope. The water not only washed the bouse, and thus enabled the boys to distinguish the ore from the stones, but it also effected a rough separation between the two by carrying the latter to the bottom of the slope, whilst the former, through the force of gravity, remained near the top. The *clean* stones were then picked out and taken to the dead heap : the pieces of pure ore were taken to the ore heap in the bingstead : the mixed pieces were taken to the knockstones, on which they were crushed by means of buckers, wielded by boys of from fourteen to sixteen years of age : the small stuff which could not be dealt with by the pickers was left to the care of the hand-sieve boy. The hand-sieve was of the same shape, and almost of the same size, as that which is used by the gardener and the plasterer in the riddling of mould and lime. The boy, having put a small quantity of the crushings from the bucker into the sieve, shook it smartly over a tub, meanwhile keeping the sieve and its contents just under the water with which the tub was almost filled. The process of sifting is explained more fully below. The buddle, the hand-sieve, and the hand-bucker, were the chief appliances in use on the old washing floor.

In the early part of the present century the buddle gave place to the grate, the hand-sieve to the brake-sieve, and the hand-bucker to the crushing machine.

The Modern Washing Floor.—The Picking.—When the bouse is brought out of the mine, it is deposited in the teams, which are generally situated in the upper portion of the washing floor. If it is very poor, the washing master sends two or three boys to pick out the larger stones; to wash them, so as to deprive them of any particles of ore which adhere to them, and then to carry them to the dead heap. If the bouse is rich, he sends as many boys to pick out the pieces of pure ore, reduce them to a proper size, and take them to the bingstead. If the bouse is neither poor enough nor rich enough to require this preliminary picking, it is taken at once to the grate (Fig. 1, Plate IX.) This apparatus is made by placing a number of iron bars parallel with, but at a distance of about half-an-inch from, each other. At each end of the grate, and nearly on a level with it, a board, or, in lieu of it, a flat stone, is firmly fixed. (See Fig. 1, Plate IX.) The grate is used thus:—A strong stream of water being allowed to fall upon it, the bouse, in convenient quantities, is placed under the stream, and is then raked backwards and forwards. During the process the small stuff passes through between the bars, falls upon the sloping stone underneath, and thence into the pit made for its reception. A mixture of rider, spar, pure and mixed pieces of ore, of various shapes and sizes, remains upon the grate. When this has been drawn upon the picking boards, the pieces of pure ore are taken out, broken to a proper size, and carried to the bingstead. The mixed pieces are then picked out and taken to the grinder, or crushing machine, where, together with the stuff from the pit, they are reduced to the consistency of gravel. The crushings are then taken to the brake-sieve. (See Fig. 2, *n*, Plate IX.)

This machine is made of strong wires, passed through thin bars of iron, by which they are kept at a proper distance—generally about $\frac{1}{10}$ of an inch—from each other, and are also firmly held together. The sieve is suspended in a tub by two upright arms made of flat iron bars, and deeply notched, which are either fastened to a lever (Fig. 2, Plate IX.), or are brought into contact

with two cog-wheels in such a way that the teeth of the wheels fit
into the notches of the arms.   When set in motion by the large
wheel of the grinder, the cogs communicate to the arms, and,
therefore, also to the sieve, a jigging motion, by which its contents
are smartly shaken up and down.   In the case of the lever, the
jigging is done by a boy.   The crushings from the grinder are
thrown into the sieve, in suitable quantities, and subjected for a
few minutes to this jigging motion, during which the heavy ore
finds its way downwards, the finer particles passing through the
sieve into the tub, whilst the larger particles (called *round*, or
sieve ore) are intercepted by the wires and collected together in
the bottom of the sieve.

The worthless matter, called *cuttings*, is found on the top.
Between the cuttings and the pure ore there is a layer of particles,
called chats, which are neither pure ore nor clean cuttings, but
a mixture of both.   A boy stationed by the side of the tub takes
off the cuttings with his limp, but, meanwhile, leaves the ore and
the chats in the sieve.   A fresh supply of stuff is then thrown in and
jigged ; the operation being repeated as frequently as the boy thinks
necessary, with the following results :—

1. The bulk of the worthless matter has been got rid of.
2. The round, or sieve ore, has been secured.
3. A quantity of chats has been collected and taken to the
   stampers.
4. A quantity of smalled ore, called smiddum, in some cases
   pure, in others mixed with fine sand, has been collected
   in the tub.   If pure, it is taken at once to the bingstead;
   if impure, it is carried to the buddle.

Smiddum Buddling.—The operation of buddling is performed
by a strong lad in this way:—He deposits a suitable quantity of
smiddum on a large flagstone, which is surrounded on the two sides
and back by a wooden frame, the front being left open.   Then
allowing a strong current of water to flow over the flagstone from
back to front, he draws the smiddum through it by means of a
col-rake (coal-rake).   During the operation, which is performed
very slowly, the water carries away the comparatively light dross
and a little of the ore, but leaves the great bulk of the ore in a

pure state on the flagstone, whence it is taken to the bingstead. The dross, with its small admixture of ore, is called smiddum tails. It is wheeled to a square box (Fig. 3, *a*, Plate IX.), into which a strong stream of water falls, where it is agitated with the shovel until the slime which it contains is set free and swept away into the slime-pit below the box by the stream. The smiddum is now taken back to the buddle, where the residue of the ore left after the first operation, is secured by a second and similar operation.

During the operations of grating, grinding, sifting, and buddling, a portion of the minutest and finest part of the ore is carried away by the water. In order to save this ore from being finally lost, *receivers*, or *slime pits*, are constructed at a little distance from the place where the former operations are conducted, into which the water is allowed to flow. These receivers are rectangular in shape, about eight or ten yards in length, one yard in breadth, and from two to three feet in depth. They are perfectly close at the sides and one end; at the other end there is an opening near the top of about nine inches wide and two or three inches deep, through which the water is discharged. It will be easily understood that when the slimy liquid flows into one of these receivers the slime gradually sinks to the bottom, whilst the water escapes through the opening. When one receiver is filled with slime the water is turned into another, the contents of the former being taken to the circular and zenner buddles and the dolly tub, where the ore is extracted from them.

Sludge and Slime Buddling.—The circular and zenner buddles are so nearly alike in shape and construction that a description of one may very well serve for the other. They differ a little in their mode of action; the bottom, or floor, of the circular being stationary, whilst that of the zenner is rotary. This floor is circular in shape, and rises rapidly from the circumference to the centre. In the centre is fixed a metal pillar, about four feet in height, which serves the double purpose of a support for a funnel-shaped box and of an axis upon which a fan-shaped wheel, fixed within the box, revolves. A stream of water being turned into this box, and its outflow being so regulated that the box is always kept full, a quantity of sludge, or slime, is next put into it. In its progress downwards the sludge is thoroughly mixed with the water by the revolution of the wheel. Passing through the narrow opening at the bottom of the box, the mixture, in its progress from the centre to the circumference, is equally diffused over the floor.   In the case of the circular buddle the dross is carried near to, or even over, the edge of the floor, whilst the pure ore, owing to its greater specific gravity, lodges near the centre.   Thus a separation of the one from the other is effected. The operation is facilitated, in the circular buddle, by a long brush, which is made to sweep over the floor in the direction of the circumference, and in the zenner buddle by the rotation of the floor itself.   When a sufficient quantity of sludge, or slime, has been put into the buddle, the boys who have charge of it turn off the water, and then proceed to remove the contents.   The worthless dross which lies near the edge of the floor of the circular is first taken away, then that portion which consists of a mixture of dross and ore, and lastly the pure ore.   The slime does not lodge on the floor of the zenner but is swept over the edge into a circular box, which is fitted to the circumference, and divided into four compartments.   During the operation of buddling the pure ore is collected in one compartment, the blende in another, a mixture of ore, blende, and other matters in a third, and the dross in a fourth.   At the end of a buddling shift the boys find the slime thus divided, and have only to empty the compartments.   The finest portion of the slime is reserved for the dolly tub.   See Plate IX., Figs. 4 and 5.

The washing of old heaps of cuttings, &c., by means of what is called hushing, is the last branch of ore dressing which requires notice.   The ore dressers generally put the cuttings into a syke, or gully.   The residuum of ore which they contain makes its way to the bottom of the syke through the force of gravity, whilst a portion of the lighter stuff is carried away by the water.   If there should be a number of large stones in the syke, the ore generally collects around them: it also collects in the holes at the bottom.   A clay bottom is best suited for hushing operations.   The husher first builds his dam and then removes all the large stones to one side where he makes a wall with them.   He then sets off his hush by lifting up the door of the dam.   The operation is repeated until the cuttings, gravel, &c., are washed off the ore, which is then found lying in holes and about earth-fast stones, at the bottom of the syke. The husher collects and carries it to the *brake-seive*, where it undergoes the operation of jigging, &c., as before described. Considerable quantities of ore have been recovered from old dead heaps by means of hushing.*

The appliances which have hitherto been described are those in general use. On large washing floors there are other contrivances for facilitating the dressing operations. The grinder is now fitted with a pair of Blake's crushers, which effect a great saving of time and labour, by reducing to the size of road-metal the large pieces of bouse (*knockings*)—such as the rollers cannot take—and which were formerly broken into smaller pieces with the hammer. The crushings are then passed through two pairs of rollers which reduce them to the consistency of gravel. In this condition they are passed through a series of graduated drum-cylinders, connected with each other at the ends and fixed in a sloping position, the largest being at the top, and the smallest at the bottom of the slope. The perforations are also graduated in size. Assuming that the diameter of those in the first cylinder is $\frac{5}{8}$-inch, the diameter of those in the second cylinder will be $\frac{4}{8}$-inch, &c. The diameters will thus be represented by the following series, $\frac{5}{8}$, $\frac{4}{8}$, $\frac{3}{8}$, $\frac{2}{8}$, $\frac{1}{8}$, $\frac{1}{16}$, $\frac{1}{32}$, $\frac{1}{64}$. Each cylinder revolves upon its own axis, and is set in motion by that which is next above it, the first, or top cylinder being set in motion, either by the large wheel of the grinder, or by a wheel specially erected for the purpose. Whilst in a state of rapid motion the crushings are washed into the topmost cylinder by a stream of water, and are thence driven downwards through the others by the motion. In their progress from top to bottom they undergo a thorough sifting. The largest particles pass through the largest holes in the top cylinder; the next in size pass through the holes in the second cylinder, &c., to the bottom; the smallest particles passing through the smallest holes in the lowest cylinder. The whole of the stuff operated upon is thus divided into as many parts as there are cylinders.

* [The contrivances for catching the ore are now so numerous and perfect that very little indeed finds its way into the gully. The hush may at some future time be utilised for the recovery of the large quantities of blende which lie buried in the dead heaps.—ED.]

The cylinder is not designed to serve as a substitute for the sieve, but is merely intended to facilitate the operations of the latter by classifying the crushings preparatory to their being taken to the sieve. It is, for this reason, called the *classifier*. If any large particles pass out at the end of the lowest cylinder they are brought back to the grinder. Under each cylinder, though a little to the left of it, is placed a large rectangular tub, which is divided into compartments, each compartment being fitted with a brake-sieve. The three tubs at the top contain each five, the others each four, compartments, with as many graduated sieves. Each cylinder, the lowest excepted, is connected with the sieve (No. 1) most directly under it by a wooden box, or pipe, which serves the purpose of a conductor for the stuff driven through the perforations, conveying it from the cylinder to the sieve. This sieve is not suspended, but fixed, in the tub. Between it and the back of the tub, a rectangular board, called the *float*, about 24 inches long by 9 inches broad and 2 inches thick, is suspended by an iron rod. When at rest the float is a little above the surface of the water. The separation of the ore from the dross (cuttings) is not, in this case, effected by jigging, but by a rapid vertical motion of the float, the downward movement raising the water to a higher level in the tub, and thus pressing it through the interstices of the sieve. By this simple contrivance the contents of the sieve are kept, for a short time, in a state of semi-suspension, and the ore, meanwhile, finds its way to the bottom. The sieve (No. 1), which is under the top cylinder, extracts the bulk of the pure ore: the sieve next to it (No. 2) extracts the remainder of the pure ore: No. 3 extracts the mixed pieces of ore, called chats, which are taken to the stamps (see Plate VIII. and description of apparatus): Nos. 4 and 5 complete the separation of the ore from the cuttings. In the tubs, which contain four compartments, sieves Nos. 1 and 2, always counting from the one nearest to the cylinders, extract the lead ore; Nos. 3 and 4, the blende.

Here it should be observed that the stuff which passes through the small perforations of the lowest cylinder, is not tubbed, but is taken to the buddles.

It should also be observed that, though all the cylinders revolve at the same time, they do not all revolve in the same direction.

If the first revolve from right to left, the second will revolve from left to right, &c. This must necessarily be the case where each revolves upon its own axis, but is driven by the one above it.

A great saving of time and labour is effected by the modern washing apparatus. The work which formerly required the labour of two men and eighteen boys can now be done by two men and four boys.

Recapitulation.—The preceding account of the operations of the washing floor may be summarised thus :—The bouse generally undergoes a first picking in the teams, and a second at the grate. The portion which is left after these pickings is taken to the grinder, where it is first reduced to the size of road-metal by Blake's crushers, and then to the consistency of gravel by the rollers. The crushings are then classified by the graduated cylinders, and are next deprived of the bulk of the ore and blende which they contain, by the sieves and smiddum buddles. The finest portions, from the lowest cylinder and the slime pits, are taken to the circular and zenner buddles, the very finest to the dolly, by which appliances the remainder of the ore is separated from the dross.

DESCRIPTION OF THE ORE DRESSING APPARATUS.

The crushing machine and stampers, represented in Plates VII. and VIII., are very essential where the quantity of bouse is tolerably large. Plate VII., Fig. 1, is a side elevation of the machine ; D is the great pit wheel attached to the axle of the water wheel, the circumference of the latter being represented by the large circle: the wheel D turns an iron cog-wheel, *e*, on the spindle of which is fixed one of the iron rollers. Concentric with the pit wheel D, and upon the axle of the great water wheel is fixed a fluted roller, which moves another fluted roller parallel with it. The bouse is brought in the waggon A, and let out by a door which opens outwards in the bottom, into the hopper, S. After passing through the fluted rollers* immediately below the hopper, the bouse descends by the two inclined planes (represented in the figure) to the two smooth rollers which are turned by the iron cog-wheel *e*. The rollers are made of cast iron: they are represented more distinctly in Figs. 2 and 3. The spindles of these rollers turn in brass bushes, fixed in two iron frames, *k k*, which are bolted down to the wood-work; these iron frames have long mortices in them, in one end of which the two bushes for the pivots of the roller, *f*, are firmly fixed. The bushes

* [Where Blake's crushers are in use the fluted rollers are not required.—ED.]

of the roller, *g*, slide in the mortices in such a manner as to allow the two rollers to be placed either in contact or at a short distance from each other, as circumstances may require. The rollers are, however, generally pressed towards each other by the weights, *r r*, suspended at the ends of the levers, whose fulcrums are at *x*, Fig. 1. The operation of these levers, in pushing up the moveable rollers, will be easily understood from an inspection of the figure. By this contrivance, when a large or hard lump is introduced between the rollers, they are allowed to recede from each other so that it can pass through without doing injury to the machine.*

The two cog-wheels, *m m*, Fig. 2, are attached to the axles of the two rollers and cause the latter to move round together. The hopper, *h*, Fig. 3, is supported at some distance above the rollers; the bouse runs out at an opening in its bottom into a trough, *i*, called the *shoe*. This trough, or shoe, is shaken by means of a piece of wood attached to it, one end of which rests upon the teeth of the cog-wheel *m;* by this means the bouse is made to fall upon the rollers in small quantities, and choking up is thus avoided.

In place of this contrivance, a boy is sometimes employed to feed the machine : he sits in a small cabin near the rollers and rakes in the bouse out of the shoe.

The rollers are kept cool by a small stream of water which flows into and through the shoe.

The stampers, Fig. 1, Plate VIII., are used for crushing chats. In this Plate the stamp mill is represented entirely distinct from the crushing machine, but in many instances the two machines are moved by the same water-wheel, the stampers being placed on one side and the rollers on the other.

In the Plate alluded to, Fig. 1, shews a longitudinal elevation of the stamp mill. A, is the water-wheel, framed on a strong octagonal shaft, B, B, which turns on two gudgeons, fixed in its ends. D, is the pit wheel, or great cog-wheel, of eighty teeth, made of cast-iron, which turns the wheel E, of thirty-seven teeth, which is fixed on a horizontal shaft, F, called the *tumbling* shaft. The beams, T, T, have cross pieces attached to them, between which the stampers, V, W, X, Y, slide up and down. The stampers are lifted up by the nippers, *n*, *m*, Fig. 2, which are fixed upon the shaft, F. These nippers take hold of the tappets, *w*, raise the stampers to the proper height, and then allow them to fall upon the chats which are placed upon an inclined plane, and which gradually slide down as the operation proceeds. The descent of the chats, down the inclined plane, is facilitated by a small stream of water, which flows in at its top.

Fig. 1, Plate IX., is a ground plan of the grate. See page 175.

Fig. 2 is a ground plan and Fig. 6 an elevation of the brake-sieve, where *a* is the end of the brake, or lever, *n* the wire sieve, and *e e*, the tub.†

Fig. 3 is a ground plan of the trunk buddle ; *a* is the box into which the smiddum is put.

---

* [The large hard lumps are now reduced by Blake's crushers.—ED.]
† [Where the jigging is done by cogs the lever is dispensed with.—ED].

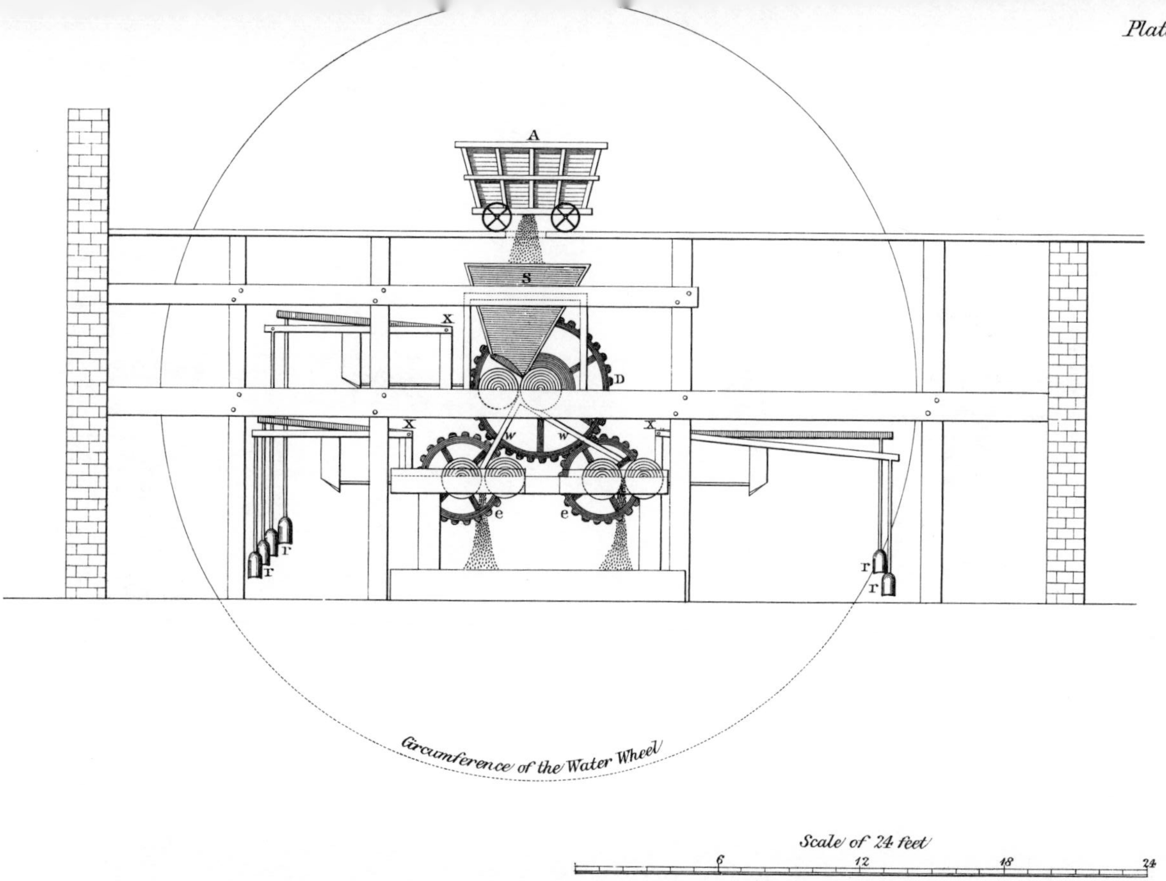

Plate 7.

Circumference of the Water Wheel

Scale of 24 Feet

Andrew Reid, Newcastle

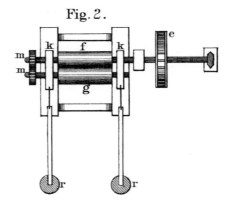

Fig. 2.

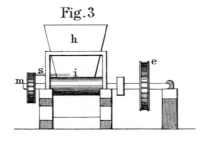

Fig. 3

Plate 8.

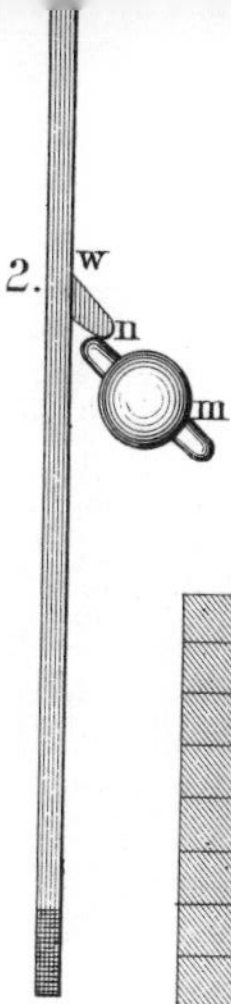

Fig. 1.

Fig. 2.

Scale of Feet

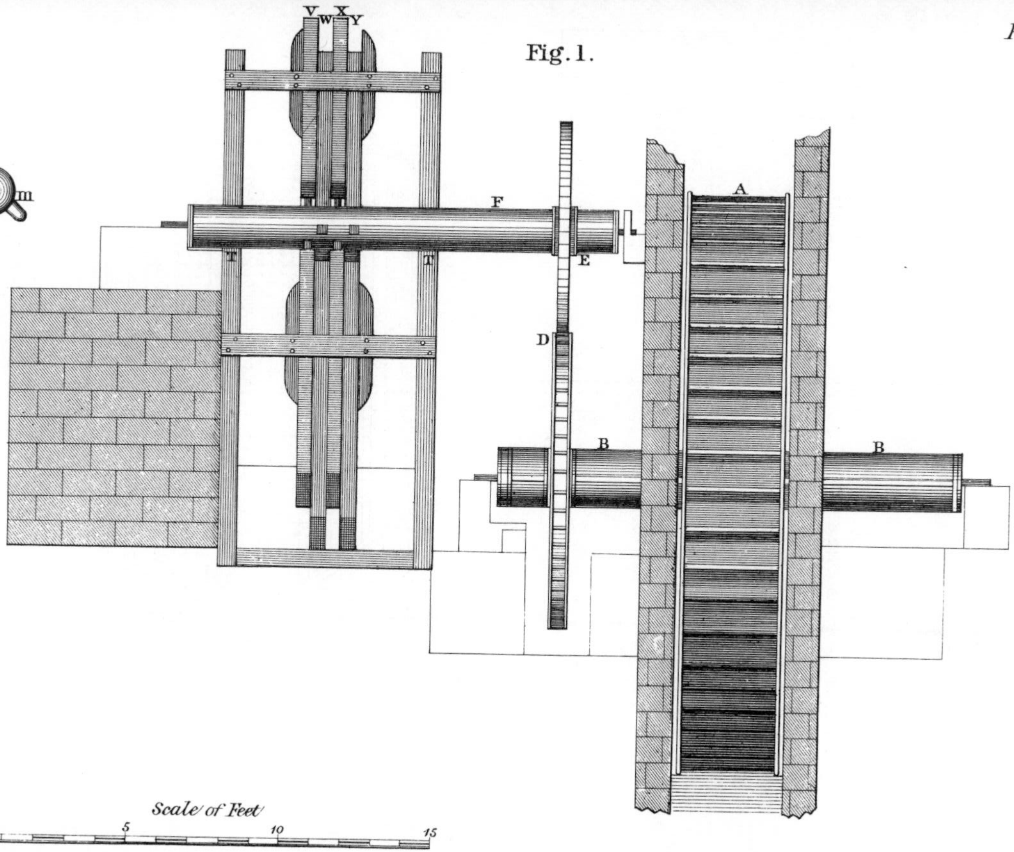

Plate 9

Fig. 1.

Water Course

Grate

Inclined Plate

Pit

Fig. 2.

a

e

e

n

e

1'6"

2'6"

Fig. 3.

a

b

3'6"

Fig. 6.

Limp

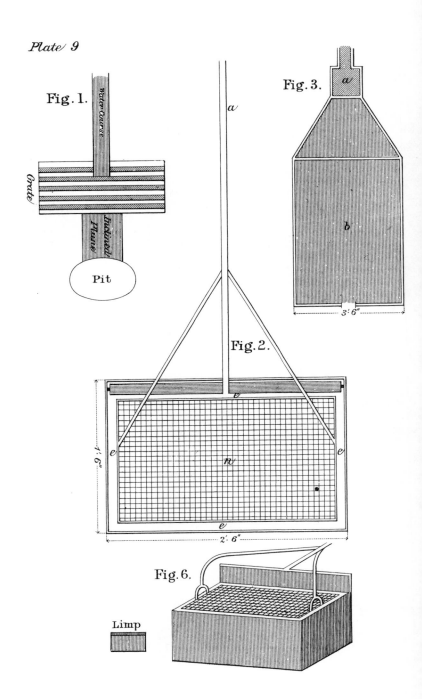

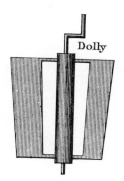

Dolly

Fig. 4

Fig. 5

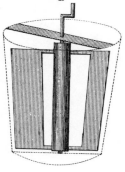

Figs. 4 and 5 represent the dolly tub and dolly ;* they are used thus:—The tub (Fig. 4) is first filled to a certain height with water ; the dolly (Fig. 5) is then introduced and turned quickly round, a circular motion being thus communicated to the water : in the meantime, a suitable quantity of slime ore is slowly put in. When the ore is thoroughly mixed with the water the dolly is withdrawn, and the workmen then proceed to beat the sides of the tub with a hammer, or heavy piece of wood, in order to keep the matter in suspension as long as possible, and thus allow it to settle gradually. The ore finds its way to the bottom through the force of gravity, and the light refuse settles upon it. The water is then let out, and the dross removed to the dead heap. The pure ore at the bottom of the tub is taken to the bingstead.

It was formerly customary in Alston Moor, and the places adjacent, for the miners to let the dressers a parcel of bouse, to dress, at so much per bing, the price depending upon the quality of the bouse. Some parcels of bouse were washed for 2s. 6d. or 3s. per bing, or even less, whilst other parcels required from 4s. to 8s. per bing. The ore-dressers are now employed by the day.

IV.—ON THE SMELTING OF LEAD ORES.

The Ancient Mode of Smelting.—It appears from the numerous boles or bayle hills, which are found in the mining districts of the counties of Northumberland, Cumberland, and Durham, and also, as I am told, in Derbyshire, that the smelting of lead ore was, in former times, conducted in the following manner:—Piles of stones were placed round a fire, which was lit on the western brow of an eminence, where it would be exposed to the west wind. These stones were placed in such a way as to leave certain openings which served as flues and blast holes. The fuel was obtained from the neighbouring wood, which, on that account, was named Hag Hill, or Hag Bank. It is unnecessary to spend time in describing more minutely these rude and imperfect modes of smelting. It is obvious that, on account of the variableness of the wind, the workmen could have very little command over the fire, a thing which is most essential in every operation conducted by heat. This was probably the method adopted by the first ore-smelters.

* Dollying the slime ore is a most excellent method, since by it, not only is the ore made purer, but more of it is saved than by any other means.

The next mode of smelting was by means of the blast *hearth*, an apparatus which is known in various parts of Europe by the name of the Scotch hearth. It was probably like the hearth now in use, though, no doubt, greatly inferior in power, since it was not equal to one-third of the work done by the present hearth.

I shall endeavour to describe this hearth, and the manual operations connected with it; but I shall, in the first place, explain the theory upon which it operates, and compare it with the third mode of smelting, generally known by the name of the Derbyshire *cupola*, or reverberatory furnace, a description of which I shall extract from Mr. Farey's "Derbyshire Report."

The ores, from which lead is obtained, are varieties of galena (sulphuret of lead), white ore of lead, which is a carbonate, and the earthy ore, or oxide of lead, the latter seldom occurring in the mines of Northumberland, Cumberland, and Durham. When this last ore does occur in those mines it is mixed very intimately with indurated clay. Were it more common the hearth and the reverberatory furnace are well adapted for the extraction of its lead. These three kinds of lead ore, exhibit numerous characteristics, or habits, in the fire, owing, chiefly, to the variable proportions of the lead and mineralizing substance or substances which they contain, and partly to the extraneous matter from which they are seldom completely separated by dressing. The first, viz., galena, or sulphuret of lead, when pure, breaks into smooth right-angled fractures, and is generally known by the name of cubical lead ore. Its composition is about eighty-seven of lead, and thirteen of sulphur. The other sorts of galena exhibit a waving cubical fracture, and always contain more or less antimony, a fact which is evident from the white sublimed oxide attaching to the doors and sides of the roasting furnace. As antimony is mineralized with about double the quantity of sulphur that is found in galena, it is evident that a small compound of it combined with the galena will increase the usual proportion of sulphur in that ore to fourteen, fifteen, or sixteen per cent. Analysis has shown that such is the case. Sulphur, or rather its oxide, also exists in galena, in an uncombined state. A portion of it can, therefore, be volatilized by combustion, and the quantity thus reduced to the mineralizing ratio. The excess of sulphur is usually got rid of by roasting. Hence the reason why roasted ore yields more lead in the blast, or ore hearth, than the raw ore. It is not only more porous, but works dryer, as the smelters would say, and thus allows the current of air from the blast-pipe to disseminate itself more perfectly through the contents of the hearth.

It is true, that the extraneous matter, which consists chiefly of argillaceous and siliceous substances, pyrites, the ores of zinc, and riders of different compositions, contain more or less of the calx of iron, and that this calx affects the habits of the ore in smelting, but it is the excess of sulphur, or rather of its oxide, which chiefly alters its composition.

White lead ore, or carbonated lead, is the second in importance, since it has been found in considerable quantities in the lead mines above-mentioned, more especially in the manor of Alston Moor, where, in the amorphous state, it has been found in the massive condition. It has been found in considerable abundance at Fair Hill, Flow Edge, and at Hudgill Burn mines, in the form of crystallized, or dog-toothed ore.

The third, or earthy ore of lead, has, I believe, been met with only at Greengill West End. The lead it contains is in the state of an oxide. It is mixed with extraneous substances; the argillaceous impurities being more prevalent in the carbonates than the sulphurets. The oxide seems to be intimately blended with this argillaceous matter.

Only these three kinds of lead ore are found in the above-named mines. They are mixed with different proportions of extraneous matter, and thus require somewhat different modes of treatment in smelting. As, however, the lead in all of them is combined with mineralizing substances; viz., with sulphur in the cubical or right-angled galena, sulphurated antimony in that of the waving-fractured, carbonic acid in the white ore, spar and oxygen in the earthy; it is clear that before the metal can be separated from these substances, something must be presented to them for which they have a greater affinity than they have for lead. Oxygen, with the aid of heat, decomposes galena, by uniting with the sulphur, and forming the sulphuric acids which are dissipated in the gaseous state, along with nearly all the antimony, the latter escaping as a volatilized oxide. Heat alone will expel the carbonic acid from the carbonates, and coal, or charcoal, &c., will abstract the oxygen from the earthy ore of lead. Lime is used to soften the siliceous, argillaceous, and ferruginous impurities of the ore, and thus cause them to form into lumps, in which state they can be separated from the contents of the blast hearth. Lime also promotes their fusion at a high temperature in the reverberatory furnace, so that they swim upon the surface of the lead ; and, when an additional quantity of it is thrown upon the fused slag, it dries it up and forms a mixture of lime and slag, which can be raked off the surface of the lead. Galena can be smelted with a sufficient quantity of grey or black slag, the separation of the lead and sulphur taking place in consequence of the oxide of the iron of the slag uniting itself with the sulphur of the galena ; hence a less quantity of such slag will be necessary when it contains a great deal of the said oxide, the presence of which is indicated by the blackness of the slag ; it is scarcely necessary to observe, that this operation must be performed in the slag hearth, which I shall describe in due course.

The Reverberatory Furnace.—I now extract, from Mr. Farey's "Derbyshire Report," a description of the reverberatory, or cupola, smelting furnace :—

"The cupola consists of a reverberatory furnace, about ten feet long* six feet wide, and two feet high in the centre, inside measurements, the flame being obtained from a fire-place at the end. The *fire-bridge*, is one foot high, and reaches within one foot and a half of the roof,† the latter descending gradually to the end opposite the fire-place, where it is only six inches high. There are two openings in this end which are separated by a triangular block of firestone. They meet in the passage, or flue, which is one foot and a half wide. This flue curves upward through a length of ten feet or more, and is covered by flat stones, closely jointed in fire-clay,

* This dimension must surely include the fire-bridge, which is upwards of two feet in length.

† I believe, it has been found, that a distance of fourteen inches, between the top of the fire-bridge and roof, answers better.

which can be taken off when the flue-glass, or melted flue dust, requires removal. The flue passes, by an easy curve, into a chimney, fifty-five feet high. One side of the furnace, or cupola, is called the labourer's side: here is situated the door for supplying the fire with coals; and here also are three small openings into the furnace, each about six inches square. They are usually closed by iron plates which can be removed when a free current of air is required, or when the furnace needs stirring. On the other side, called the working side, are three similar openings, closed in like manner, and also two other openings below them, which are used for tapping the slag and the lead (see below). The ash-hole also opens on this side, which has conveniences for raking, and for opening the grate-bars from below, in the case of their slagging up and impeding the draft. The floor of the furnace, which is composed of old furnace-slag, roughly pounded, and brought to the proper form by rakes (or strong iron hoes) whilst in a semi-melted state, is raised almost to the level of the small doors on the labourer's side; but is eighteen inches below the middle door on the opposite, or working side. The tap-hole for running off the lead into a large cast-iron pan, called the lead pan, is on the working side. From this tap-hole, the bottom rises on all sides, thereby forming a receptacle sufficiently large to contain the lead in a charge of ore. On a level with the bottom of this receptacle, and under the door which is furthest from the fire-place there is another tap-hole for running off the slag.*
In the centre of the top of the furnace there is a small opening, called the crown-hole, which is covered with a thick iron plate when the furnace is at work. Above this crown-hole there is a large hopper of wood, and under the hopper an iron tube which reaches down almost to the plate which covers the crown-hole.

---

* When the reverberatory furnaces were first erected, by the London Lead Company, at Whitfield Mill, in the county of Northumberland, they were constructed with two taps, as here detailed; but as the bottom of the furnace declines, both from the fire-bridge to the flue, and from the labourer's to the foreman's or tapping side, it was found necessary to discontinue the slag tap, as it was so close to the lead tap, that the workmen were very much burnt in casting the lead; instead of running the slag off in the way described here, they added lime to the fluid slag, until it was sufficiently dried up to be fit for removal.

The hopper is furnished with a shuttle, or sliding valve, and, together with the tube, is suspended by framing from the roof of the smelting house. The charge of ore is put into the hopper, from whence it passes into the furnace.

"In the cupola, or furnace, thus constructed, the process of roasting the ore, in a moderate heat, to expel or sublime the sulphur, arsenic, &c., can first be performed, and then an intense heat can be applied for expelling the oxygen and reducing the metal. The charge, which is not introduced gradually, but is shot down into the furnace at once, usually consists of five, six, seven, or even eight sorts of ore from different mines, and dressed in different ways. The perfection of the process depends upon the proper mixture of the ores. Sixteen hundredweight of ore (of one hundred and twenty pounds each) is the usual charge.* It is spread over the floor of the furnace, and the doors are closed until a proper heat has been got up. They are then opened, and the ore is raked and stirred about, first from one side of the furnace and then from the other, so as to expose every part of it to the action of the heat and to the air. The doors are again closed and the heat increased to an intense degree, and thus the reduction of the metal is effected. The molten lead is collected in the bottom of the furnace, and the slag swims on the top of it to the depth of two or three inches. The tapping is then effected by poking out the stopping of lime, when the slag flows out like melted glass. It soon cools on the stone floor of the building. In the solid state it is opaque, of a whitish grey colour, and moderately heavy. It is sometimes used for road metal. When the bulk of the slag has been run off, the smelter proceeds to scatter upon the melted lead two or three shovelfuls of quicklime, in the state of powder, which has the effect of stiffening the portion of slag which was left. He then draws it carefully off the metal, and rakes it upon the floor in a semi-fluid state. This is called drawn slag, and is, when cold, of a very dark or black colour, and very heavy.

"The lead pan is now cleared out, if necessary, and, the stopping of lime being removed, the lead is suffered to run out of

---

* At Whitfield Mill the smelters found that a charge of twelve hundredweight of ore was sufficient; it was generally worked off in six hours.

the furnace into the pan, where it is skimmed, the dross being thrown back into the furnace. The molten lead is then taken out with ladles and poured into seven or more cast-iron moulds with round ends, which are placed in a row. A new charge of ore is now let down into the furnace, through the crown-hole, and the same operations are repeated."

Roasting.—The first process in the smelting of lead ores is that which is known as roasting. It is done in' the roasting furnace (see Plate XII. and the accompanying description).

Roasting dissipates a portion of the sulphur and antimony which exist in the ore, and thus facilitates the operation of the hearth.

During the process the furnace requires very careful management. The heat must be diffused as equally as possible over every part of the furnace—a thing which is not easily done. The temperature must also be carefully adapted to the ores which it is proposed to roast, some ores requiring a much higher temperature than others.

From nine to eleven hundredweight of galena, according to the nature of the ore, is thrown into this furnace for a charge, without any mixture whatever: three of these chargings are usually worked off in eight hours. The fire is introduced in such a manner as to produce a copious smoke over the surface of the ore; if any part of the ore becomes soft or clammy, a fresh surface is presented to the flame and the oxygen of the atmosphere by stirring or raking the ore transversely, or longitudinally, the workmen taking care to raise as much heat as the operation requires, in order to keep the ore from slagging; because, whenever this occurs the oxidizement of the sulphur, antimony, &c., or the expulsion of the fixed air, is very much or entirely retarded. The process is intended to bake, or cake, the slime ore and the small metallic particles which are brought from the horizontal chimneys, as well as to expel the excess of sulphur and antimony.

The roasting furnace operates upon the same principles as the ore hearth and reverberatory smelting furnace. In fact it is precisely the same as the latter so far as it goes; but the ore, or whatever it is charged with, is drawn out in as friable a state as possible,

Q

and is not reduced to lead. It is similar in form to the reverberatory furnace, differing from the latter only in the bottom, which is made perfectly level, as it is not intended for the reception of lead. The roasting furnace has, on that account, been considered by some as only an imperfect copy of the reverberatory; but a little reflection will show the fallacy of this supposition. Smelting by the united means of this furnace and the ore-hearth possesses many decided advantages over the reverberatory furnace. The work is done more economically through the saving of coal which is effected, and it is also done more quickly. The lead is always much purer; so much so, in fact, that where it has to be refined the loss of lead, I am told, is about one-ninth of the whole in reverberatory furnace smelting, as against one-twelfth, or one-thirteenth, in ore hearth smelting, which I shall now proceed to describe.*

Ore Hearth Smelting.—The smelting, or ore hearth, now in use consists of a cast-iron pan, which is rectangular in shape, and measures twenty-four inches by thirty-one inches: the depth is about twelve inches. On its top is cast a ledge which runs round the two sides and back, and is about eight inches broad and an inch and a half thick. The work-stone, which, in 1821, was a separate piece, is now cast on the front edge of the pan, in a sloping position; the fall from the front of the pan to the outer edge of the stone being about four inches. It also has a ledge of an inch or an inch and a half in depth. The back of the hearth is raised with a piece of cast iron, called a back-stone, thirty-one inches long and six and a half high, upon which rests the muzzle of the blast pipe. Over this pipe is placed the pipe-stone, which is of the same length as the back-stone, and eight inches high, and is so called because of the semi-circular hole which it contains for the reception of the blast pipe.† Upon, or along, the two side ledges of the hearth-bottom are placed two castings, called the bearers: they are each about twenty-four inches long and eight inches square. The hearth is set in

* [Some kinds of ore can be treated in the ore hearth equally as well without, as with roasting. Most kinds, however, require the preliminary process.—ED.]

† [The back-stone and pipe-stone now form one casting, which contains a hole through the centre for the reception of the blast-pipe, and is furnished with a contrivance, in the shape of a projection, for disseminating the blast.—ED.]

masonry of brickwork, and in front of it is placed a melting pot for the reception of the lead as it issues from the pan, and which, after running through the channel made for that purpose, falls over the ledge of the work-stone.

From the above description it will be seen that the blast issues from the back of the hearth. The bottom, or, as it is called, pan, of the hearth forms a reservoir capable of containing thirty hundred-weight of lead, which is altogether below the action of the heat ; consequently as the lead in smelting oozes down in drops, this reservoir of cooler lead tends to lessen the waste of volatilization.

At the termination of every finishing* shift a part of the ore, called browse, remains in a semi-reduced state, and in a state of mixture with the cinder and slag. This browse is better suited for the commencement of the succeeding operation than raw, or even roasted ore. The mode of working the ore-hearth is as follows :— The interior having been filled with wood, a shovelful of fire is thrown in and the blast turned on. Coal is then thrown upon the wood. After the fire has acquired sufficient strength, first a portion of the browse and then, after a few minutes, the whole of it, is gradually thrown in. In a little while the greater part of the contents of the hearth are brought upon the work-stone, by means of a large iron poker. The refuse part of the ore, which is desig-nated grey slag, and is known to the practical smelter by its bright appearance, having been picked out with a shovel and thrown into the right hand corner of the outside of the hearth, the browse is put back, with a little coal, if heat be wanting, and with lime, if the browse is not sufficiently disengaged from the slag—a circum-stance which is known by the whole of the mass exhibiting a tendency to fusion, which tendency the lime corrects by forming the earthy matter, for which it has a strong affinity, into lumps, and thus drying it up. The lumps of slag which are formed, contain from one-tenth to one-fiftieth of the lead in the ore, which is afterwards extracted by the more intense heat of the slag-hearth (see below). The heat of the ore-hearth is just sufficient to sweat

* [The ore-hearth is now worked from Monday morning until Saturday night, in shifts of eight hours ; the last shift from 4 p.m. to 12 p.m. on Saturday is called the finishing shift.—ED.]

out the best of the lead, leaving the other matter in a solid, or
fixed state; hence the reason why the hearth produces the finest
lead.   When the browse has been returned into the hearth, a
suitable quantity of ore is spread over the top of it.   After the
lapse of about ten or fifteen minutes, the contents are again
brought upon the work-stone, the grey slag picked out, coal
and lime, in the necessary proportions, added, the browse returned,
and a fresh supply or charging of ore thrown over it.   The same
operation repeated for eight hours forms a smelting shift, during
which fourteen to twenty-eight hundredweight of lead is obtained.

In this manner the best of the lead, together with the silver, the
two metals being in a complete state of union, is, as it were, sweat
out, without fusing any of the other substances with which they
are combined.

The *slag hearth*, with considerable modifications, has been used
in this country upwards of one hundred years.   Its inner cavity is
a parallelopipedon of twenty-six inches long, twenty-two broad,
and thirty-three in depth.   The bottom is composed of a plate of
cast-iron, two inches thick, which slopes gently from back to front.
Upon this bottom are placed, longitudinally on each side, the
bearers, which are castings similar to those of the ore-hearth.
Upon these are placed the fore-stones,* which consist of two pieces
of cast-iron, of about twelve inches in breadth, and twenty-six in
length, an opening being left between them and the hearth bottom,
of about seven inches; the additional height of two inches is obtained
by placing a course of fire-brick betwixt these metal stones.   The
sides of the hearth, above the bearers, are of brick-work, and the
back above the blast-pipe is of the same material, but the back
below, being twenty inches in height, is of cast-iron, or brick-work.

Prior to the last twenty years, the slag, in the liquid state, was
run off into the pot which was placed on the outside of the hearth
for the reception of the lead.   On cooling, it formed cakes over
the surface of the lead, which were reduced by stampers, in order
to prepare the material for dressing operations.   It is now run over
the ledge of a pot into a cistern, six feet long, four deep, and four
in breadth, into which a stream of cold water is made to fall.

* [Brickwork has been substituted for these fore-stones.—ED.]

When the slag comes into contact with the water it flies to pieces. To adapt it for the operation of washing, if this should be necessary, and to prepare it the better for that purpose, the stream of water and the flow of slag are made to fall into the cistern, very nearly at the same place.

The slag-hearth is worked in this manner:—The interior is filled up to the height of seventeen inches, that is, to within two inches of the blast-pipe, with small ashy cinders, beaten closely together. The pot, for the reception of the lead, is also filled with these cinders, which, in each case, answer the purpose of a filter. A little waste wood, or peat, is placed inside the hearth, and upon this is thrown a shovelful of burning coals ; the blast is then turned on. When sufficient heat has been obtained, coke is thrown upon the wood, and over all is spread a stratum of grey slag, or whatever other matter is to be smelted. From time to time, as occasion requires, the grey slag and coke are added. In this process the slag is made perfectly fluid as well as the lead. The latter separates from the former, by finding its way through the filter of ashy cinders, which the former cannot do on account of its viscidity. At the very moment when the slag becomes melted upon the filter (which is soon after the commencement of the shift), the workman makes a hole through the latter of about an inch in diameter, with a poker, through which the molten slag flows in a red hot stream, and after passing over the lead pot, which is placed between the hearth and cistern, falls into the latter.

The lead, obtained by slag-hearth smelting, is not so pure as that obtained from the ore-hearth. It is never so entirely freed from the mineralizing substance, and it is hardened by the carbon of the coke. The former should never be used but in cases where the latter fails, or else is extremely slow in smelting the carbonates.

The Refining of Lead was introduced into this country in the reign of William and Mary. How far the process was similar to the present mode of proceeding, I do not know. Most probably it was much the same. The rate of doing the work has been nearly doubled within the last fifty years.

Refining is performed in a reverberatory furnace, the fire-place of which is about twenty-two inches square and is separated from the furnace by a partition, called the fire-bridge, fourteen inches broad, which prevents anything but the flame entering the furnace itself. The flame passes over the surface of the lead in the cupel, or test, towards the two draught flues on the opposite side of the furnace, which terminate in a chimney nearly forty feet high.* The cupel, test, or vessel, in which this operation is conducted, consists of an oval iron frame, surrounded with a rim five or six inches in depth. Its greater diameter is four feet and a half, and its lesser three feet It has four cross-bars at the bottom, each bar being about five inches in breadth and of the same thickness as the frame itself. The first of these bars is twelve inches from the fore-part of the rim : the second is about the same distance from the first, the third from the second, and the fourth from the third. This test-frame, as it is called, is filled with a mixture of bone and pearl ash, beaten very closely together with flat-headed iron beaters, the heads of which are about two inches in diameter. The pearl ash has the property of semi-vitrifying the bone ashes or destroying their friability, and making them more durable. The ashes are then scooped out with a small spade, made for that purpose, until there is left upon the test-frame and upon the sides a coating of about an inch and a half to two inches thick, excepting in the fore-part, called the breast, where the coating is twelve inches. In this breast a channel is cut from the inner side of the frame, one inch and a quarter in width and nine inches long, with which the passage, or gateway, for the litharge communicates.

The test thus prepared is placed in the refining furnace (in fact it may be called the furnace bottom), and is supported at a proper height against, or close to, an iron ring, which runs round the furnace. The height of the furnace roof, from this ring, is fifteen inches at the fire-bridge side, and twelve at the flue.

The fire must be applied to the test very cautiously, because an intense heat evaporates the water, with which the ashes were moistened, too rapidly, and causes the test to fly to pieces. When the test has been slowly brought to a reddish heat, it is nearly filled with melted lead, previously fused in a cast-iron pot, five hundred-weight being required for the purpose. The lead soon becomes

---

* [The flues are now conducted into the condensing chambers, or long flues.—ED.]

covered with a grey pellicle, called dross, which is a mixture of the first oxide of metallic lead. After the heat of the furnace has been intensified, the lead becomes of a whitish-red colour, and its whole surface covered with litharge, the latter being composed of about ninety-one of lead and nine of oxygen. The blast is then made to play upon the surface of the lead from the hind-part of the test, and thus force the litharge up to the breast, and over the gateway, whence it falls upon a cast-iron plate in clods, in which state it is taken to the reducing furnace to be re-converted into lead.

The blast of air, not only acts mechanically by sweeping off the litharge from the surface of the lead, but also furnishes oxygen for its formation, the refiner taking care to command the proper heat. As the surface of the lead must necessarily become depressed by its oxidizement to, or below, the level of the gateway, more lead is allowed to flow in from the melting pot in order to raise it to the proper height. The operation is continued in this manner until the workmen consider that the lead which is left in the bottom of the pan is too rich for proper and easy management. This rich lead is, therefore, taken out of the test. After such a quantity of rich lead has been obtained as, by assay, is found to contain sufficient silver for a cake, it is melted down again, and the silver is obtained in a test which is hollowed out so as to contain the silver, and leave a margin of the bottom of the test uncovered. The slag can thus be raked off the edges of the silver. Thus the lead, copper, tin, &c., are entirely separated from the silver by the aid of the oxygen of the atmosphere, when the operation is properly managed. Copper is not so easily separated as lead, owing to its greater affinity for silver. Tin is rarely found in combination with silver: when so found it is extremely difficult to separate, on account of its small affinity for oxygen.

The next process, called *reducing*, is the opposite of refining, since it is a converting of the litharge into lead. It is sometimes conducted in a hearth, similar to that used in ore smelting; but more frequently in a reverberating furnace, which is six feet long and nearly six broad, at the middle doors, inside measure. The fire-place is twenty-five inches square, and is divided from the furnace by a partition, or fire-bridge. It sometimes has only one, though generally two, draft flues, through which the flame enters the chimney.

In the refining furnace, as has been observed, nothing but the flame is permitted to act upon the lead, because coal, or charcoal, if brought into contact with that metal would not only (by its greater affinity for oxygen) prevent the conversion of lead into litharge, but would abstract the oxygen from the litharge that had already been formed. In reducing, the litharge is carefully mixed with small coal, and the bottom of the furnace is covered with a two-inch layer of the same fuel previously to the commencement of the operation. The flame from the fire-place very soon sets the coals in the furnace on fire, and in a little time they are burnt to red hot cinders. The mixture of litharge and coal is then thrown upon them, and the heat is raised to the necessary temperature. The oxygen is thus extracted from the litharge, and the lead being set at liberty flows into a cast-iron pot It is cast into pieces, and marked *refined lead*. Care should be taken that something short of the necessary quantity of coal is mixed with the litharge previously to its admission into the furnace, because the workmen, upon seeing the want of it as the process goes on, can throw in a supply whenever it is required. This is a point which should be always carefully attended to, since a redundancy of coal necessarily increases the quantity of slag. The operation here described is continued by re-charging the furnace with the mixture of litharge and coal. Six tons of lead can thus be reduced in nine or ten hours. Supplies of litharge can be thrown into the furnace during the first six hours of the shift.

The work is neither done so well nor so quickly when the coal and litharge are broken into very small pieces; because the operation is then either altogether, or in a great measure, confined to the surface, in consequence of the air, which is necessary for the proper combustion of the coal, being shut out. But when a part of the litharge is cloddy, or in pieces of the size of a hen's egg, the charge of the furnace works more in a mass, and the bituminous part of the coal becoming volatilized, pervades the interstices of the litharge and promotes its reduction by the abstraction of its oxygen.

Assaying.—Having now described the processes which are adopted for the smelting of lead ore, I shall next make a few observations upon assaying.

Apparatus for that purpose are variously constructed. The simplest consists of a rectangular fire-place, thirteen inches long, eight broad, and eleven in depth, with a fire-bridge of the thickness of a brick, dividing it from the furnace. The bottom of the latter is about twelve inches square, perfectly level, and about six inches distant from the under side of the roof. The flue passes into a chimney, fifteen or sixteen feet from the floor. A furnace of this size is sufficient for the assaying of two hàlf-pounds of lead at the same time. The operation is conducted in circular cupels, each five inches and a half in diameter, which are made of the same materials as the refiner's test, and surrounded with an iron ring.* The depth of the rim is nearly one inch and a half.

The most eligible mode of placing these cupels is to put the one before the other, since they work off more nearly at the same time when thus placed. When the furnace is used for the assaying of the ores of lead, the crucible is placed in the fire-place among the hot cinders. The two operations can thus go on at the same time.

There are various methods of assaying galena and the other ores of lead. The most common for galena is performed either by metallic iron filings or the grey oxide of iron, in scales.† The black flux is also very much used. Both these methods are objectionable. The first is no criterion for either the lead or silver, excepting only in a case where the ore is perfectly free from antimony. The decomposition of the ore is obtained by the union of the iron, or its oxide, with the sulphur of the galena, but when antimony is present, a compound of antimony and lead is formed. The silver also, on account of its strong affinity for iron and its oxide, unites with the scoria of these substances and with the sulphur. When the process is properly conducted the scoria, in the fluid state, floats upon the surface of the lead in the crucible. Small coals are then thrown upon it, which become caked, and

---

* The crucible should be forged out of a short solid piece of round bar-iron by hammering it hot over a core or mandril of the same form and size as the interior of the crucible.—*Vide* Dr. Percy on " The Metallurgy of Lead," page 104.

† The reducing agent now generally adopted is wrought-iron, and for this purpose the metal in the form of hoop, rod, and nails is suitable, but not iron filings, of which any excess remains entangled in the reduced lead, and vitiates the result. —Dr. Percy, page 106.

form a sort of lid, and thus hinder the scoria, but not the lead, from running out, when the crucible is inclined to one side. The lead having been obtained, it is put into a melting pan, and a little coal or charcoal diffused over it. The pellicle which forms upon its surface is reduced by a low heat. When this is carefully done, there remains nothing but metallic lead and its silver, provided the iron, or its oxide, has been used in proper quantities for the absorption of the whole of the sulphur. In nice assaying, the iron is used sparingly in order to obtain all the silver possible. But, as sulphur exists in ores in different proportions, it is safest not to use above a quarter of the weight of iron to the ore (the proportion for pure galena); and if, after the remelting of the lead, any scoria remains unacted upon by the coal or charcoal, it will be found to consist of sulphuretted lead, which should be returned to the crucible, from whence it was taken, with the addition of more iron, &c.

The other method of assaying, viz., by the black flux, is not so objectionable, though it is well known that the vegetable alkali which it contains acts upon the lead. I prefer to assay galena, with or without antimony, by the following method :—

Pound the ore very fine, in a mortar ; give it a partial calcination upon a fire-brick, scooped out like a table plate, and placed in the body of the assay furnace ; stir it repeatedly, for the oxydizement of the sulphur and antimony, for the space of three hours, then introduce this roasted ore into a black or grey crucible, putting one of the legs of a small porcelain tube, bent at a right angle, to the bottom of the crucible, the other leg being attached to a pair of small bellows. The crucible, with its contents, having been placed in the fire-place of the assay furnace, and the ore brought to a red heat without any indications of fusion, strew over it, a covering of small coal, upon which, when formed into a cake, place a piece of stone, or anything to keep this lid of coal close down, whilst the blast is being made to play upon the fire in a gentle manner ; by maintaining a proper degree of heat, the lead and silver will, in the course of three-quarters of an hour, be disengaged from the ore in a manner perfectly analagous to that of the blast-hearth.

As to the assaying of the carbonates and oxides of lead, it is only necessary, in the former, to put it into a crucible, placed as above, and apply a sufficient heat to expel the carbonic acid gas; but it is better in most cases to add a little lime. The oxides must be mixed with combustible matter, say coal or charcoal, as in reducing. I should also add lime or chalk when the presence of sand or clay is suspected.

The lead, thus obtained, when assayed for silver, must be treated as follows :—

The cupel (before described) being brought to a red heat in the furnace, from one-half to two ounces of lead is put into it, which soon melts, and becomes covered with litharge; a part of this litharge is volatilized, but the greater part is absorbed by the cupel, and the silver is left behind in a globular form. It scarcely needs to be remarked that the ores and their products must be accurately weighed, and the necessary calculations made.

Assaying by the *muffle* is conducted in the same manner as by the naked fire. The use of it is to prevent the draught of air in the furnace from taking off small particles of the metal; but it is inconvenient for common practice, since it must obviously screen the lead from the heat of the flame, and thus delay the operation; though, when it has once begun to operate, it is very quick, since the smoke of the naked flame (when it comes in contact with the lead) reduces the oxide of the lead in the cupel.

Where it is necessary to assay lead for silver from the ores of different mines, a furnace may be constructed to take off four of such assays at one operation, by enlarging the fire-place and furnace about one-fourth; and, instead of placing one of its sides against a wall, as is commonly the case, let that end contiguous to the flue stand against such wall, so that access may be had to both sides of the furnace, which is furnished on each side with a sliding door and valve, or two doors without a valve, and a moveable flue between it and the chimney. The cupels being arranged in a square, the operator carefully adjusts the flue and admission of air through the valves in such a manner as to make the process go equally forward in each cupel. Allowing three hours for starting, a dexterous hand will take off sixteen assays, of two ounces of lead each, in less than six hours, which will be equally as well done as if only one was going forward.

DESCRIPTION OF SMELTING APPARATUS.

I.—THE ROASTING FURNACE.

Plate XII., Fig. 1, is a perpendicular section of the roasting furnace: *a*, is the inside; *b*, the fire-bridge, over which the flames pass from the fire-place; *c d*, one of the grate-bar supports—there are two or three; *e*, the ash-pit; *f*, the teas-hole, where the coals are introduced into the fire-place, *c;* *g*, one of the flues; *h*, one of the door-ways through which the ore is raked and stirred longitudinally; *j j j*, doors for raking and stirring the ore transversely; the middle one, being larger, is also used for charging and drawing: the other side of the furnace has similar doors; attached to each of the middle doors is a flue, on the outside of the furnace, which communicates with the chimney, and takes away the smoke; *k*, is an opening, to which are affixed two doors, for taking the coal slag out of the fire-place; *l*, is a hole for cleansing the chimney, which is closed when the furnace is at work; *m*, ends of the grate-bars; *n*, roof of the furnace, being a nine-inch brick thick; *o*, passage for the smoke and flame to the chimney, *p;* *q*, passage round the furnace; *r*, is the gable wall of the house.

Fig. 2 is a horizontal section of the roasting furnace: *a*, is the furnace bottom, composed of fire-brick set edgewise upon cast iron plates; the whole thickness of the bottom is six inches, the space below being hollow; *b*, the fire-bridge; *c c c c*, the fire-place; *d d d*, supporters of the grate-bars; *e*, the ash-pit; *f*, the teas-hole; *g g*, the flues; *h h*, doors through which the ore is raked and stirred; *j j j j j j*, doors of the furnace; *k*, steps into the ash-pit.

NOTE.—The space between the external and middle line is the casing of the furnace, and is made of stone, bound, longitudinally and transversely, with iron; and the space between the middle and internal line is the lining of the furnace, made of fire-brick.

II.—THE ORE-HEARTH, SLAG-HEARTH, AND ASSAY FURNACE.

Plate X., Fig. 1, is a horizontal section of the modern cast-iron ore-hearth; *b c a*, is the bottom, and *r* the work-stone of cast-iron; *z*, is the pot for receiving the lead.

In this and the other figures, the orifice of the blast-pipe should have been advanced to the inside of the hearth.

Fig. 2 is a perpendicular section of the old ore-hearth, taken longitudinally in the middle, or line of bellows pipe; *g*, is the solid part of the hearth bottom; the space betwixt *g* and *a* is its ledge, of four inches and a half, which is here made too small; the dotted space *w* is five inches wide, and is stopped with bone ashes, &c.; *c d*, is the work-stone, its thickness being about four inches and a half, but is here made less than that; *a b*, is one of the bearers; *g h* is the back-stone, which the bellows pipe rests upon, and ought, in the figure, to have been placed on a level with the bearer ; it is six inches and a half high, and is one inch and a half above the bearers at the top, their height being five inches ; *h k*, is the pipe-stone, eight inches high, upon it is another back of five inches in height ; *e*, is the top of the back part of the hearth ; *f*, the floor of the house ; *m*, is the fore-stone, and the cavity below the work-stone, at *d*, the pot for receiving the lead ; the height, from the end of the workstone, at *d*, to the floor is, in this figure, only about one half of what it should be, namely fifteen inches, though the whole height of the hearth is correct, as is also the order of placing the various castings, excepting the back. There are a few inaccuracies in the dimensions.

Fig. 3 is a horizontal section of the bottom of the slag hearth and appendages ; *m m*, the sides; the space *a b f c*, the pot; *w* the pipe for filling the reservoir, indicated by the lines projecting from the pot ; the line or partition, *b c*, stands a little higher than the top of the pot, but does not go within three inches of the bottom ; through this space the lead, after passing through the filter of cinder, flows into the triangular part of the pot, *b f c*, from whence it is ladled.

NOTE.—There is a mistake in this drawing : the sides, *m*, ought to have been continued up to the line *b f*, so that the wide part of the pot, which is six inches more than the line *b c*, might enter the inside of the hearth, to allow the slag, when in its highest state of fluidity, to fall upon the filter of ashes in the pot, in order that the lead may the more completely escape through the filter.

Fig. 4 is a sketch, or foreside view of a slag-hearth when off work : *a* is the top, in which the matter which is to be smelted and the fuel are put ; *b b*, fore-stones of cast-iron ; *c c*, the cheeks or sides, of freestone ; *d d*, cast-iron bearers ; the inner curved line in front of the fore-stones, *b b*, represents the side of the slag-hearth pot, and the outer one its ledge or lip, over which the slag falls into the space before it, being a reservoir of water.

Fig. 5 is a sketch of the same when at work.

Fig. 6 is a perpendicular section of a slag hearth : *a a*, are the fore-stones ; *e*, the pipe-stone or back ; *f*, the back, of cast-iron, below the bellows pipe ; *s*, the line of blast.

Fig. 7 is a perpendicular section of an assay furnace : *a* is the fire-place ; *b*, the fire-bridge ; *c c*, two bricks for covers to the fire-place, to be taken off for the admission of fuel ; *d*, the cupel ; *f*, a flue or chimney to take off the smoke which escapes from the covers *c c ;* *e*, the flue of the furnace, which communicates, as well as the former one, *f*, with the chimney.

Fig. 8 is a horizontal section of an assay furnace : *a* is the fire-place, with grate-bars ; *b*, the fire-bridge ; *c*, the cupel in the furnace ; and *d*, the flue.

III.—THE REFINING FURNACE.

Plate XIV., Fig. 1, is a test frame; Fig. 2 is a test fit for work, A, being the gateway for the litharge.

Fig. 3 is a perpendicular section of two refining furnaces, with part of the chimneys ; *a a*, the fire-places ; *b b*, the fire-bridges ; *c c*, tops of the same, where the flame passes over to the test in the furnaces, *d d; e e*, the flues; *f f*, the inside of the chimneys; *g g*, holes, on the back part of the chimneys, for taking out the fume ; they are closed up when the furnace is working; *h h*, the ash-pits.

NOTE.—This Figure is the back representation on the bellows side of the furnace.

Fig. 4 is a horizontal section of two refining furnaces, showing the test in the one full of lead, as when at work, and the other, with a test also in it, with the common position of a cake of silver, represented by the internal oval; *a a*, the fire-place of each furnace ; *b b*, fire-bridges ; *c*, the test at work, full of lead ; *d*, that with a cake of silver in it ; *e e e e*, passage from the flues to the chimney ; *f f f f*, feeding holes ; *g g*, teas-holes ; *h h h h*, holes for taking out the fume on each side of the furnace chimneys, *i i;* at present the two holes in the front are left off since the chimneys may be cleaned without them ; and in, or adjoining, that part of the chimney between the two furnaces, are placed two melting pots, the flues from which enter each of the furnaces at the two inside holes, *f f*, at which the lead used to be put ; *k*, is the litharge falling from the test, and forming into clods.

IV.—THE REDUCING FURNACE.

Plate XIII., Fig. 1, is a perpendicular section of the reducing furnace ; A, is the inside of the furnace ; B C, the fire-bridge, the part B is of fire-brick, and the other part, C, is made of bone ashes, prepared with a mixture of fern ashes, in the same manner as in the making of a refiner's test ; D, the fire-place ; E, the ash-pit ; F, the teas-hole ; G, the flue ; H, the chimney ; J, the gable wall of the hous ; K, one of the grate-bar supporters ; L, ends of the grate-bars ; M, the drawing door, opposite to which on the other side is that for charging ; N, door to take the slag from the fire-bridge ; opposite to it on the other side is a similar one, by which means the fire-bridge is kept a proper size, since the slag which attaches to it can be taken off in a hot state without injuring the furnace bottom, which would be the case if taken off cold ; O, roof of the furnace, which is a nine-inch brick in thickness ; P, a hole for cleansing the chimney, which is closed when the furnace is at work.

Fig. 2 is a horizontal section of the reducing furnace : the furnace bottom, is made of black slag, run about four inches thick, supported by common brick edge-wise upon cast-iron plates of one inch thick ; a better bottom is made by beating a layer of the ashes which the refiners use for making tests, an inch thick upon the plates ; the slag bottom should decline a little on all sides to the tap-stone to allow the lead to run off ; the part below the plates is hollow ; *b c*, the fire-bridge, made of fire-brick and refiners' ashes, as before-described ; *d d d*, the fire-place ; *e*, the ash-pit ; *f*, the teas-hole ; *g*, the flue ; *h*, the bottom of the chimney ; *j*, gable wall of the house ; *k k*, grate-bar supporters ; *m*, the drawing door ; *n n*, doors for cleansing the fire-bridge of slag ; *o*, the charging door ; *p*, the tap-stone, along which the lead issues to *q*, the pot for receiving it.

NOTE.—The inside of the furnace is made of fire-brick, and the outside of stone, bound like that in the roasting furnace.

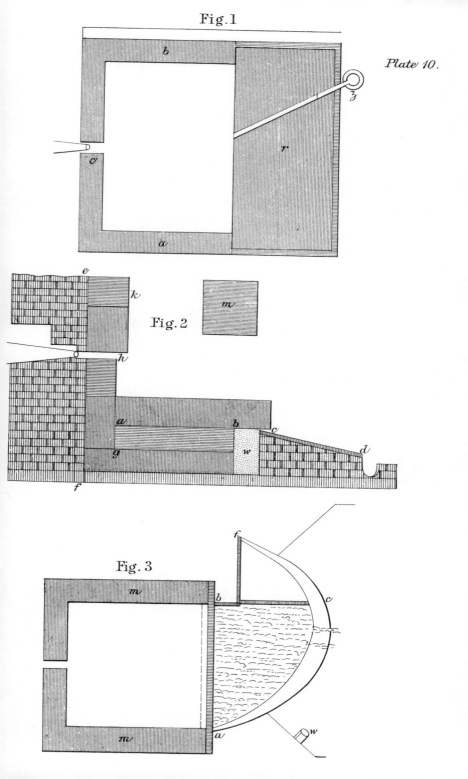

Fig.1

Plate 10.

Fig.2

Fig.3

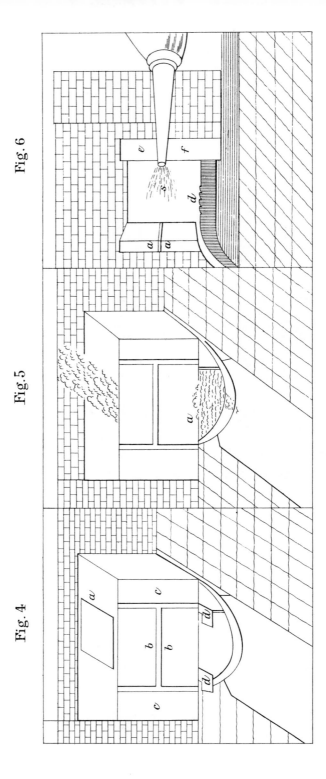

Fig. 4

Fig. 5

Fig. 6

Fig. 7

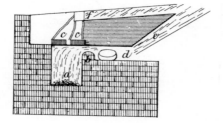

Fig. 8

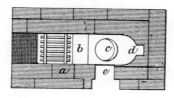

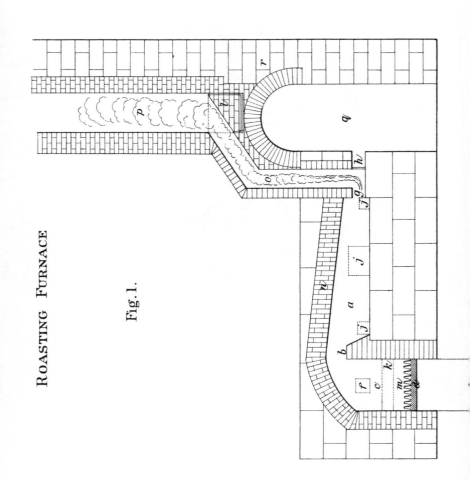

ROASTING FURNACE

Plate 12

Fig. 1.

Fig. 2.

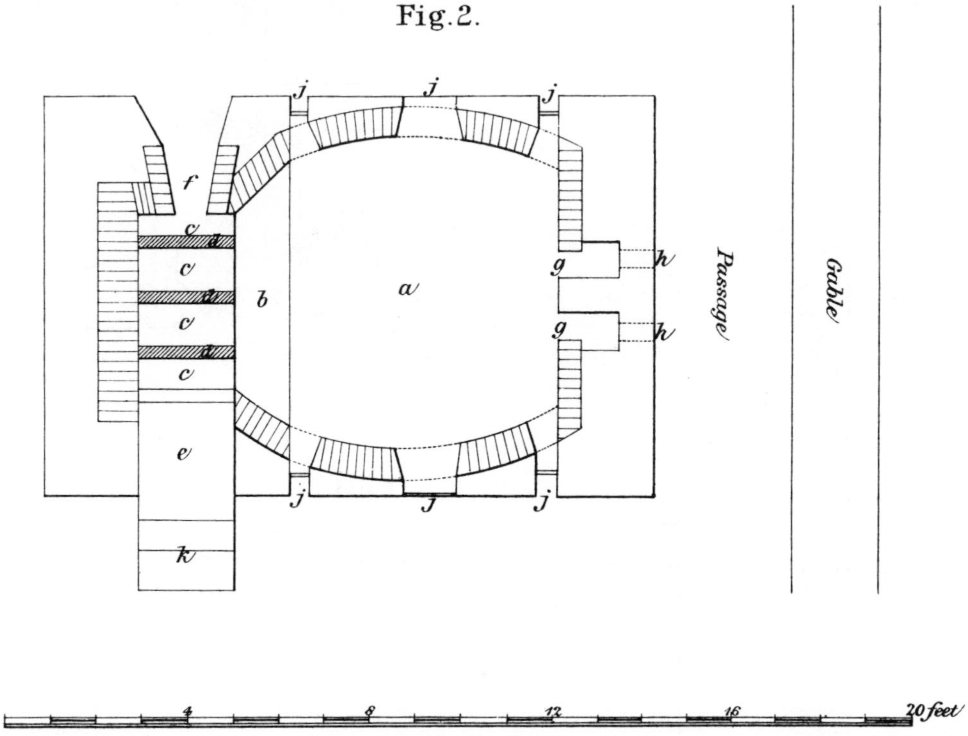

Gable

Passage

Andrew Reid, Newcastle

20 feet 16 12 8 4

Plate 13.

REDUCING FURNACE

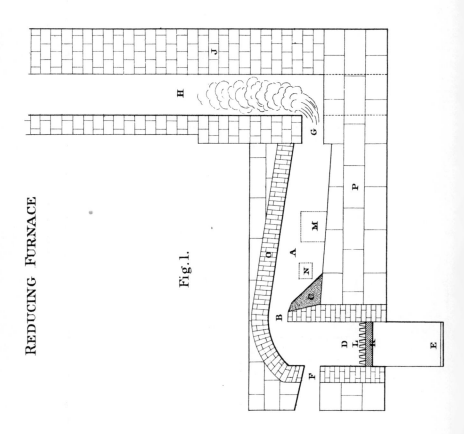

Fig. 1.

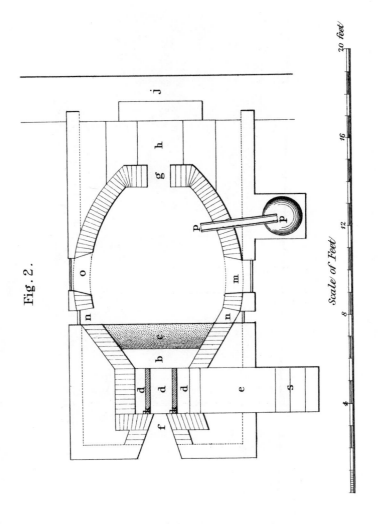

Fig. 2.

Scale of Feet

Plate 14.

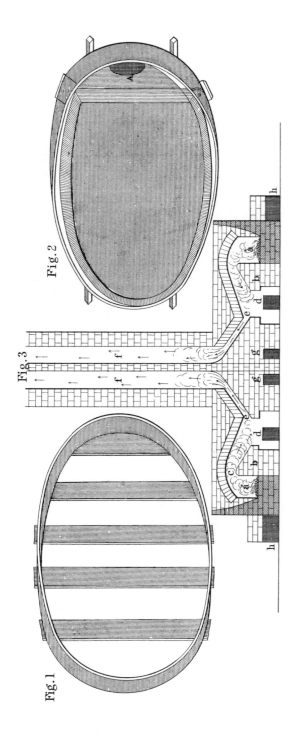

Fig. 2

Fig. 3

Fig. 1

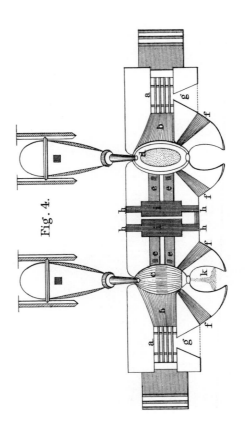

Fig. 4.

APPENDIX.

LIST OF LEAD MINES IN THE DERWENT DISTRICT.
(*Received after going to press.*)

1. *Derwent Mines*, Blanchland.—Lead, in the low grit; occupied by the Derwent Lead Mining and Smelting Company.
2. *Edmondbyers*, Edmondbyers.—Lead, in the grit; occupied by the Hexham and Edmondbyers Lead Mining Company.
3. *Harehope Gill*, Edmondbyers.—Lead, in the grit; occupied by the Harehope Gill Mining Company.
4. *Healey Field*, Blackill.—Lead, in the grit; occupied by the Healey Field Mining Company.

ALSTON DISTRICT.

5. *Brownley Hill*, S.E. of Alston.—Lead, from slate sills to four-fathom limestone; occupied by the Brownley Hill Mining Company.

EXTRACTION OF SILVER FROM LEAD.

THE PATTINSON PROCESS.
(*Extracted from Dr. Percy's Treatise on "Lead."*)

" During the prosecution of some experiments in 1829, Mr. Pattinson required lead in a state of powder, and to obtain it, adopted the mode of stirring a portion of melted lead in a crucible, until it cooled below its point of fusion, by which the metal is obtained in a state of minute subdivision. In doing this he was struck with the circumstance that, as the lead cooled down to nearly its fusing point, little particles of solid lead made their appearance, like small crystals among the liquid lead, gradually increasing in quantity as the temperature fell. After observing the phenomenon once or twice, he began to conceive that possibly some difference might be found in the proportions of silver held by the part that crystallized and the part that remained liquid. Accordingly, he divided a small quantity of lead into two portions, by melting it in a crucible and allowing it to cool very slowly with constant stirring, until a considerable quantity crystallized, as already mentioned, from which the remainder, while still fluid, was poured off; an equal weight of each was then submitted to cupellation, when the button of silver from the liquid lead proved to be very much larger than that from the crystallized lead; and thus the somewhat curious fact was discovered, that fluid lead, holding silver in solution, suffers a portion to escape from it, under certain circumstances, in the act of becoming solid. The lead used in the original experiment was what is considered rich in silver; it contained 40 ounces 15 dwts. 8 grains per ton, and was divided into a crystallized portion found to contain 25 ounces 4 dwts. 21 grains, and a fluid portion holding 79 ounces 11 dwts. 12 grains per ton, the latter being necessarily much smaller than the former in quantity. The experiment was repeated a great number of times upon lead of every variety, as to content of silver, with the same general result; but, being always performed in a crucible upon small quantities of lead, which of necessity cooled quickly, the crystallized portion was never entirely deprived of its silver, nor, indeed, reduced below two or three ounces per ton.

" 'If my memory does not deceive me,' says Dr. Percy, ' Mr. Pattinson told me that he accidentally dropped a crucible containing lead which had partially solidified, the still liquid portion running out upon the floor. He assayed both portions, and found that the liquid contained notably more silver than the solid portion.'

" Subsequent experiments, conducted on a large scale, were attended with similar results."

THE ROZAN PROCESS.

(*See Pamphlet published by the Patentee in* 1873.)

" Instead of stirring the melted lead during crystallization, with an iron paddle, as in the ordinary Pattinson method, or by means of iron flails set in motion by steam, as in the Laveissiere system, the direct agency of steam is employed. The steam, in escaping, produces a bubbling like that of a very dense liquid in ebullition. This violent and continuous agitation is very favourable, as experience has proven, to the separation of the silver from the lead. The action of the steam is essentially mechanical. In regard to its chemical action, although weak, for the reason that it has to deal with metals (lead, copper, silver, antimony) which do not decompose at a temperature of about 330°, the point at which it is employed, it is nevertheless perceptible to some extent, since the lead is subjected during the operation to a softening, independent of that which it undergoes during the fusion at red heat which precedes crystallization. Previous calcining of indifferently hard lead is even dispensed with, that which is very hard being alone subjected to a preparatory calcining. A fact which tends to show that the steam plays an active part in the softening is that the skimmings which are produced, at first yellowish and earthy at the commencement of the operation (crystallization), become, towards the completion, black and highly charged with copper—a circumstance which does not occur in the Pattinson process, notwithstanding the most energetic stirring. Towards the end of each operation, while the steam is still bubbling in the liquid, where together with the silver, copper, antimony, and arsenic are concentrated, the lead is found more and more free from the copper it contained. In regard to the antimony no such phenomenon is observed, but it is gradually eliminated during the successive meltings in consequence of the oxidizing action of the external air. It has even been noticed that soft leads yield a greater quantity of oxides than hard, especially than the antimonial leads, and that, too, under circumstances which prove that antimony in combination with lead is the first and to become oxidized, to protect, in a measure, the latter from oxidation. In short, whatever explanation may be given of the action of steam in softening, it is unquestionably certain and efficacious. It is a fact, proven by experience, that the market leads obtained by this process, are perfectly soft, while the amount of silver contained varies from 1 gr. to 2 gr. at most, per 100 kilogrammes.

LIST OF SUBSCRIBERS.

Admiralty, Lords Commissioners of the.

Armstrong, Joseph, Hardriding, Bardon Mill.

Armstrong, James, Newcastle-upon-Tyne.

Arnison, Dr. Charles, Stanhope.

Armstrong, Sir W. G., Cragside.

Armour, L. H., Gateshead-on-Tyne.

Allison, Thomas, Guisboro.'

Atkinson, Frederick, Maryport.

Allison, Henry T., Jarrow-on-Tyne.

Atkinson, A. A., Fence Houses.

Adams, William, Cardiff.

Argyll, His Grace the Duke of.

Brown, T. Forster, Cardiff.

Blenkiron, James, Yorkshire.

Boyd, E. F., Leamside.

Boyd, R. F., Leamside.

Bolton, Thomas B., Stanhope, Darlington.

Bolton, Anthony, Nenthead, Alston.

Benson, Thos. W., Allerwash.

Backhouse, Edmund, Darlington.

Booth, Robert L., Morpeth.

Bryham, William, Wigan.

Bowman, Rev. E. L., Alston.

Byng, Colonel, Bishop's Stortford.

Beaumont, W. B., M.P., Bretton Hall, Yorkshire.

Bowes, John, Streatlam Castle, Darlington.

Bell, John, Newcastle-on-Tyne.

Bute, the Most Hon. the Marquis of.

Blackett, Sir Edward, Bart., Matfen, Morpeth.

Bewick, Thomas J., Haydon Bridge.

Brown, Rev. Dixon Dixon, Unthank Hall, Haltwhistle.

Buccleugh, His Grace the Duke of.

Bainbridge, R. W., Middleton-in-Teesdale.

Bainbridge, Charles E., Middleton-in-Teesdale.

Barnes, Dr. Henry, Carlisle.

Brown, William B., Garrigill, Alston.

Bartholomew, C., London.

Brown, Robert, Lesbury.

Bell, Robert, Nenthead, Alston.

Brown, A. Walton, Newcastle-on-Tyne.

Beckingham, J. H., Newcastle-on-Tyne.

Bell, Thomas, Durham.

Cheesman, B., Lesbury.

Cranston, J. E., Newcastle-on-Tyne.

Crawhall, Thomas, Stanhope.

Clapham, Henry, Newcastle-on-Tyne.

Courant, Editor of, Newcastle-on-Tyne.

Cleveland, His Grace the Duke of.

Chadwick, David, London.

Craig, Jacob, Garrigill, Alston.

Childe, Rowland, Wakefield.

Cain, Joseph C., Newcastle-on-Tyne.

Croudace, John, Haltwhistle.

Croudace, Thomas, Haltwhistle.

Cowen, Joseph, M.P., Blaydon-on-Tyne.

Cole, R., Walker.

Collis, W. B., Stourbridge.

Corbitt, John, M.P., Droitwich.

Corbitt, John, Gateshead-on-Tyne.

Clough, James, Bedlington.

Cain, John, Bedale.

Crawhall-Wilson, Thos. Wilson, Alston House, Alston.

R

Devonshire, His Grace the Duke of.
Dickinson, John, Alston.
Dent, Robert, Garrigill, Alston.
Durham, The Right Reverend the Lord Bishop of.
Dickinson, Thomas, Alston.
Dickinson, Joseph, sen.
Dickinson, Joseph, jun., Alston.
Dawkins, W. Boyd, Owen's College, Manchester.
Dixon, George, Gateshead-on-Tyne.
Dodsworth, F. & W., Newcastle-on-Tyne.
Dodd, M., Scotswood-on-Tyne.

Elliot, R., London.
Ecclesiastical Commissioners.
Embleton, Thomas, Newcastle-on-Tyne.
Eddy, J. Ray, Skipton.

Forster, G. B., Backworth.
Fraser, D., Newcastle-on-Tyne.
Forster, James, jun., Hull.
French, J. T., Alston.
Fleming, William, Appleby.
Farrar, James, Barnsley.
Fletcher, Herbert, Bolton.
Farrell, F. Milnes, Stoke-on-Trent.
Featherstonhaugh, W., Blackhill.
Forster, C. Le Neve, North Wales.

Garth, Francis, Yorkshire.
Gray, Thos., Newcastle-on-Tyne.
Geach, Edward, Ventnor.
Geach, H. H., Ventnor.
Goddard, Fred. R., Newcastle-on-Tyne.
Gresley, W. S., Ashby-de-la-Zouch.
Gibson, James, Cardiff.

Herdman, W., Weardale.
Hind, William, Newcastle-on-Tyne.
Hothfield, The Right Hon. Lord.
Harrison, C. W., Newcastle-on-Tyne.

Hutchinson, Arthur, Keswick.
Hildyard, J. R. W., Eastgate.
Hunter, Joseph, Chesterfield.
Holliday, M. F., Crook.
Hall, John, Garrigill.
Hurst, Thomas G., Corbridge-on-Tyne.
Hedley, Edward A., Newcastle-on-Tyne
Harker, Thomas, Richmond.
Howard, Stafford, M.P., Thornbury.
Heslop, Christopher, Marske-by-the-Sea
Heppell, Thomas, Durham.
Hodgson, J. Duncan, Newcastle-on-Tyne.
Hay, James, jun., Northumberland.

Joicey & Co., James, Newcastle-on-Tyne.
Jordan, Robert, Monmouthshire.
Johnson, William, Whitfield.
Johnson, John, Chesterfield.
Jackson, W. Geoffrey, Normanton.

Little, William, Carlisle.
Lancaster, Isaac, Garrigill.
Leithart, James, Newcastle-on-Tyne.
Lonsdale, the Right Hon. the Earl of.
London Lead Company.
Lee, William, Darlington.
Lamb, Robert, Cumberland.
Landale, Andrew, Fife, N.B.
Lishman, William, Fence Houses.
Lyon, Robert B., Newcastle-on-Tyne.
Leach, C. C., Bedlington.

Mitchell Main Colliery Company, Barnsley.
Morris, William, Chester-le-Street.
McCulloch, David, Kilmarnock, N.B.
Moffatt, T., Whitehaven.
Millican, John J., Hexham.
Morpeth, John, Northumberland.
Milner, Rev. J., Middleton-in-Teesdale
Maddison, Henry, Darlington.

Monks, Colonel, Durham.
McLay, James, Dysart.
Marshall, F. C., Tynemouth.
Monkhouse, Joseph, Cockermouth.
Monkhouse, Rev. T. G.
Monkhouse, Rev. G., Heathery Cleugh, Weardale.
Millican, John, Alston.
Millican, John, Farnberry, Alston.
Makepeace, Hugh R., Airdrie, N.B.
Morrison, John, Dalkeith.
Marriott, C., Stockton.
Millican, T., Fence Houses.
Manchester Geological Society.
Martin, James S., Manchester.

Nevin, John, Mirfield.
North, Fred. W., Stafford.
Northumberland, His Grace the Duke of.

Pickering, J., Blackhill.
Peacock, William, Richmond.
Pritchard, Henry, Newcastle-on-Tyne.
Pritchard, H., Newcastle-on-Tyne.
Peart, John, Alston.
Pattinson, John, Gateshead-on-Tyne.
Paull, Joseph, Nenthall.
Pease, Sir Joseph W.
Pease, Henry Fell, Darlington.
Pickering, L. S., Appleby.
Pullan, Samuel, Otley.

Race, Featherstone, Middleton-in-Teesdale.
Robson, Thomas, Fence Houses.
Robertson, William, Glasgow.
Rutherford, William, Lintz Green.
Rogerson, John, Croxdale Hall, Durham.
Robinson, Wm. H., Newcastle-on-Tyne.
Richardson, Thomas, Ashgill.
Rosslyn, the Right Hon. the Earl of.
Raisbeck, Matthew.

Russell, Robert, New Main, N.B.
Rodwell, J. A., Bedale.
Richardson, Thomas, Alston.
Ridley, John, Allenheads.

Spencer, Thomas, Ryton-on-Tyne.
Slinn, Thomas, Newcastle-on-Tyne.
Steavenson, A. L., Durham.
Spark, James, Wearhead.
Straker, John, Corbridge-on-Tyne.
Stewart, T. B., Abington, N.W.
Swan, J. Cameron, Newcastle-on-Tyne.
Stobart, William, Northallerton.
Smyth, Warrington, London.
Spark, Jonathan, Garrigill, Alston.
Simpson, William, Alston.
Shaw, Walton, Leadgate, Blackhill.
Stephen, W. Davies, Newcastle-on-Tyne.
Sample, Thomas, Bothal Castle, Morpeth.
Slack, John, Durham.
Science and Art Department, South Kensington, London.
Scarth, William T., Darlington.
Siddle, John, Ashgill, Alston.
Spence, Faraday, Newcastle-on-Tyne.
Spencer, Michael, Newcastle-on-Tyne.

Thompson, John, Darlington.
Taylor, John C., and Sons, London.
Teasdale, Thomas, Weardale.
Tallantyre, I. B., Haltwhistle.
Thompson, Lieut.-Colonel, Carlisle.
Taylor, Hugh, Northumberland.
Thompson, George, Alston.
Tredegar, The Right. Hon. Lord.
Thompson, Joseph.

Vipond, Leonard, Garrigill.
Vipond, James, Garrigill.

Willis, James, Newcastle-on-Tyne.
Wood, Lindsay, Chester-le-Street.
Watson, S., Weardale.

Wilson, Lloyd, Carlisle.
Watson, Thomas, Darlington.
Walton, Robert, Stanhope.
Ware, Thomas, Fourstones.
Wallace, George, Darlington.
Whitwell, William, Kendal.
Watson, Joseph, Penrith.
Walton, Jacob, Glenwood House, Alston.
Wood, Thomas, Fence Houses.

Walton, Jonathan, Donk's Villa, Nenthead.
Whaley, John, Haltwhistle.
Walton, William, Haltwhistle.
Watson, Matthew, Morpeth.
Wallace, John, Backworth, Newcastle-on-Tyne.
Wilson, Ald. Thomas, Riding Mill.
Walton, Robert, Stanhope.

CORRIGENDA.

On pages 52 and 149, for "North Riding" read "North and West Ridings."

On page 180, line 9 from top, for "five" read "three."

On page 180, line 9 from bottom, omit the sentence "Nos. 4 and 5" to "cuttings."

On page 204, line 6 from bottom, for "and to become oxodized," read "to become oxodized, and to protect."

NOTE.—The mines which are now occupied by the Nenthead and Tynedale Lead and Zinc Company, were formerly occupied by the London Lead Company.